TO

H. T. K.

GENERAL PREFACE

THE present work is an exposition of the facts and principles of psychology in accordance with a definite method. This is, in general, *the method of psychophysiology*. In greater detail, the treatment is based upon an analysis of the process of neuromuscular response, together with the familiar postulate that consciousness is correlated with, but distinct from, the *cerebral* factor in these physiological operations. The scheme is thus that of traditional "physiological psychology," brought up to date, but I believe that its refinement and modernization may prove to be as important as is its historical core. Small changes in point of view may reveal new aspects of the system of psychology as a whole, enabling one to straighten out some very ancient tangles in a quite satisfactory manner.

My aim in preparing this work has been rather complex. Aside from irrelevant personal motives, the main purposes which I have had in mind may be summarized as follows. Firstly, to examine the foundations of psychology as a science, in order to arrive at a satisfactory statement of its problems and methods. Secondly, to formulate a plan for treating these problems and facts which would thrust aside nothing that is of real human importance. Thirdly, to present, in accordance with this plan, what seem to me to be the most important facts and theories of psychological science. Fourthly, to reconsider the question of the mind-body relationship from the philosophical standpoint. Finally, to formulate certain philosophical developments of all of these studies.

In connection with my first purpose I have been stimulated by a desire to refute the position which is taken by the modern behaviorists in psychology, and

yet to preserve what is valuable in behavioristic practice. In a sense, this work in its entirety is presented as a
detailed, demonstrative, reply to the behavioristic contention
that the introspective method in psychology is worthless.
However, I have not rejected, but have, rather, adopted
the behavioristic methods insofar as they are positive. I
have insisted upon viewing the organism as a physical machine, the operations of which can be described without reference to consciousness. Nevertheless, this very reference
creates the principal purpose and problem of the book. I
shall be greatly interested to know what objections the behavioristic psychologists can raise against the arguments and
analyses which I have offered, and I shall be surprised
if there are any introspective psychologists who disagree
seriously with the general system which is developed in this
book.

It is therefore my hope that the work may accomplish
something towards effecting a reconciliation between the
behavioristic and the introspectionistic schools, and may thus
aid in unifying the progress of psychological science. The
present controversial situation certainly constitutes an undesirable distraction from the many important problems which
are pressing upon psychology for solution. Also, because
of the apparent deadlock which exists between the opposing
schools, psychology is losing the respect both of the scientific world and of the public. This is occurring at a time
which is, in general, quite favorable for an increase in such
respect. The world to-day has a greater interest in philosophical and psychological problems than it has ever had
before. People are beginning to realize that these fields of
study should be capable of supplying information which
may be of the greatest possible value in regulating the
conduct of life.

The second of my purposes is concerned with the details of the psychophysiological method. This method recognizes the existence of consciousness as a distinctive psychical entity, which cannot be reduced in any sense to terms
of physics or of physiology. However, consciousness, as I

have conceived it, is a very concrete and real thing, nothing less than a section of experience itself. I have assumed, with the classical physiological psychologists, that the individual consciousness is correlated with processes occurring in certain areas of the cerebral cortex. Such processes are, of course, stages or links in a chain of neuromuscular events, all of which must be conceived ultimately in physical terms. This chain of events takes the form of a physical propagation, starting in the environment, and being transmitted along neural channels until it finally reaches the environment again. I have considered the task of psychophysiology to be that of determining the relationships which hold between consciousness and various segments of this propagational series.

The natural subdivisions of the response propagation furnish the cue for a classification of such psychophysiological relationships. Under the caption of *perception,* I have discussed those relationships which obtain between consciousness and the world outside of the organism, at the beginning of the propagational series of events. I have taken the term, *sensation,* to stand for the relationship between consciousness and processes in the afferent nervous arc, including the sense-organs and their immediate stimuli. Under the heading of *cerebration,* I have considered the direct psychophysical relationship between consciousness and brain activity, as well as indirect relationships with other central processes. I have taken the word, *action,* to stand for psychophysical relations which hold between consciousness and events on the efferent, or outgoing, sector of the response path. It is true that these applications of the terms, perception, sensation, cerebration and action, involve some redefinitions, but I believe that the changes in meaning which I have introduced are scientifically advisable.

When we come to the third of my expressed purposes, I may expect to encounter some adverse criticism of its presented realization. It is impossible in any book of practicable size to set forth all of the facts of psychophysiology. It would be even more difficult to expound all of the theories which have been offered in this field of thought. Hence I have been compelled to select those facts and theories which seem to me to be the most important, and I have necessarily chosen these from my own stock of information. Doubtless there are some regrettable omissions, but it has been my endeavor to prepare a reasonably comprehensive and detailed treatment of the facts. I shall be indebted to anyone who may care to communicate to me criticisms which may have a bearing upon the contents of possible later editions of this work.

Some may feel that I have been particularly presumptuous in my treatment of theories. Here I have followed the suggestion of my colleague, Dr. Beebe-Center, and have neglected to consider what he designates as "duds," or doctrines which are definitely out of date and in clear disagreement with established facts. This procedure is quite contrary to the conventional practice in textbooks of psychology. It is customary to present a long list of alternative hypotheses. The danger comes, of course, in attempting to distinguish between the "duds" and the live ideas, in particular instances. The writer himself must take the chances which are involved in making such decisions. I have contented myself, as a rule, with formulating a single theoretical interpretation of the facts which seems to me, in the given situation, to be the most satisfactory one in the present state of our enlightenment, and I have done this without much reference to the historical sources of the theory in question. Those who are interested in a review of classical guesses are referred to other textbooks, or to historical treatises.

I have divided the treatment of the facts and theories of psychophysiology under the four headings of Perception, Sensation, Cerebration and Action, each of which corresponds to a unit Part of the present work.

Under the influence of the fourth of my expressed purposes, I fear that my presumption has reached extreme limits, for here I have dared to suggest a scientific basis for what passes as philosophy. In the time of the Greeks, the word philosophy stood for all knowledge. Gradually, one by one, the definite sciences have emerged from its womb, but certain forms of inquiry still remain in an embryonic condition. The principal ones are known as epistemology, ontology (or cosmology) and ethics. I believe that these disciplines, also, can be made scientific; but, in order that this may be accomplished, their status must undergo a shocking transition, which cannot fail to bring pain to academic philosophy. (However, these pains may be the agonies of parturition.) It is necessary, according to my view, to regard epistemology, cosmology and ethics as *developments from the facts of psychophysiology*.

To an unbiased thinker, this thesis will not appear unreasonable. Knowledge is surely a mental function, and knowledge of the physical world must be regarded as a psychophysical relationship. Knowledge of a *metaphysical* world may conceivably involve some fundamentally new terms, but it is my contention that, in fact, the latter are basically those of introspective psychology and of physical theory. The key to a cosmological inquiry into the nature of "things in themselves" is to be found in the psychophysical relations which are demonstrated by psychophysiology. Ethics should be interpreted as a practical development of human motivational and of cosmological principles. I have endeavored to present these ideas in definite form in the fourth volume, and to provide schematic developments for the disciplines in question.

In concluding my general comments, I may be permitted to say that I have presented in this book what seems to me to be the living substance of modern psychology. Psychophysiology is something more than a special way of viewing psychological facts. It is the essence of what we have learned that is valuable in the domain of psychological inquiry. I stoutly maintain that the behaviorist's view of the science is a fearful error. I assert, with equal firmness, that a psychology by pure introspection is possible and necessary. But I do not believe that a purely introspective psychology can be made *valuable* unless it is correlated with the facts which the behaviorists are emphasizing. Either extreme in method yields a result which is not only less than the facts, but something which, by itself, is practically worthless. Strict behaviorism and strict introspectionism are, indeed, artificial academic creations. The living and growing truths of psychology are psychophysiological. Both behaviorists and pure introspectionists unwittingly contribute to the development of this science, but their accomplishments for posterity would be increased if they would envisage all of the facts with a clear and open mind.

Something should probably be said here concerning the relation of my treatment of psychology in the present work to the modern controversy between the *Gestalt* (or configurational) and the structural schools of psychology. I confess that the arguments of the configurationists and the methods of the Titchenerian structuralists both appeal to me very strongly. As in the behavioristic debate, I consider that the positive contentions on both sides of the argument are generally correct. The problem before the constructive thinker is to eliminate the negative propositions and to arrive at a satisfactory compromise which will permit the theory to check with the facts. A sympathetic and tolerant *Gestalter* will, perhaps, consider the present book a contribution to his own movement. I shall not be at all displeased at such a reaction. On the other hand, I believe that Professor Titchener, himself, if he were still alive to read this work, would not be offended by its methods.

The following comments may be made regarding the physical make-up of this work. It is essentially a continuous treatment of psychophysiological problems, but it has been divided into four volumes in the hope of increasing its general usefulness. Some readers will not be interested in the more philosophical discussion. Other readers may be concerned primarily with the higher mental processes, still others with sensation, and there may be some who are interested only in the foundations of psychology.

The first volume embraces the first three Parts, dealing with the definition of psychology, with the methods of psychophysiology and with perception, respectively. The inclusion of perception in this volume is due primarily to the desirability of a reasonably even subdivision of pages. However, it has the advantage of offering a concrete example of the psychophysiological method, which is pursued throughout the work, to those who may not care to read the volumes on sensation and on cerebration and action. Perception deals with the common sense facts of psychophysiology, while the later Parts are concerned with more subtle and esoteric matters.

The second volume provides a unified treatment of sensation, as I have defined this concept above. Action and cerebration are discussed in the third volume, and fall together quite naturally. The fourth volume is devoted wholly to the philosophical developments of psychophysiological facts and principles: an analysis of the ultimate significance of the mind-body relationship, and an attempt to found a new philosophical methodology.

For the benefit of those who may wish to use the later volumes without consulting earlier ones, summaries of essential points in the argument of the book as a whole are presented at the beginning of each volume. Essential matters of detail are repeated in fine print at appropriate places in successive volumes or are dealt with in footnotes.

I wish to acknowledge my indebtedness to the following persons for the assistance which they have given me in the preparation of this work: Dr. J. G. Beebe-Center, for a preliminary reading of the manuscript, numerous helpful suggestions, and in particular for many references in the literature on the topic of affection; Mr. A. D. Fuller, Jr.; Dr. T. F. Karwoski and Mr. Eugene F. McCarthy for assistance with the proof; and to Dr. Karwoski and my wife for help in preparing the reference lists, the index and other details of the manuscript.

L. T. TROLAND

CAMBRIDGE, MASS.,
JUNE, 1929.

CONTENTS

PART ONE

PROLOGUE: THE DEFINITION OF PSYCHOLOGICAL KNOWLEDGE

Contents

LIST OF ILLUSTRATIONS

PART ONE

PROLOGUE: THE DEFINITION OF
PSYCHOLOGICAL KNOWLEDGE

THE PRINCIPLES OF
PSYCHOPHYSIOLOGY

Introduction

The Present Status of Psychology

1. The Importance of Psychology.—The modern world
is slowly awakening to the fact that psychology is humanly
the most important of all the sciences. This importance has
both theoretical and practical aspects. On the practical side,
it appears that the principal factors in social organization
and disorganization, in business, politics, religion and war
are psychological. The present social order is largely an
adaptation to our natural human nature, a psychological
entity. On every hand, at the present day, the practical
world is turning to psychology for assistance. It is asking
that psychologists guide men in the choice of vocations, that
it find the proper individuals for particular tasks, that it
advise in questions of business policy, that it show how to
advertize commodities and services successfully, that it teach
the principles of effective salesmanship, instruct public speak-
ers in the best methods of presenting educational or political
topics to an audience, and that it do many other things.

Psychology offers practical assistance to the human individual in his own private life, as well as in his social relationships to others. Psychology should have the effect of
turning a man's attention to many realities and principles
which he might otherwise miss because of the general objective tendency of thought. The conceptions and laws which
are revealed by psychology should help us constantly to
understand our own experiences, our sensations, thought
processes, emotions and moods, and should aid us in regu-

lating our conduct more rationally with respect to them and to our fundamental life purposes. Psychology should liberate us, to some extent at least, from irrational and dangerous impulses and enable us to control scientifically— as certain religious schemes endeavor to control emotionally —the tendencies and feelings which govern our lives.

Still further, we might be tempted to look to psychology to provide us with the guidance which is required for a fundamental improvement in human ideals. Psychology should be able not only to assist us in the pursuit of our more or less accidental and occasional purposes, but to generalize the purposive tendency of mind and reveal the universal goal of sentient life. It should solve the problem of theoretical ethics and show humanity the way to the greatest moral achievement.

On the theoretical side, nothing can have more meaning than a discussion of our own natures, what human beings are in themselves, how they develop, and their possibilities for the future. From the philosophical standpoint, we see that not only the inner world of feeling but also the external world of sensation and perception, so far as we know it immediately, presents a psychological rather than a physical problem. Philosophically, also, psychology links itself with the great mysteries of metaphysics, religion, and theory of knowledge. The relation of body to mind, which is an integral feature of the psychological problem, is at the same time one of the cardinal problems of metaphysics, upon the solution of which depend the understanding of the nature of knowledge and, perhaps also, a clear conception of the nature of being in general.

2. The Scientific Status of Psychology.—When we view modern psychology in the light of these demands and possibilities, we can hardly escape a twinge of disappointment. Perhaps in part because of the very fact that psychology deals with the cardinal reality of man himself as a sentient being, it has been very slow in developing as a positive science. The natural course of intellectual application, both in the individual mind and in the history of science appears

to be centripetal. Our attention is directed first to the things which are farthest away. Science began with the Chaldean study of the stars. It came to earth in geometry or earth-measure. It went on into physics, into chemistry, into biology, and finally, in psychology, is now endeavoring to penetrate the nucleus of the observing and thinking process itself.

Psychology, like all other sciences, began as a subdivision of philosophy, and its departure from the fold of philosophical disciplines is one of the most recent. As a branch of philosophical inquiry, it is nearly as old as any other line of investigation or thought. At present, in many college curricula, psychology is listed neither under philosophy nor under science. It appears to be in the act of obtaining a separation from philosophy and not yet to have been admitted into the group of positive sciences. It seems to be in a transitional state, moving between the purely speculative or discursive method of philosophy and the empirical, mathematical form of modern scientific thought.

Nevertheless there can be no question that the trend of current psychological effort is towards a more and more scientific treatment of the subject. Psychology, as an empirical science, is well out of its swaddling clothes and is even entering upon its adolescent period. That it should lack the maturity of older sciences is no aspersion upon its character or its possibilities. On account of its youth, as well as the tremendous importance of the problems which it envisages, the appeal of psychology to the investigative mind should be singularly intense. In many other fields of science, such as mechanics or mathematics, most of the major problems appear to have been solved, so that the remaining questions may seem to be of minor importance. In psychology, however, nearly all of the great problems are still open for original investigation; and any one entering the psychological field with the firm purpose to make significant contributions to human knowledge will find rich opportunities.

3. **The Problem of the Problem of Psychology.**—The contemporary adolescence of psychology is naturally char-

acterized by a phase of self-examination and internal criticism.[1] At the present time, psychology is endeavoring strenuously to determine just how its problems and methods should be defined. This critical process takes the form of disagreement and controversy among psychologists with regard to these questions. From the standpoint of an outsider, the effect may be that of complete chaos. Approaching the camp of psychology in the hope of securing practical or theoretical guidance, he comes upon a scene of dissension among disagreeing factions. It would not be surprising if, under these conditions, the outsider should beat a hasty retreat and thereafter view the science with greatly lessened respect.

As a member of the psychological camp, I should certainly argue against this persuasion. Nevertheless, I am forced to admit that, to a psychologist who is interested in preparing a systematic presentation of the essential truths which have been gleaned concerning mind and its relationships, the present controversial situation is somewhat disconcerting. If we pick out a dozen current texts on psychology, we are almost certain to find at least twelve different interpretations of the science; and some of these interpretations will seem to be entirely antithetical in character. One psychologist will define the science as the description of behavior, whereas another will restrict it to the analysis of consciousness. One will devote half of his book to the physiology of the sensations, whereas another will exclude the sensations on the ground that they are non-psychological. For one psychologist, analysis is an indispensable tool, whereas for another it is a snare and a delusion.

Under such conditions, it is clearly impossible to write a psychological textbook without an introduction dealing with the fundamental concepts and methods of the science. Such an introduction must present and attempt to justify a particular point of view, which will necessarily conflict to some extent with other current interpretations of psychology. Practically all contemporary psychological texts have such introductory chapters devoted to the questions: "What is psychology?" "What is its subject matter?" "What are its methods?" If we open a textbook of physics we may find only a paragraph dealing with such topics; in a textbook of geometry, perhaps not even a sentence. If, on the other hand, we inspect textbooks of ethics, we find in the majority of cases that the entire book is devoted to a discussion of this type of problem, leaving no room at all for the development of an actual system of knowledge. The variations among sciences in this respect are naturally correlated with their respective states of advancement. Increase in the definiteness of the concepts of any science goes hand in hand with its empirical and theoretical progress.

The question as to the subject matter and the methods of any science would appear not to be a problem in that particular science itself. For example, it is not a problem in physics to determine what physics is, although in the case of psychology some aspects of the determination of its nature may well turn out to be psychological. Strictly speaking, the definition of any science is a task for some such line of inquiry as epistemology (theory of knowledge) or logic. However, we are forced to admit that, as a practical matter, epistemologists and logicians are not in a position to define particular sciences, excepting their own. Consequently it seems to be necessary for students of special sciences to clarify the epistemology and logic of their particular fields of investigation. So it is peculiarly requisite that we should pay attention, in the opening chapters of the present book, to the problem of the problem of psychology: the definition of the science, its fundamental concepts and methods.

Chapter I

An Outline of the History of Psychology

Section 1

THE PSYCHOLOGY OF THE SOUL

4. The Historical Basis for Defining Psychology.—It was asserted by Comte, the French philosopher, that the only way in which to understand a science is through its history.[2] The truth of this assertion is inversely proportional to the degree of crystallization of the concepts of the science in question. It is certainly not essential to an understanding of mathematical reasoning to know the history of the subject; but it is somewhat more important in physics or in chemistry to know something of the histories of these respective departments of knowledge. In biology, the history of the science becomes much more enlightening, and Comte's statement applies with particular force to psychology, especially when we find ourselves compelled to approach the study of this science by asking the question as to what it is about.

Conceptions such as that of psychology must be permitted to have an evolution, but such development should never involve radical discontinuity. It seems that the present controversy regarding the problem and methods of psychology centers about the *definition* of the term, *psychology*. The customary criterion of correct definition is *usage,* and usage stands for the history of the given concept. Apart from such a test, there would appear to be no fundamental way of determining what psychology "really is." We might say, of course, as some critics have done, that

6

psychology is whatever psychologists are doing; but this will apparently lead us to no decision, since the deeds of present-day psychologists are naturally as varied as are their opinions concerning the proper nature of their science.

We have seen that the present is a period of fierce debate concerning the definition, scope and methods of psychology. We find, in America and in England, two contesting groups known as behaviorists and introspectionists who disagree flatly concerning the definition of the word psychology.[3] One group maintains that psychology is the science of behavior, while the other regards it as the science of consciousness. Within the camps of the behaviorists and of the introspectionists there is further dissension. The behaviorists are not united on the definition of behavior while the introspectionists are even less united in their definitions of consciousness or of the psychical. If we are seeking an authoritative answer to the question "What is psychology?" we must review the history of this conception and of the allied conceptions from which it grew. Only by doing this, and by following as best we may the indications thereby obtained, can we preserve the continuity of thinking which is essential to progress.

5. Psychological Origins of the Soul Theory.—The word psychology is of comparatively recent origin, but its essential root, *psyche,* the Greek term for soul, preserves a continuity in history which takes us back to some of the earliest phases of human thought regarding the nature of mind. Following this thread of thought, we find it possible to divide the history of psychology into two general phases: first, what may be called "the psychology of the soul," which is characterized by the development of a constantly increasing dualism between soul and matter, culminating in the work of the French philosopher, René Descartes (1596–1650); and, second, what we may designate as "the psychology without a soul," following Descartes and being characterized by a multiplicity of unsuccessful attempts to avoid the dualistic assumption. The psychology without a soul may be divided into two subsidiary phases, the one philosophical and speculative in method, the other empirical and psychophysical in its attack. These several phases and sub-phases, of course, overlap to a very considerable extent, but the division of the historic problems which they indicate is justifiable as a general schema for purposes of exposition.

All sciences naturally begin with the conceptions of common sense and involve an attempt to make common sense more adequate and explicit. However, common sense itself is not a God-given system of knowledge but has a course of development similar in general character to that which is followed by science. The common-sense beliefs from which the science of psychology has sprung are to be found in the primitive and prehistoric doctrine known as *animism*. This doctrine, the hypothesis of the soul as spirit or air, is the consequence of rational and even scientific thinking on the part of primitive man. It will repay us to place ourselves for a moment in his position and see how, in all probability, he arrived at the doctrine in question.

There was apparently a fairly definite period in the history of mankind [4] when men began to use language articulately and started to think in terms of words as symbols. Even before this, however, there must have been mental processes resembling those which were ultimately formulated in words. Primitive man must have found himself presented with an experience very much like ours, but not in the beginning, like ours, 'sicklied o'er with the pale cast of thought.' He had at the outset no theories, but plenty of data. Now, the simplest intellectual act which he could perform upon his experience would be one of classification, and the simplest useable classification of experience as a whole would appear to be its division into two contrasting parts, comprising an inner or private region and an outer or external one. The inner part of experience would consist of desires, thoughts, images, organic and motor sensations and the like, while the external part would consist of the seen, heard and felt world. A section of the latter would be the thinker's own externally perceived body. Such a division would involve a separation of the world and the self within experience and would demarcate, approximately, the domains of physics and of psychology, respectively.

The causes which led primitive man to make this bipartite division of his experience were probably to be found in part in the inherently different natures of the two portions. Even more important, however, must be reckoned the characteristics and the correlations of the *changes* occurring within and between the two divisions. Even before he began to think explicitly, primitive man must have been aware of the striking connection which existed between the postures and movements of his own externally perceived body and his internal feelings or ideas. He must have recognized also, that the remainder of his external experience could become correlated with, or controlled by, internal factors only through the mediation of his body in the external world. Although the correlation of inner with outer bodily experience is apparently not perfect, it is sufficiently thoroughgoing to lead to the recognition of a very general relationship of interdependency between the two. The body appears to respond to changes in the inner consciousness, while changes in the body produced by external influences are reflected, as in the case of physical injury, by powerful modifications of inner experience. This sort of inner connection between internal and external corporeal experience must have impressed upon the thought of primitive man a rudimentary conception of *causation* or *activity*. The predominant phase of this activity was undoubtedly that which appeared to proceed from within outwardly, and brought the states and processes of the external body under the dominion of the internal feelings and images. This externally directed activity provided primitive man with his notion of *will*, a notion which was destined not only to play an important part in primitive psychological speculation but also in more advanced general theories of the universe.

6. Animatism and Animism.—In the beginning, of course, our prehistoric philosopher did not formulate his observations in words, but merely carried them in his mind by means of images which were linked together by the principle of association. Such systems of images, however, provide a basis for thought which is nearly as satisfactory as is an expression of the same ideas by the use of language. Thinking thus, in his rudimentary way, the primitive philosopher noted, or reacted to, the *similarities* which existed between his own externally perceived body and the bodies of other men, and even of animals, which formed portions of his own external experience. These similarities, operating through the principle of association, aroused in his mind images of corresponding internal experiences. He saw other men behaving as he had seen himself behave and accordingly inferred the existence, in connection with their behavior, of internal experiences which were distinct from his own. He regarded these foreign internal experiences as the active causes of the motions which were exhibited by the other human or animal bodies. Thus, our primitive thinker arrived at the notion of truly objective minds. Such objective minds were not restricted in the beginning of human thought to other human beings, or even to the animal kingdom in general, but were extended to apply to all nature insofar as it showed spontaneous or otherwise unexplained changes. The point of view thus achieved is that of *animatism,* which may be defined as the theory that all spontaneous processes occurring in the external world are attributable to the activity of specific individual systems of internal experience, or in a word, to *will.*

The doctrine of animatism is to be distinguished sharply from that of *animism,*[5] which definitely propounds the hypothesis of the *soul.* This hypothesis is a daring speculation, introduced with the appearance of explicit thinking about the problems of experience, in an attempt to synthesize and thus to explain the complex conditions which surround the phenomena of sentiency and of volition. The soul is conceived to be an entity distinct in character from both inner experience and spontaneous movement, but providing the basis or substance for both. Some of the circumstances which justify this hypothesis are: the temporary suspension of animation in sleep, accompanied by a fantastic continuation of both internal and external experience in the form of dreams; the phenomenon of death with its complete lapse of animation and apparently complete disappearance of sensibility; the phenomenon of the breath streaming from the nostrils, visible in winter, together with its disappearance in death and its slowing in sleep; reflection images seen in water and shadows cast in a bright light; and hallucinations and after-images, which are interpreted by primitive man as being ghosts or fantastic external appearances. The close association between the breath and life caused the former to be seized upon by the primitive thinker to play the part of the substance which underlies sentiency and spontaneity. The soul thus appeared as a form of air, spirit, or an anima which is the bearer of will, of self and of activity, the explanation of motion as well as of internal sensation. The soul, thus conceived, does not differ very radically from the conception of matter which subsequently arises, although it is a definite sort of diaphanous matter, possessed of peculiar sensibility and dynamic power.

7. **The Beginnings of the Theory of Matter.**—Because feeling and spontaneity coerce the attention, the demand for an explanation of these phenomena naturally precedes that for an explanation of external experience in general. However, with the expansion of explicit thinking, which occurred very rapidly among the free-minded Greeks, a need arose for an explanation of nature at large. With the Greek philosophers [6] we find both philosophy and science taking their origins, and we find the beginning of a search for a substance which is capable of explaining the characteristics, not only of the living and sentient, but of non-living and inactive, factors in the world. The Greek philosophers introduced the idea of a natural cause, or *fusis,* a substance conceived by analogy with the soul but underlying the phenomena of external and, possibly, of internal experience in their entirety. Just as psychology harks back to the *psyche* or *anima,* so does physics find its roots historically, as well as etymologically, in the Greek conceptions of the *fusis.* Both matter, in this sense, and the soul are hypotheses

added to the data of immediate experience in an attempt to explain the interconnections and resemblances which are observed between these data.

The earliest Greek philosophers, those of the Ionian school, were monists, their doctrine being that of a universal single substance, underlying not only inactive phenomena in external experience but also the phenomena which had previously been explained by the hypothesis of an anima. Their views may be regarded as extension and modification of the animistic hypothesis in an effort to explain the totality of experience on a single assumption. Thales (640–546 B.C.), the first of these thinkers, suggested that the essence of all things was *water*, a substance capable of assuming liquid, solid or vaporous states. But water, as conceived by Thales, possessed all of the properties of the soul, being both sentient and active. Anaximenes (*ca.* 575 B.C.) expanded the *anima* itself into a universal substance, making air the essence of all things. Anaximander (611–547 B.C.) adopted a different and more mystical view in regarding the ultimate substance as an "Infinite One," a sort of numerical or mathematical entity, which foreshadowed in its properties the characteristics of the Absolute in modern idealism.

The subsequent course of Greek philosophy, however, proved the difficulty of maintaining a monistic explanation of all experience. The doctrine of a special substance underlying feeling and movement insisted upon reinstating itself, but the demand for an explanation of the facts of external experience at large insured the persistence, also, of an independent conception of physical reality. In the atomistic theories of Leucippus (*ca.* 500 B.C.) and Democritus (born *ca.* 465 B.C.) which were continued by Epicurus (342–270 B.C.) and his school as well as by the Roman poet, Lucretius (93–55 B.C.), we find the beginnings of the modern physical scientific theory of the material world. Modern atomism is, of course, vastly more intricate, and is more accurately and adequately conceived, than was that of the Greek thinkers, but its essential nature and function as an explanatory hypothesis remain the same. The Greek atomists, like the modern physicists, attributed activity to atoms, but they nevertheless felt compelled to postulate the existence of a special very light and refined species of atom to account for psychical phenomena. Here, in effect, they simply atomized the anima of earlier philosophy.

In the arguments between the Greek thinkers, the character of both the soul and of matter changed kaleidoscopically. Matter was divided into diverse elements while the soul was partitioned into sub-souls or what later came to be known as faculties. Empedocles (490–430 B.C.) found everything to be made of various combinations of fire, air, earth and water, and Heraclitus (540–475 B.C.) selected fire to play the part of the soul and to be the flickering agency of change in all things. Among the many elements which were postulated by Anaxagoras (500–428 B.C.) there was a special one, the *nous,* which was conceived as the basis of feeling and of motion. Through all of these vicissitudes of the soul, however, the anima theory persisted and reappeared in the *pneuma* doctrine of the Roman Stoics.[7]

8. Experience versus Reality.—As a part of the Greek research into the ultimate nature of physical reality, there arose the method of investigation by argument or reasoning. The source of this method is undoubtedly to be sought in the developments of the science of geometry, where it was found possible to pass dialectically from certain self-evident propositions to other propositions which were later verifiable by experience. This method, that of logic or mathematics, constitutes a second permanent contribution of the Greek intellect to the advancement of science; particularly, of physical science. By the method of reason, the Greek philosophers hoped to attain certainty as to the nature of ultimate reality. However, the conclusions to which they were led by the application of this method were not always verified by experience and in many cases quite contradicted the latter. Consequently there arose a conception of *illusion* or "appearance," as contrasted with "reality." The reasoning of Parmenides (born *ca.* 539 B.C.) led him to agree with Anaximander that ultimate reality is a pure numerical unity, while the world of experience is but a system of hallucinations devoid of any rational structure. By supposedly strict logical analysis, Zeno showed that motion and other phenomena were impossible and was thus led to a general denial of the validity of perception. The great geometer, Pythagoras (born 582 B.C.), and his school, endeavored to conceive the universe in terms of pure number and looked for the essence of the world in certain relations between numbers. For the Pythagoreans, the soul was a harmony among the elements, a doctrine which presages Plato's notion of the soul [8] as the idea of life and Aristotle's conception of it as organic form.[9] This rationalistic tendency among the Greeks is of importance in the history of psychology because it led, at least implicitly and in some cases (Parmenides) quite explictly, to the recognition of a system of appearances distinct from that of reality. This system of appearances is practically identical with the field of immediate experience which is considered by modern structural psychology. It comprises *all* of the data with which the thought of primitive man began.

9. The Development of Dualism.—Among the Greek thinkers, we find the beginnings, not only of theories of matter and of mind but also of empirical observations upon psychical phenomena. Plato (427–347 B.C.) and Aristotle (384–322 B.C.) are preëminent in this latter field, but we may reserve consideration of their empirical observations for a succeeding section of our discussion, confining ourselves for the present to the evolution of the concepts of soul and matter. As philosophy passed out of the hands of the Greeks, through Aristotle to the Romans, interest in the nature of matter decreased, as that in the character of the soul was augmented. The soul was divided into *departments,* of which Aristotle distinguished a hierarchy of five, the highest being responsible for thought and creative reason. In the hands of Christian and Stoic philosophers, the soul became essentially a religious conception, carrying with it in enhanced form its implication of immortality and independence of the body, which attached to it even in primitive animism. In Christian philosophy, the soul became the focus of ethical influences and was set over against matter, the main theoretical function of which became that of subserving the forces of evil. Saint Augustine [10] (died *ca.* 613 A.D.) distinguished within the soul the three faculties of memory, intellect and will, emphasizing the ethical importance of the latter. The medieval Schoolmen, represented, for example, by Saint Thomas Aquinas (*ca.* 1227–1274),[11] elaborated similar faculty doctrines and did all within their power to widen the chasm between the soul and matter, in the interests of religious teaching. In the philosophy of Francis Bacon (1561–1626), at the termination of the medieval period, we find the soul divided into the faculties of intellect, reason, fancy, memory, appetite and will.

All through the Middle Ages, with their astonishingly meager contributions to science and philosophy, we find the notion of the soul becoming more and more mystical, losing the distinctness of its conception as an anima and being endowed more and more with abstract and intangible attributes. It continued, however, to function as the mysterious entity underlying mental activity and voluntary movement, and carried with it the immortality of personal character with which it was endowed in primitive theory. With Bacon and the Renaissance, however, men suddenly turned away from this easy plan of abstract speculation and began to consider afresh the data of experience itself. The Greek ideas of matter and the contemplation of the nature of the external world at large were revived. Galileo [12] (1564–1642) initiated both experimental and mathematical physics, while Copernicus (1473–1543) and Kepler (1571–1630) turned anew to astronomy, and revolutionized existing conceptions of the solar system. With Newton (1642–1727), the laws of motion and of gravitation, as well as the principles of optics, assumed distinct mathematical form. Physical science, which had been nursed by the Arabians during the Middle Ages, was delivered once more

to the Europeans.   The nature of matter became clearer
and more distinct while, by contrast, that of the soul assumed an enhanced mysticism.

The climax of this dualistic tendency appeared in that
stupendous intellectual figure of the post-Renaissance, René
Descartes (1596–1650).   Descartes' philosophy[13] foreshadowed most of the cardinal ideas of modern thought.
As the basis for philosophy he returned to immediate experience with his famous formula, *cogito ergo sum.*   The
essence of the soul is *to think,* while that of matter is *to
be extended;* the widest of all conceivable contrasts.   Animals, according to Descartes, are to be regarded as mechanical automata operated by the mechanism of the reflex arc,
which he was the first to schematize clearly.   Probably
through fear of ecclesiastical censure, Descartes restricted
the doctrine of automatism to the lower animals and taught
that, in man, the soul interacts with the mechanical organism
at a small point in the brain within the pineal gland.   There
is no more unique figure in the history of intellect than this
energetic and universal thinker, who crystallized the philosophy of all of his precursors and laid the paths along
which most of his successors were to trudge.   But, as we
shall see, their travels along these paths were directed toward an escape from the dualistic doctrine which he so
clearly enunciated.

Section 2

THE PSYCHOLOGY WITHOUT A SOUL;
PHILOSOPHICAL PHASE

10. Paths of Escape from Dualism.—The movement of
psychological theory after Descartes may be characterized
as an attempt to escape from his categorical dualism of
soul and matter.   This theoretical endeavor was accompanied by two lines of empirical development which began
with Descartes himself: first, the analysis of experience or
consciousness from the introspective point of view, an em-

pirical study independent of soul theory and, second, an effort to arrive at a definite conception of the relation of consciousness to organic processes or to the data of physiology.   In the present Section, we shall consider post-Cartesian psychological theory and the development of psychology as the introspective study of consciousness, leaving for consideration in the next Section the history of the relations between psychology and physiology.   There are three evident methods by which one might attempt to escape from the dualism of soul and matter, as it was formulated by Descartes, and each of these methods was utilized by a considerable number of his successors.   The methods in question consist, first, in the identification of the psychical and the physical, second, in the rejection of mind as an illusion or delusion and, third, in the denial of the existence of matter.

11. Spinoza and Leibnitz.—The principal monistic philosophers, immediately following Descartes, were Spinoza[14] (1632–1677) and Leibnitz[15] (1646–1716).   Spinoza propounded the view that mind and matter are two different aspects of a single universal substance which he called God. The apparently intimate relations of mind and matter are to be explained as a consequence of their symmetrical dependencies upon the single underlying substance.   Although the terminology of Spinoza's theory has ethical and religious connotations it is by no means a sentimental philosophy, but more closely resembles a deterministic mechanism in its form.   Spinoza's doctrine is the prototype of many so-called *double aspect theories* of the interrelations of mind and body, a species of theory which is still far from being extinct in psychological discussion.   For Spinoza, the substances soul and matter were both submerged in the universal substance of God.

Leibnitz, however, retained the hypothesis of the individual soul and constructed a theory of soul atomism, or a "monadology," as he called it.   He supposed the universe to consist of a hierarchical organization of individual souls of varying orders of complexity.   Each of these souls, or

monads, possessed a double aspect, as it appeared to itself
and as it appeared to any other soul. In the former rôle,
it constituted a psychical phenomenon, but, in the latter, it
was material. Within each of the monads, there was supposed to be an actual or potential representation of all of
the other monads, this system of representation comprising
the physical universe for the given monad. The individual
monads were conceived to be the ultimate substantial realities lying back of the phenomena which make up the world
of perception. However, the representations, within any
monad, of the monadic universe outside of it, were not to
be regarded as direct effects of the latter but, rather, as the
product of internal processes within the monad which were
exactly synchronized with the outside cosmic structures and
events.

This non-causal, but absolutely accurate, correspondence
in a universe of souls—as Leibnitz expressed it—"without
windows," was explained as a consequence of a "preëstablished harmony," ordained by the Creator, the greatest of
all monads, the monad of monads. The Leibnitzian doctrine of preëstablished harmony is the source of the modern
theory of psychophysical parallelism, which assumes a relation of interdetermination or correspondence between psychical and physical events without interaction or transfer
of influence between the two series of processes. The
Leibnitzian monadology was utilized later in the teachings
of C. Wolff (1679–1754), R. H. Lotze, J. F. Herbart
and other psychological thinkers. Both Spinoza and Leibnitz made valuable contributions to general psychology, the
former writing at considerable length on the association of
ideas and on the emotions, while the latter proposed the
idea of unconscious perception and developed the conception of the unity of consciousness.

12. The Materialistic Path.—The escape from dualism
by the method of rejecting the psychical concepts and adopting a strictly materialistic view of the universe is represented
by a contemporary of Descartes, Thomas Hobbes [16] (1588–
1679). Hobbes attempted to reduce all reality to matter

and motion, regarding all other aspects of experience as
illusions or phantasms. He distinguished clearly between
the characteristics of perception which are significant of the
actual nature of bodies and those which are mere accidents,
imposed by the reactions of the sense-organs and brain.
This distinction, which in his successors becomes that between *primary and secondary qualities,* respectively, enabled
him to discard from the domain of serious philosophy all
of the characteristics of external, as well as of internal,
experience which would not fit into his materialistic system.
The secondary qualities, such as color, sound, etc., were
regarded as ephemeral by-products of mechanical motions
within the brain. Hobbes' conception of bodily activity was
strictly mechanistic, applying the automaton theory of Descartes to man as well as to animals. This mechanistic conception was also developed in great detail on the purely
physiological side by Borelli [17] (1608–1679) another contemporary of Descartes. The same views were continued
by later materialists such as J. O. de La Mettrie [18] (1709–
1751), in his book on *The Human Machine,* P. J. G.
Cabanis [19] (1757–1808), P. H. D. Holbach [20] (1723–1789)
and others.

   13. The Idealistic Path.—The third path of escape
from dualism, involving the rejection of matter as a real
substance, is represented by the line of philosophical thinking
which began in modern times with the British philosopher,
Bishop Berkeley [21] (1685–1753). Hobbes and Locke had
shown that the so-called secondary properties of bodies are
mental or subjective creations. Berkeley, by an analysis of
the mechanism of stereoscopic vision which still possesses
considerable scientific value, demonstrated that the primary
qualities of extensity and motion are just as dependent
upon the reactions of the nervous system as are secondary
qualities such as color and hardness. This view is latent
even in Hobbes' analysis, as well as in the Leibnitzian philosophy, but Berkeley boldly drew the conclusion that, because all of the contents of external experience without
exception are dependent upon sensory mechanisms, there is

no basis whatsoever for a belief in the objective reality of
matter. He regarded the hypothesis of matter as an explanatory addition to the facts of immediate experience, a
useless fiction. The subjective idealism which he thus established virtually makes all experience psychical, but, as
he himself repeatedly pointed out, this doctrine cannot correctly be accused of tampering with any of the actual facts
of perception.

Although Berkeley rejected the hypothesis of matter, he
retained that of spirit or soul, and postulated the existence
of a universal soul or God to be responsible for the generation, within finite souls, of the phenomena of the external
world. The Scottish philosopher, David Hume [22] (1711–
1776), now took the obvious next step and rejected spirit
as well as matter from the domain of reality, thus returning
to primitive, unamplified experience as the only reliable subject matter of scientific or philosophical discussion. This
was a position of universal skepticism in which all that we
know is the flux of experience, even causation being reduced
to an habitual concatenation of impressions or ideas. Such
an impoverishment of the subject matter and methods of
science seemed to Immanuel Kant [23] (1724–1804) to im-
pugn the validity of all scientific inquiry, and he therefore
proceeded to attempt a vindication of science, by showing
that, although the world of external experience is a purely
mental construction, this construction is inevitably made according to certain general principles or "categories of the
understanding," as he called them. The nature of these
principles can be known *a priori* or independently of concrete experience because they are the laws of the knowing
mind itself. The phenomena of the external world thus
necessarily obey the laws of geometry, of temporal succession, of causation, and the like. Whether or not we admit
that Kant's arguments actually provide a way of escape
from the skepticism and empiricism of Hume, we must
acknowledge that his doctrine of the constructive activity of
perception is a valid psychological principle.

Although it appeared to the German Idealists, who followed Kant, that he had succeeded in escaping from the skepticism of Hume, it still seemed that he had left them in what the modern Realist would call an "egocentric predicament," for he denied completely our ability to know objective realites, or things-in-themselves, as they actually are. Accordingly, the strivings of subsequent idealisms have been directed toward a harmonization of idealistic tenets with a belief in truly objective reality, attempting to replace the subjective idealism which began with Berkeley by an objective idealism.   Although the main interests of these thinkers have been ontological or metaphysical rather than psychological they have made many incidental contributions to psychology, and their metaphysical doctrines are extensions of psychological principles into the realm of metaphysics. Among German thinkers of this school we must count J. G. Fichte (1762–1814), who found in the imperative of the moral consciousness an implication of the existence of objective realities as objects of duty.[24]   The influence of Fichte's teachings upon modern psychology can be traced in such systems as Münsterberg's purposive psychology.[25]

F. W. J. von Schelling's [26] (1775–1854) *Naturphilosophie* and G. W. F. Hegel's [27] (1770–1831) dialectic and phenomenology contain many psychological reflections, but are less suggestive than the works of Arthur Schopenhauer [28] (1788–1860) and his follower, K. R. E. von Hartmann [29] (1842–1906), who conceived the universe throughout in psychological terms.   According to Schopenhauer's pessimistic philosophy the substance of external, as well as of internal, experience is to be found in what he called the *Will* which, in its struggles out of unconsciousness into consciousness, creates all of the miserable phenomena of experience. In von Hartmann's philosophy the "Unconscious" replaces the *Will* of Schopenhauer.   Besides being full of many keen incidental psychological observations these pessimistic philosophers made many contributions to our modern theories of the subconscious mind.

14. The Analysis of Consciousness by Introspection.—
We must now turn to consider another phase of mental
science which assumed constantly increasing importance after
Descartes and finally came, in the rôle of "the psychology
without a soul," to occupy the center of the psychological
stage. This phase, as typified in its extreme form by the
philosopher Hume, involved a complete neglect or rejection
of hypotheses, either of soul or of matter, and an attempt
to formulate a strictly empirical description of given phenomena of experience, whether internal or external in character. Such an effort was evident in many of the writings
of Descartes himself as well as of some of his predecessors,
and is still more obvious in his follower, N. Malebranche [30]
(1638–1715), but it only comes to full flower in the British
empiricists of the Enlightenment period.

The beginnings of empirical psychology, of course, overlap the development of the soul theory and are to be found
in Greek philosophy. We have already mentioned the subjectivism of Parmenides and of Zeno, who defined a system
of appearances or illusions and described some of the characteristics of this system. The emphasis which was laid by
Socrates upon self-knowledge is well known, and his pupil,
Plato, not only dilated at great length on different forms of
knowledge, including those of "illusion" and "opinion," but
stated definite principles, derived from observation, regarding the association of ideas by similarity and contiguity and
concerning the principles of memory or reminiscence. In
Democritus and Empedocles we find rather carefully elaborated theories of sense perception. Aristotle has well been
called "the father of empirical psychology," since he is the
author of treatises on the principles of idea association, on
memory and on dreams. Saint Augustine laid great emphasis upon self-observation, but the Medieval Scholastics
made very little progress in this direction, as they were by
nature theory-spinners rather than observers. Prior to
Descartes, we find in the Spanish thinker, J. L. Vives [31]
(1492–1540), a definite apostle of the empirical study of
the activities and physical effects of the soul, in place of the

attempt to determine its inherent nature. Descartes' own idea of the fundamental certainty of consciousness virtually makes introspection the starting point of all knowledge, and empirical psychology by introspection was clearly conceived by Malebranche.

However, it is only in the British philosopher, John Locke [32] (1632–1704), that we arrive at a point of view regarding experience which is comparable with that of modern introspective psychology. Although Locke accepted, philosophically, both the hypotheses of soul and of matter he laid little emphasis upon them and was concerned, in his own thinking, almost exclusively with an analysis of experience or consciousness into its given components, and an ascertainment of the modes and laws of combination of such components. He found that all knowledge was dependent upon experience and that experience was resolvable into units known as ideas. Ideas are either simple or complex, the latter being built up from the former by "association." He distinguished between "sensations" and "reflections," reflections being products of introspective analysis. He also drew a clear line of demarcation between the primary and secondary qualities of bodies as we experience them, regarding the secondary qualities as properties of consciousness only. In Locke's teachings we find the explicit beginnings of modern structural psychology.

The empiricistic and associationistic schools of mental philosophy which began with Locke were continued by a long series of British thinkers. We have seen how Hume reduced the subject matter of all science to the immediate data of experience, and how he explained even physical causation in terms of the principle of association. Naturally, in the course of this line of thought, he developed many specific ideas regarding the principles of association by similarity, contiguity, etc. David Hartley [33] (1705–1757) and Joseph Priestley [34] (1733–1804) also considered these questions, and advanced physiological theories to account for the processes of association and memory. Thomas Reid [35] (1710–1796) clearly advocated a psychology by pure introspection. During the nineteenth century the association school was continued in England by James Mill [36] and by his son, John Stuart Mill,[37] who introduced the conception of "mental chemistry." According to this latter view the associative combination of ideas is accompanied by a qualitative change in the nature of the integral group, analogous to the alteration which occurs in chemical union. Sir William Hamilton [38] (1788–1856), influenced to a large extent by the Kantian philosophy, vigorously championed the study of the inner life. In France, a similar view was developed by E. B. de Condillac [39] (1715–1780) in his sensationalistic psychology. All of these thinkers of the association school denied the existence of innate ideas and the possibility of any knowledge apart from experience, assuming that the mind is originally a *tabula rasa* upon which sensation writes its records in the form of reproducible images. Knowledge arises exclusively from this process and consists in a definite concatenation of such images.

15. Herbart and Lotze.—In Germany, J. F. Herbart [40] (1776–1841) developed a theory of mental chemistry which was a sort of combination of the Leibnitzian monadology with the empirical analysis of the associationists. Psychology, for him, consisted in the theory of the combination and interaction of certain psychical units which he called "soul reals." These psychical units were conceived to exist primarily in the subconscious mind where they interacted not only according to principles of association, or attraction, but also under the influence of a principle of inhibition or mental repulsion. Herbart endeavored to work out the interactions of such units by means of a mathematical symbolism. His doctrines have influenced later theories of the subconscious, such as that of repression in the psychology of Freud. Another psychologist exhibiting tendencies similar to those of Herbart was R. H. Lotze [41] (1817–1881). Lotze elaborated a monad theory with a definite division of faculties of the soul, on a dualistic basis, but his works contain much detailed and careful thinking about specific psychological problems. He clearly advocated the empirical study of the correspondence between mental and physiological states, thus aligning himself with the psychophysiologists, whose efforts in conjunction with the advancing science of biology it will be our duty to consider in the next section.

Section 3

THE PSYCHOLOGY WITHOUT A SOUL; PSYCHOPHYSICAL PHASE

16. The Rise of the Science of Biology.—We have seen that, after Descartes, the study of mind turned more and more away from the hypothesis of the soul to an empirical description of the facts of consciousness. However, the strict adherence to these facts, without reference to any supposedly underlying realities or conditions, proved difficult. The hypothesis of the soul had provided the conception of a substance having properties capable of explaining mental phenomena, and, with the rejection of this hypothesis, a quest naturally arose for some other principle which might take its place and furnish a basis upon which to synthesize the complex and incoherent data of experience into a scientific system. The substitute for the soul which appeared in this situation was *the living physiological organism.*

We have seen that Descartes himself not only epitomized the soul theory but also outlined the fundamental principles of both introspective and physiological psychology. He clearly expressed the idea of the reflex arc, which has dominated nerve physiology since his time, and the problem of the relation of mind to matter was distinctly formulated in his writings. The Cartesian doctrine of animal automatism definitely established the task of modern physiology, to explain in mechanistic or in physicochemical terms all of the operations of the living organism, without reference at all to mind. Modern physiology, itself, may be said to begin with William Harvey's (1578–1657) discovery and demonstration of the circulation of the blood. His contemporary, G. A. Borelli (1608–1679), endeavored to explain various animal movements, such as the flight of birds, on purely mechanical principles. For most of the great advances in biology, however, we are compelled to wait until the beginning of the nineteenth century.

Biology, as a general science of living things, was first clearly defined by G. R. Treviranus [42] (1776–1837) in his work, appearing at the dawn of this century, entitled *Biologie* (1802–1805). Biology appears in the nineteenth century essentially as a subdivision of the general science of physics, dealing with living matter, or protoplasm, and its products. Although, from time to time, there have been vitalistic tendencies in biology, maintaining that forces other than those studied by physics and by chemistry are active in the life process, the general trend of biology has been throughout mechanistic, denying the intervention in organic functions of other than physical agencies. This mechanistic tendency has also led the majority of physiologists to exclude from their theories any alleged psychical influences. They have tended to regard psychical phenomena, with T. H. Huxley [43] (1825–1895), as ineffective associates of restricted physiological activities—such as brain processes—which are not properly the subject matter of biology and are left for the psychologist or the student of mental science to consider.

Although biology, regarded as a physical science, has thus little to gain from attention to psychological facts, a similar statement certainly does not apply to the relations of psychology to biology. The advances in general biological theory, in the methods and discoveries of anatomy as well as of physiology, have been of the utmost importance for the development of psychology. At nearly every point, the conceptions of the biological sciences have been clearly reflected in psychological thought. The beginnings of laboratory experimental physiology in the work of Claude Bernard (1813–1878) and Paul Bert (1833–1886) laid the foundations not only for further advances of physiology but also for the development of laboratory psychology, which is forced to employ physiological methods of attack. The theory of evolution, beginning with J. B. P. de M. Lamarck [44]

(1744–1829) in his doctrine of development by effort and the transmission of acquired characters, and arriving in Charles Darwin's [45] (1809–1882) theory of evolution by natural selection and the survival of the fittest at the status of a definitely established theory, made possible the genetic point of view in psychology. Darwin himself wrote on a psychological topic from this point of view when he discussed "the expression of the emotions," and Herbert Spencer's [46] (1820–1903) elaborate treatise on psychology was explicitly undertaken from the evolutionary standpoint.

Among other psychological writers of this time who were influenced by the development of biology must be mentioned G. H. Lewes [47] (1817–1878) and W. K. Clifford [48] (1845–1879) as well as T. H. Huxley [49] (1825–1895), who discussed philosophical problems of mind and body. The literature of the period following Darwin was highly controversial and speculative but led to important progress in our conceptions of the relation existing between life and mind. Among other names which stand for the influence exerted upon psychology by biology we must mention that of Sir Francis Galton [50] (1822–1911) whose studies on the heredity of mental traits and on image types are classical, being continued in the researches of such modern investigators as Dr. F. A. Woods [51] (1873–   ). The biometric method, or the application of statistical mathematics to biological problems, which was introduced by A. Quetelet [52] and elaborated by Karl Pearson [53] (1857–   ), was rapidly adapted to psychological or psychophysical data. Another important biological advance, which was made initially by Mendel [54] (1822–1882) in the middle of the nineteenth century, began to bear fruit only at the end of this century when Mendel's writings were rediscovered by De Vries [55] and others. The doctrine of unit characters, which was formulated by Mendel, has revolutionized our conception of the nature of heredity and has been found applicable to a number of psychological traits.

17. Studies on Sensation and Nerve.—It is natural that the first definitely experimental studies in physiological psychology should have been concerned with sensation. It will be recalled how, with the development of physics, the majority of the qualitative characteristics of the world of external experience came to be regarded as secondary or subjective in character, therefore becoming chattels of the psychologist. Color and musical tone, as well as feelings of pain, warmth and cold, were clearly regarded, even in the eighteenth century, as mental rather than as physical facts. It is true that some of the early physicists, such as David Brewster [56] (1781–1868) and W. H. Wollaston [57] (1766–1828), and the poet, Goethe [58] (1749–1832), regarded color as an objective property of physical bodies, but Sir Isaac Newton [59] very clearly conceived color to be an effect produced in the eye or optic nerve by the action of light, which in itself was regarded as an uncolored, corpuscular form of matter. Similar views were entertained by Thomas Young [60] (1773–1829) in connection with the wave theory of light, which eventually replaced Newton's corpuscular hypothesis. In a famous lecture delivered by Young at the very beginning of the nineteenth century, we find clearly formulated that trichromatic theory of color vision which has played so important a part in physiological optics ever since. Johannes Purkinje [61] (1787–1869) published, in 1823, an important work, dealing with "the physiology of the sense organs," in which he described many interesting subjective appearances due to peculiarities of the organs of sense and, especially, of the eye.

This pioneer work of Purkinje was soon followed by very important contributions from Johannes Müller [62] (1801–1858) who wrote works on "the comparative physiology of vision" and on "the fantastic visual sensations," [63] as well as concerning many other problems lying in the borderland between physiology and psychology. Müller's doctrine of "the specific energy of nerves," according to which the sensory quality which results from the action of a stimulus depends not upon the nature of the latter but upon the identity of the nerve channel, has played an extremely important rôle in psychophysical thinking ever since his time.

Among the pupils of Müller were two psychophysiologists who became even more eminent than their great teacher. One of these was Emil Du Bois-Reymond [64] (1818–1886), who discovered and studied in great detail the electrical processes occurring in nervous tissues, thus laying the foundations for our modern conceptions of the essential nature of nervous activity. Du Bois-Reymond also wrote upon the problems of mind in relation to matter from a philosophical point of view. Another pupil of Müller, Hermann von Helmholtz [65] (1821–1894), was probably the greatest scientific intellect of the nineteenth century: the discoverer of new facts and new principles in many diverse fields of science, a great physicist and mathematician as well as a master of anatomy and physiology. His clear conception of the principle of the conservation of energy laid the basis for many of the most important subsequent advances in physics, while his demonstration of the finite velocity of the nerve impulse paved the way for the development of modern neurology. The most elaborate and systematic phases of his work lay definitely in the field of psychophysiology, resulting in two great handbooks of physiological optics [66] and physiological acoustics,[67] respectively, works which in their respective domains have never been equaled.

Among the successors of Helmholtz and of Du Bois-Reymond in the study of nerve physiology must be counted the German physiologist, Max Verworn [68] (1863–   ), whose work on the nature of excitation and inhibition has thrown a great light upon psychological as well as upon purely neurological questions, and the two English investigators, C. S. Sherrington (1857–   ) and Keith Lucas (1879–1916). Sherrington's even now classical work on *The Integrative Action of the Nervous System* [69] made very clear the fundamental principles which are involved in the coördination of functions between the many individual components of the nervous system. The researches of Lucas [70] further elucidated our conception of the nature of nerve action and culminated in the establishment of the so-called "all or none" principle for the nerve impulse. In the field of sensory psychophysiology, the epoch-making work of Helmholtz has been continued by such men as Ewald Hering [71] (1834–1918), Johannes von Kries [72] (1853–), Arthur König [73] (1856–1901) and Wilibald A. Nagel [74]. Hering's theory of color vision and his allied theories of other psychophysical processes have exerted a tremendous influence upon psychology, while von Kries' demonstration of the so-called duplicity or rod-cone theory, in vision, places his name high on the list of psychophysical investigators.

18. Psychophysics and Laboratory Psychology.—Another line of research which was to be of great systematic importance for physiological psychology was initiated by E. H. Weber [75] (1795–1878), a German physiologist who carried out elaborate quantitative investigations of cutaneous and auditory sensations and demonstrated the constancy of the relative threshold in many departments of sensory experience. Weber's Law, named after him, provided physiological psychology with a quantitative principle which was comparable in definiteness, if not in accuracy, with some of the mathematical laws of physical science. G. T. Fechner (1801–1887) utilized Weber's Law as the basis of a comprehensive theory of the relations holding between psychical and physical reality. In his *Elemente der Psychophysik*,[76] published in 1860, Fechner formulated principles which laid the groundwork for laboratory experimental psychology. He outlined definite methods for mental measurement and endeavored to show that the psychical and the physical are interrelated at all points by a universal logarithmic law, which he derived mathematically from Weber's principle. Fechner's thought is characterized by a rare combination of scientific diligence and accuracy with deep philosophical insight and sympathy, in the study of mental phenomena.[77] His conceptions of psychophysical law and of panpsychism still stand as bulwarks of scientific psychology.

The first avowedly psychological laboratory in the world was founded in Leipzig in 1879 by Wilhelm Wundt [78] (1832–1920) who must be accounted one of the most com-

prehensive minds of the late nineteenth century. His voluminous writings on mental science and the many pupils whom
he educated in his laboratory strongly stimulated the subsequent advances of scientific psychology. The first psychological laboratory in America was established by G. Stanley
Hall [79] (1846–1924) at Johns Hopkins University in 1890.
One year later William James [80] (1842–1910) started a laboratory at Harvard University. Although James retained
his definite connection with the laboratory for a period of
only one year, his interest in psychological problems never
waned and his continuous contributions to the facts, theories
and philosophy of mind earned for him at his death the title
of Dean of American Psychologists. James was replaced at
Harvard by Hugo Münsterberg [81] (1863–1916), in 1892
who remained as director of this leading psychological laboratory until his death, exerting an important influence upon
the development of experimental methods in the study of
mental phenomena. An even greater figure among American experimental psychologists was E. B. Titchener [82]
(1867–1927), whose laboratory at Cornell University has
been the constant source of new data and ideas, standing
firmly for the application of methods of observation and
controlled experiment to strictly psychological subject matters. In the laboratories of Wundt, Münsterberg and Titchener, as well as in the myriads of other psychological laboratories which sprang up in the early twentieth century,
not only problems of sensation but all sorts of questions relating to mind were attacked by experimental methods. If
the results have not always been uniformly illuminating, the
blame is to be laid not on the general method of attack, but
on the difficulty of the problems and the youthfulness of the
science.

19. The Development of Brain Physiology.—Another
path of progress in the domain of physiology which inevitably
led over into that of psychology lay in the study of the
functions of the brain. A path which met this, starting on
the side of psychology, was that of the scientific study of
insanity or mental abnormality. As long as the soul theory

dominated man's conception of his own mental nature, he was content to regard insanity as an expression of possession by evil spirits, and hence to endeavor to cure the disorder by exorcising the evil spirit, using methods painful to the patient and fruitless in results. With the beginnings of physiological psychology, however, it gradually became clear that the state of the mind depends upon that of the nervous system, in particular upon conditions within the brain. This dependency of personality upon the character of the brain was expressed with highly exaggerated definiteness by F. J. Gall [83] (1758–1828), during the first quarter of the nineteenth century, in his theory of phrenology. According to this doctrine, elaborated from the historic faculty psychology, different mental faculties were to be regarded as localized in different portions of the brain, the degree of physical development of these various portions being proportional to the dominance of the given faculty in the personality under analysis. This hypothesis naturally substantiated the idea that the form of the cranium could be relied upon as an index of character. Although the doctrine of phrenology, with its thirty-five independent faculties, was fantastically conceived by its originator and, in the hands of his disciples, degenerated into a form of charlatanism, it nevertheless foreshadowed the modern principle of the localization of functions specifically in different portions of the brain.

M. J. P. Flourens [84] (1794–1867), reacting against the exaggerated form taken by phrenology, denied (in 1824) that there is any localization or partition of functions whatsoever within the cerebrum, maintaining that this region of the brain operates as a unit for all mental functions, and this doctrine held sway for nearly fifty years. However, in 1870 G. T. Fritsch and E. Hitzig [85] (book, 1874) demonstrated, beyond peradventure, the existence of a definitely delimited area in the cerebral cortex for the control of the voluntary muscles of the body. They established this by means of local stimulation of the cortex in living dogs, their observations being corroborated by David Ferrier [86] (book, 1881). Shortly thereafter a definite area for the control of speech was located by J. Bouillaud and P. Broca [87] (1824–1880). This was followed by Paul Flechzig's [88] (1847–   ) work on the ontogenetic development of the brain tracts, which indicated clearly that the motor and sensory fibers from the periphery are definitely projected upon selected areas of the cerebral cortex. The work of F. Goltz [89] (book, 1881) and H. Munk [90] (book, 1881) established the existence of specific visual and other sensory areas in the cortex, the functions of such areas being proven not only by experiments upon lower animals but by an accumulating mass of evidence drawn from pathological observations upon human beings. Modern investigations in this field tend more and more towards the view that all mental functions and phenomena are specifically represented in the mechanisms of the brain, although the dividing lines thus established between mental functions are very different from those drawn by phrenology.

20. Theories of Mental Disease.—The identification of the various portions of the brain which are involved in specific mental functions, has been aided tremendously in the human subject by observations upon mental disease, and the dominant theory of insanity at the present day is psychophysical, seeking to cure mental disease, where possible, by correcting abnormal conditions in the nervous system. However, side by side with this line of attack, there has developed a system for treating mental disease by psychological methods, although this procedure has been restricted in the main to a specific class of disorders known as psychoneuroses, such as, for example, hysteria. The French psychiatrists, Pierre Janet [91] (1859–   ) and J. M. Charcot [92] (1825–1893) showed that it was possible to trace hysteria to an emotional shock or mental trauma in the psychical biography of the patient, and they found that, in many cases, they could remove the pathological symptoms by hypnosis and suggestion.

This conception of mental disease and its cure has been developed into an elaborate psychological system by Sigmund Freud [93] (1856–   ) and his followers, the psychoanalysts.

According to this doctrine, a great many mental disorders are due to repressed emotional influences or inhibited subconscious purposes, and the cure for the trouble lies in relieving these repressions or inhibitions and integrating all of the mental tendencies into a consistent whole. This general scheme has been applied, by the psychoanalysts, not only to what are ordinarily regarded as pathological states, but also to certain phenomena of everyday life, and these extensions of the psychoanalytic theory lead us eventually to very general ideas concerning motivation and character. In the Freudian psychology we find the idea of the subconscious mind utilized, as it was in Herbart's system, to explain the dynamics of the mental life. By thus laying stress upon the problem of motivation, the psychoanalysts have given psychology a tremendous impetus in a direction along which it must travel progressively if it is to be of maximum human utility. The Freudian emphasis upon sex, fear and other primitive motives has opened the eyes of psychologists to the importance of instincts, for an understanding of mental life.

In connection with the present topic we may mention briefly the progress which has been made in recent times in our knowledge of the influence of various chemicals and toxins upon "the mind." The use of ether and chloroform to produce anæthesia during surgical operations has been followed by an understanding of the manner in which these substances act upon nervous tissue, and hence, in part, of the conditions of consciousness in nerve activity. The effects of other narcotics and excitants, such as strychnine, alcohol, morphine, etc., have been carefully studied experimentally. Furthermore, it has been found that, within the body itself, there are produced specific chemical substances called hormones, secreted by the ductless glands, which play an important part in the regulation of the mental as well as of the physiological characteristics of the individual. The study of these relationships seems to be developing at the present day a sort of chemical phrenology. Although the importance of the so-called endocrines is undoubtedly exaggerated by certain of their exponents,[94] the basic fact of their existence and influence cannot be denied. The part played by certain specific internal secretions, such as adrenin, in states of emotion has also been definitely proved by the work of W. B. Cannon [95] and others.

Section 4

MODERN MOVEMENTS IN PSYCHOLOGY

21. The Roots of Modern Doctrines.—As we stand amid the modern turmoil of controversy in psychology, and look back into the history of the science, certain movements are salient as the sources of present opinions. The British empiricists and the French sensationalists find their legitimate modern representatives in the school of structural psychologists, who regard psychology as the science of the analysis of consciousness by the introspective method. This school, for the most part, conceives the relationship between consciousness and physiological processes in terms of the principle of parallelism. The latter took origin in Leibnitz's doctrine of preëstablished harmony and it has been followed, with some deviations and modifications, by the line of physiological psychologists leading down to the present day. The influence of physiology and of the physiological mode of attack upon psychology is seen in all of the modern doctrines, even the most subjective of them. Consciousness appears, psychophysically, as an aspect of response, the properties of the response arc being stamped in symbolic form upon the constitution of the mind. The psychical phenomena seem to symbolize the transition from sensory integration to motor expression.

This "motor theory of consciousness," which assumed distinct form in the thought of William James,[96] has many ramifications, but is a leading idea in all modern psychology. It influences the strictly structural psychologists the least, and the behaviorists the most, since the latter deny that

anything at all exists for psychology except the response
mechanism. The so-called *functional psychologists,* represented for example by J. R. Angell,[97] have departed, at any
rate in their mode of thinking, from the assumption of psychophysical parallelism and have tended to regard consciousness as actually playing a part in the response activity,
thus truly possessing a "function" in the physiological sense.
They have felt that a bare introspective account of consciousness was not adequate, and that to give psychology completeness it was necessary to consider the part played by consciousness in behavior. The philosophical and practical difficulties encountered by this attitude have encouraged the
behavioristic or purely physiological point of view.

Behaviorism apparently arises in modern times as a consequence of the failure of animal psychologists to arrive
at a satisfactory criterion for the existence of mind in the
lower organisms. The seeming futility of arguments concerning the presence or absence of psychical activity in connection with the responses of lower animals led to the appearance of a purely physiological line of attack upon animal
behavior. The animal physiologists, represented for example by Bethe, Beer and von Uexküll,[98] were largely successful in their effort to eliminate psychological terminology
from their accounts of animal action, thus encouraging the
application of similar methods of analysis to human behavior. This suggested, in the minds of Watson and other
American psychologists, the conception of psychology as
a science of behavior, pure and simple. The ultimate
roots of the behavioristic movement, however, are certainly
to be found at the beginnings of physiology in the work of
Harvey and Borelli, and in the ideas of animal and even
human automatism which appear in Descartes and La
Mettrie.

Philosophical views have played a large rôle implicitly
in modern psychological thinking. The introspectionists,
particularly of the structuralist school, have been influenced
by, and have tacitly assumed, the standpoint of idealism,
whereas the behaviorists and objective psychologists have

based their thought upon a realistic interpretation of experience. It would appear that neither the introspectionists nor the behaviorists have kept in very close touch with the development of modern physical science, with its tendency to reduce the physical universe to a system of electrical particles and its relativistic doctrines of space, mass and time. From the metaphysical point of view nearly all of the modern schools in psychology present an aspect of naïveté. Only here and there, as for example in the doctrine of psychical monism as expounded by the Dutch psychologist, G. Heymans,[99] do we find an attempt to reconcile the conflicting metaphysical assumptions which underlie modern psychological thought.

As we shall see in the following section, the various doctrines concerning the problem of psychology, which are represented in current debates, by no means form a closely knit system nor one which is throughout modern and progressive. The most ancient psychological teachings continue to have their apostles. Some psychologists, although a dwindling number, still uphold the soul theory. Others, such as the French philosopher, Henri Bergson,[100] champion a confused dualistic view with vitalistic implications. The psychoanalytic line of development has very few points of contact either with introspective structural psychology or with physiological psychology, although some borderline thinkers, such as E. B. Holt,[101] have endeavored to establish such interconnections. In general, the picture which psychology presents at the present day is one of incoherence and even of disruption, but the scene discloses an intense activity, so we may feel hopeful that the outcome of the struggle will be the appearance of a truly synthetic and vigorous conception of the science, consistent at once with the diversified lines of historical development which have entered into its making and with the demands of progress and human utility.

22. The Behavioristic and Gestalt Movements To-day. —In the year, 1929, we find two outstanding battles raging in the domain of psychological methodology. One of these controversies is somewhat more general in its bearing than is the other, but both are attracting a great deal of attention. The first is the general argument between the behaviorists and the introspectionists, which began with the pronouncements of John B. Watson,[102] in 1913, and which, after the passage of sixteen years, seems to be no nearer a decision than it was in the beginning. The second point at issue is one as to the method of psychological report or description, rather than as to the definition of the problem of psychology at large: the controversy between the *Gestalt* (configurational) and the older "structural" schools of psychology. Behaviorism is essentially an American propaganda, while the *Gestalt* movement is characteristically German. Probably, during the past few years, the *Gestalt* doctrine has created more interest in America than the behavioristic views have as yet aroused abroad. However, we find such *Gestalters* as Kurt Koffka [103] discussing the behavioristic program very seriously, and rejecting it as a central plan for psychology. Although the outstanding applications of the *Gestalt* proposals have thus far been to introspective topics, such *Gestalters* as W. Köhler have demonstrated their relevancy to a behavioristic as well as to an introspective statement of the psychological problem. Behavioristic teachings concerning organic unity in bodily response (as opposed to atomistic physiological analysis) have a configurationistic flavor (*vide infra*).

Behaviorism. Although Watson is properly regarded as the founder of behaviorism, his views were foreshadowed, as we have seen, by proposals of earlier workers. E. P. Frost [104] actually antedated Watson by several months in recommending that psychology dispense with introspective concepts and limit itself to an objective statement of its problems. Behaviorism has important connections, historically, with functional psychology, as well as with the arguments of the animal physiologists and with earlier materialistic views in general.

As formulated by Watson, behaviorism is essentially an attempt to redefine the problem of psychology in non-introspective terms. The outstanding feature of Watson's behaviorism is its rejection of all such notions as consciousness, feeling, sensation, perception and memory. The doctrine is, to this extent, a negative one. On the positive side, it attacks the phenomena of neuromuscular response with renewed vigor and attempts to formulate psychological problems in terms of various behavior concepts. Although Watson regards psychology as a biological science, he refuses to identify it with any branch of physiology. The problem of psychology, according to him, is to consider the stimulus-reaction system as an organic whole, whereas physiology breaks it down into components.

It must be acknowledged that Watson's teachings have made great progress among American psychologists. The youthful militancy of behaviorism and its promise of new results have made many converts. Prominent among the latter may be mentioned A. P. Weiss,[105] E. C. Tolman [106] and W. S. Hunter.[107] Tolman has presented many reformulations of psychological concepts in behavioristic terms. Weiss has developed the behavioristic standpoint in a thoroughly physical manner, which savors of old-time materialism brought up to date. Weiss' views contrast rather sharply with the "organic unity" notions of such writers as E. B. Holt, R. B. Perry [108] and Watson himself. Hunter has taken a less radical and more constructive position, with an eye for facts rather than concepts. We shall consider the doctrines of various behaviorists in greater detail below.

Configurationism. The origin of the Gestalttheorie or the doctrine of configurationism appears to lie in M. Wertheimer's studies on motion perception.[109] These were published in 1912, but the development of a general systematic view was delayed until the more recent writings of Kurt Koffka [110] and of Wolfgang Köhler.[111] The notion of Gestaltqualität, or of "form-quality," which is fundamental to configurationism, was clearly stated by C. von Ehrenfels [112] in 1890. The Gestalters are now the dominant school in Germany but there are relatively few American or English psychologists who have definitely affiliated themselves with this movement. R. M. Ogden [113] and Harry

Helson [114] are the most prominent American exponents of the configurationist tendency. In Austria, the so-called Graz school of configurationists included V. Benussi, S. Witasek and A. Höfler, while Karl Bühler combats their doctrines. In Germany, the *Gestalters* are opposed by that patriarch of psychology, G. E. Müller.

The *Gestalt* movement consists primarily in an attack upon atomistic analysis in psychology. According to the configurationists, modern structural psychology treats the mind too much after the plan of an old-fashioned physics. It assumes that conscious states and process are built up from separable units and can properly be described in terms of such units. As a matter of fact, according to the configurationists, each conscious state and process is a unified system with properties peculiar to itself, and it must be described as an integral *form*, or *Gestalt*, rather than as a combination of elementary units. However, the *Gestalt* school is far from being purely negative in its teachings and results. A new kind of experimental attack upon psychological problems has arisen from the point of view established by Koffka and Köhler, and this has led to many new discoveries, especially in the domain of perception. We shall consider further details of the *Gestalt* criticism in our chapters on psychological method, and the principal positive doctrines and demonstrations of the *Gestalters* in our discussion of cerebration. (See pages 108–113 and Volume III.)

Section 5

AGREEMENTS CONCERNING PSYCHOLOGY AS A SCIENCE

23. Psychology An Experimental Science.—The existing dispute with regard to the exact field and methods of psychology should not be taken to mean that there is complete disagreement, even between the most variant opinions. The ambiguity of the definition of psychology is great only when compared with that of other more advanced sciences, and does not mean that its position within the entire domain of knowledge is not fairly determinate.   In spite of the seeming discrepancies between the various subject matters and methods which have been advocated as psychological, it is easy to demonstrate the existence of a close historical and functional affiliation between them.   The field of psychological inquiry is restricted to a definite realm, under all of its alternative interpretations, although within this realm there is much variability.   There is some confusion between the domains of psychology and of physiology, but they have never been so defined as exactly to coincide; and no one as yet has suggested that psychology is the science of the stars or of the weather.

All modern psychologists are agreed that psychology is, or should be, an empirical or inductive science [115]—no longer what it once was: a branch of speculative philosophy.   This proposition seems to be quite straightforward, but its full meaning cannot be made thoroughly intelligible except through a presentation of the actual applications and results of scientific psychology.   To regard psychology as a science is to imply that it is a description of some form of existence, established by observation and logical reasoning.   It means that psychology is not influenced by supposed *a priori* necessities or evaluations.   It derives nothing from concepts of mind or spirit, except in so far as these are descriptive formulations from experience.   A science cannot cater to any prejudices, whether they be intellectual or emotional in their foundations.   To label psychology as a science is to require, moreover, that it should strive constantly for generality and accuracy.   It must seek out principles or laws, as well as systems for classification; and it must formulate and measure mathematically wherever possible.

However, the definition of psychology as a science does not mean that its aims and methods must be the same in all particulars as those of other and older sciences.   For example, it is not an essential of science that its point of view should be "objective," or that it should endeavor to "reduce" its subject matter to so-called physical terms. Scientific observation is not necessarily confined, as it usually is in physics, to vision. In psychology it embraces all of the departments of sense and even extends beyond sense. Moreover, the exact schemes of generalization which are employed by the physical and biological sciences are not necessarily to be forced upon psychology. The devices for classification and the formulation of laws must follow methods which are appropriate to the subject matters which they concern. Even such a general conception as that of *quantity* may well present a somewhat different aspect in psychology from that which it has in the physical sciences.

A second point of agreement among contemporary psychologists is that psychology is, or should be, an *experimental* science. This means that its subject matter is conceivably amenable to methods of laboratory control. Certain kinds of psychological experiments may possibly be carried out without special apparatus or any explicit reference to physical or physiological conditions. However, in the great majority of cases, experimentation demands the establishment and control of physical determinants, so that the notion of psychology as an experimental science practically implies the functional dependence of psychological data upon physiological factors. But this cannot be interpreted to mean that the subject matter of psychology is necessarily, in itself, physiological, either in part or in its entirety.

24. **Psychology Involves Physiology But No Soul.**— There is an even more specific point of agreement among the teachings of practically all contemporary psychologists, namely, that psychology is, in fact, the study of certain phenomena which occur in functional connection with living organisms and, especially, in association with the action of nervous systems. There may be a difference of opinion as to whether these processes are identifiable with physiological activities or whether they constitute an entirely different form of existence; but no modern psychologist denies the relationship in question. Whether the point of view of the psychologist is introspective or behavioristic, he is concerned

with stimuli, sense-organs, nerves, motor reactions, etc., and their bearing upon his preferred conceptions. The process of neuromuscular response may therefore be regarded as an index of the existence of material for psychological study. The more complex the process in question, the more liable it is to involve important psychological data. Some psychologists view this neuromuscular activity as being in itself psychological; others would consider only certain limited aspects of the process; while still others concern themselves with facts which are distinct from, but correlated with, the response.

There is still a fourth point concerning which practically all modern psychologists are in agreement. This is that psychology is not what it would seem to be on the basis of its etymology: the science of the soul. The history of psychology has apparently put a definite quietus upon this literal interpretation of the word. There may still be some dissenters from this conclusion, but they are very few in number. The rejection of the soul as a subject matter for psychology is to be attributed, certainly not to any inappropriateness, but rather to the fact that its existence has never been demonstrated by scientific methods. Those who still continue to believe in the soul or some equivalent (self, subject or ego), do so on the basis of alleged logical necessity or religious emotion rather than of empirical demonstration. But such reasons cannot play a part in determining the conclusions of psychology as a science.

Section 6

PSYCHICAL SUBJECT MATTERS FOR PSYCHOLOGY

We may now briefly review some of the problems or subject matters which are being advocated for psychology at the present time. These may be divided conveniently into the psychical and the physical (including the physiological).

25. The Psychology of Self.—We still find certain residues of the soul theory, masquerading in modern discussion as accounts of empirical or quasi-empirical realities. The subtleties of thought which characterize philosophical discourse—particularly among idealists—have established notions, such as those of subject, ego, transcendental ego, and so on, which can play the part of the soul in propositions, without explicitly assuming any of its intelligible properties. In his more philosophical writings, William McDougall [116] has defended the notion of the soul and the animistic hypothesis in general, although in his recent *Outline of Psychology* he seems to abandon it as an instrument of psychological explanation. However, he still insists upon the hypothesis of "mind" as something which underlies the empirical facts of sentiency and behavior. He says that the notion of the subject is "an indispensable hypothesis." [117] "All experiencing or thinking is experiencing or thinking of some one, some subject, some person, some organism."

A similar view is adopted by Mary W. Calkins in her discussion of self-psychology.[118] She says: "I cannot be conscious of an idea, except as an idea of self; implicitly, if not explicitly, I am always conscious of a self, as having the idea of experience." Accordingly, she believes that the self is "a basal fact in psychology." She regards the self as "distinct from the body, but related to it."

26. The Psychology of "Act."—Psychologists, such as McDougall and Calkins, who believe in the subject or self, either as a logical necessity or as an empirical fact, usually regard consciousness or experience as a *process* or a *relationship,* rather than as a self-sufficient "thing." Thus, McDougall says: [119] "Whatever phase of experience we think of, we make an object of our thinking; and we tend to regard every object of our thinking as a thing. But experience is not made up of things; it is a process and perhaps in all cases a train of activity." The first step away from the self theory is apparently to define psychology as the science of the *activities* or relationships which occur between subjects and objects, while admitting that the subject itself is not a psychological datum. The object, in turn, can be left to physics or some other "objective" science, such as "phenomenology." The notion of "activity" as a subject matter for psychology has been defined from a number of different points of view: firstly, one which is very similar to that of common sense; secondly, from a philosophical or "logical" standpoint; and, thirdly, from a physiological angle. The term, *awareness,* may be employed to designate such supposed activities or relationships.

The first notion of psychical activity may be exemplified by quotations from G. F. Stout, who says: [120] "Psychology is concerned with the relation of what is perceived or in any way thought of, to the percipient or thinker." "Psychology is the science of the processes whereby an individual becomes aware of a world of objects, and adjusts his actions accordingly." Similar propositions have been laid down by G. T. Ladd, Bertrand Russell and others. The processes or activities, according to this school of psychologists, are not to be identified with any physiological operations, but are distinctive psychical phenomena or facts. Although it would appear that relations between subject and object might conceivably be either static or dynamic, this school almost invariably regards them as being dynamic. The active relations in this sense between subject and object— and constituting awareness—may be of several different types, such as cognition (incoming), affection, and conation (outgoing), representing the psychical categories of knowledge, feeling and will, respectively.

The "logical" approach to the same sort of doctrine is made by Brentano, Witasek, and others.[121] According to Brentano, all psychological subject matters are "acts," which have the unique property of always referring beyond themselves to "objects" or "contents." The latter are said to be intentionally immanent or "inexistent" within the psychical "acts." There are three fundamental classes of such acts: ideating, judging, and loving-hating. For Brentano, the *contents* of acts are physical, but for Witasek, Husserl, and others the contents are psychical. Stumpf classes them as *phenomenological.* The act psychology is evidently a logician's creation, in that it derives its fundamental postulates from the classical forms of speech or predication regarding mental facts, rather than from straightforward empirical analysis.

27. The Psychology of "Consciousness."—The third notion of the subject matter of psychology as activity is that of the functional psychologists, whose point of view has already been sketched above. Their doctrines are perhaps closer to those of behaviorism and physiological psychology than they are to the principles of the "act psychology." The functionalists, exemplified by J. R. Angell and C. H. Judd,[122] characterize psychology as "the science of consciousness" and state that "everyone knows what consciousness is although it cannot be defined." They then proceed to treat consciousness as if it were a semi-physiological entity or process which takes an active part in the adaptation of the organism to its environment. This teaching is evidently rather vague.

It shades into definitions of psychology, such as that of William James, according to which "psychology is the description and explanation of states of consciousness, as such." Again, James says:[123] "Psychology is the Science of Mental Life, both of its phenomena and of their conditions. The phenomena are such things as we call feelings, desires, cognitions, reasonings, decisions, and the like." He then says: "the pursuance of future ends and the choice of means for their attainment are . . . the mark and criterion of the presence of mentality in a phenomenon." Such notions of consciousness-undefined are among the commonest in the psychological texts of the past twenty years. Although, in some cases, the authors may regard consciousness as an activity, in the sense of awareness, they are ordinarily more inclined to treat it as a "thing," as a form of existence which is associated with organic processes, but which differs radically from the latter. Consciousness may be identified with "internal experience," as opposed to external experience which comprises the common-sense world. In general, there is a tendency to conceive it in accordance with the formula of Descartes, as being non-extended or spaceless in character.[124] Very frequently, it is a "consciousness of," having objects to which it refers, as in the case of the "act."

28. The Psychology of Private Experience.—The systematic study of the various types of consciousness—thought, feeling, memory, volition, attention, sensation, perception, etc.—has the effect of constantly extending the domain of the conception of consciousness. However, the latter is supposed to be characterized by some sort or degree of "subjectivity"—in contrast with the "objective" subject matter of the physical sciences. Nevertheless, it gradually comes to include such phenomena as color, musical tone and even spatial relationships, which are external rather than internal; so that the notion of consciousness has to be revised and tends to become coextensive with that of *experience,* combining the "external" with the "internal" in one system. Still, in order to distinguish between psychology and other empirical sciences, it is deemed necessary to regard experience in some special manner.

Numerous different interpretations of this view have been offered. The simplest one is probably that of Royce,[125] who says that psychology is the science of experience regarded as "private," while physics is that of the same experience regarded as "public." Münsterberg [126] also defines the mental as that which is accessible only to the individual; while James Ward [127] says that psychology is "the science of individual experience."

This view is made more definite in such doctrines as those of R. Avenarius, E. Mach, O. Külpe and E. B. Titchener (in his *Text-book of Psychology*),[128] according to which psychology is the science of the whole of experience insofar as it is dependent upon (correlated with) some particular physiological organism. The "individual" in this case becomes the physical body, and the criterion of "subjectivity" is the demonstration of an empirio-physiological relationship. The "objective" sciences are conceived to deal with the aspects of experience which are determined by objects outside of the organism, particularly through the senses of vision, touch and audition. Color is a psychological subject matter insofar as it relates to the retina, the optic nerve or the brain, but is physical as an index of wavelength or intensity of radiant energy.

A recent and very interesting scheme of this sort is that of Hollingworth,[129] who says that "psychology is the science which concerns itself with mental processes and with subjective events." Mental processes are "redintegrative sequences, in which a detail is substituted for a larger antecedent context, in the instigation of consequents." Subjective events are "natural events which are inconsistently reported or are reported by but one or a few individuals." These formulae mean that events and relationships in experience which are peculiar to the given individual system and which, in particular, follow the principles of association rather than of objective law, are psychological subject matter; but that those aspects which are accurately reduplicated in all appropriately related experiences are non-psychological or physical in character.

Titchener's later views suggest that the subject matter of psychology is *experience viewed and treated from the standpoint of psychological method* or under the psychological attitude. This is characterized by the elimination of judgments of intrinsic meaning or value: the treatment of experience as purely existential, and as the material for special analytic *Aufgaben*. Experience, as it appears under these conditions, may be quite different from what is given under the common-sense attitude or that of physics.

29. The Science of Immediate Experience.—Views such as these are capable of a still further expansion and clarification, leading to the notion that psychology is the science of experience—of whatever sort—as *immediately given,* or *per se:* considered without hypothesis, interpretation or abstraction. This point of view is quite clearly stated by Wundt, who says:[130] "The point of view of natural science may . . . be designated as that of *mediate experience,* since it is possible only after abstracting from the subjective factor present in all actual experience; the point of view of psychology, on the other hand, may be designated as that of *immediate experience,* since it purposely does away with this abstraction, and all its consequences." Wundt does not quite succeed in escaping from the act-content dichotomy, since he says: "Every concrete experience immediately divides into two factors: into a content presented to us, and our apprehension of this content."

If we carry Wundt's doctrine to its logical limit, we may say that the subject matter of psychology is *experience,* considered solely as material for pure systematic description, and not under any further more special attitude. Other sciences must be characterized by more complicated—if not more artificial—ways of dealing with experience: abstracting, interpreting, explaining, etc. But psychology gives a scientific account of experience exactly as it *is,* without additions or subtractions. There is thus no problem of defining the special attitude of psychology, but only one of eliminating the attitudes which characterize other forms of inquiry. Psychology, from this standpoint, would be the only science which is concerned, for example, with *colors* as *such.* Art is interested in them as aesthetic media. Physics considers them as indices of wave-length composition, etc. To this task of psychology we may add, as Wundt did, the problem of determining the laws which link immediate experience with the processes of the individual organism: the problem of *physiological* psychology.

From standpoints such as those of Titchener or Wundt, the term *consciousness* may be interpreted in a number of different ways. Ordinarily, it signifies the totality of any given individual experience at any given moment of time, such as the present. It may stand for the unity or coherence of any given moment of experience, or its pattern or configuration. On the other hand, it may be restricted to a limited group of relations found within experience as a whole, such as that existing between an image and the perception (or sensation group) which the image represents.

However, there is a much reduced tendency to speak of the "consciousness of." The general method of psychology by introspection becomes the analysis of structures rather than of processes: an enumeration of the qualitative constituents of any moment of experience, together with a statement of the arrangement and changes of these constituents.

30. Psychoanalysis.—In addition to the above more or less discrepant subject matters which have been advocated for consideration by the psychologist, there is another, which thus far has not been offered seriously as the exclusive and characteristic province of the science, although possibly the views of Tansley [131] should be interpreted in this manner. This is the hypothesis of the unconscious or subconscious mind, which has been developed most industriously by Sigmund Freud and his fellow *psychoanalysts.* These thinkers base their doctrines primarily upon psychopathic phenomena, which have been little considered by the main line of descent of academic psychologists; and the psychoanalysts, for their part, pay practically no attention to the psychology of the schools. Consequently, it is difficult to fit the psychoanalytical subject matter into the general scheme of psychological systems. From one standpoint, psychoanalysis can be regarded as an account of the supposed nature of a mind lying behind the demonstrable consciousness or experiences, and serving as a means of explanation for them. But, it is a mind which is highly complicated and frequently disintegrated; and, so, quite different from the hypothesis of the soul or the "subject" of "rational" psychology.

From another standpoint, psychoanalysis may be viewed as the beginning of an empirical psychology of *motivation,* a subject much neglected by academic psychologists.[132] The success which has been achieved by Freud with his hypothesis of repressed unconscious drives in the treatment of hysteria and allied pathological conditions, has encouraged others to attempt explanations of all human desire and conduct, by similar methods. In the majority of cases, these psychoanalytic explanations have been narrowly conceived, attempting to derive almost all human motivation from some single impulse, such as that of sex, egotism, fear, or the like. However, as this general way of thinking has spread, it has come into contact with biological influences which are gradually broadening its conceptions. Freud's teachings are couched exclusively in psychical or mental terms, but the writings of William McDougall, Morton Prince, E. B. Holt and others are bringing his principles into contact with physiological notions, such as those of instinct and the conditioned reflex.

Section 7

PHYSIOLOGICAL SUBJECT MATTERS FOR
PSYCHOLOGY

31. Compromise Psychophysiologies.—Although structural psychologists of the Titchenerian type make use of the principle of psychophysical parallelism to permit them to establish "explanatory" relationships between the results of their introspective analyses and the ideas of physiology, the fruits of their work have seemed to many critics to be quite meagre. Their introspective descriptions have appeared to be either academically perverted translations of common-sense accounts, or else as elucidations of unimportant sensory relationships. These dissatisfactions, beginning with the ideas of James, were responsible for the appearance of the so-called functional psychology—already considered above—which, although admitting the legitimacy of a purely introspective account of consciousness, lays the main emphasis upon the relation of the given consciousness to the physiological processes of response.

It is possible to pass from functional psychology to the most radical form of behaviorism by easy stages of doctrinal change. Thus, H. C. Warren [133] defines psychology as "the science which deals with the mutual interrelations between an organism and its environment," and classifies psychology as a subdivision of biology, while at the same time pro-

testing against ruling out the data of consciousness. Warren conceives behavior so as to include the entire response
arc, afferent as well as efferent, and looks upon consciousness as an index of the central or brain process. He
attempts, in fact, to *identify* consciousness and the central
activity by the use of a "double aspect" theory. Even
McDougall, in his *Physiological Psychology,* defined psychology as "the positive science of the behavior of living
things," but did not hesitate at the same time to believe in
the existence and importance not only of consciousness, but
of the soul! Warren and McDougall feel that psychology
must study behavior and consciousness simultaneously, as
two coördinate manifestations of mind.

It is generally conceded, even by the strictest of introspective psychologists, that it is an integral part of their
science to study the relations which hold between psychical
subject matters and physiological processes. Physiological
psychology is sometimes treated separately from general
psychology, but as a rule its essential principles are included
in the general textbooks. Experimental and laboratory
psychology can hardly escape physiological considerations,
in any instance. Physiologists, for their part, have laid no
claim to the relation of mind to body as a portion of their
science, although they have taken a marked degree of interest in the topic—to the extent even of being its most
effective supporters. Apparently, no psychologist has seriously advocated the view that the mind-body relationship
is the sole subject matter of his science, although such doctrines as those of Külpe, Warren and Bentley[134] suggest
this interpretation.

32. Behaviorism.—The beginnings of the behavioristic
movement in modern times are probably to be found in the
promulgations of the German school of "animal physiologists," whose work was stimulated by a disgust at the efforts
of animal psychologists to translate animal behavior into
psychological terms and thereby to "explain" it. A quotation from Bethe[135] will serve to indicate the attitude of the
animal physiologists. He says: "While the comparative

psychologists debate concerning the amount of sensation, memory and reflection that one should attribute . . . to animals, there arises in the growing science of comparative *physiology,* an enemy to the death of all comparative psychology. . . . Before objective observation, the sensations, the memory, and the thoughts of animals disappear like fluttering forms of vapor. The iron chain of objective changes, which began with the stimulation of the sense-organ, and finished with the movement of a muscle, is welded together in the middle. Nowhere remains the smallest spot for the psyche of the animal. Basing itself upon these incontestable facts, comparative physiology pronounces the psychological conclusions mere superstitions, and denies to comparative psychology the right to call itself a science."

It is quite clear that the animal physiologists did not present their science as a form of psychology, although they obviously regarded it as a substitute for the latter. However, behaviorism—as advocated by J. B. Watson—is a redefinition of the science of psychology, which adopts much the same attitude towards subjective lines of inquiry as does Bethe in the above quotation. According to Watson, behaviorism is a purely American product, which cannot be tied up with any past revolt in psychology, nor with the objectivism of Bethe, Beer, von Uexküll, Nuel or Ziegler. These objectivists (including Bechterew) are regarded by Watson as perfectly orthodox psychophysical parallelists who, however, prefer to confine their attention to the physical side of the parallelism. Watson denies that the behavioristic program is merely a subdivision of the general natural science of physiology, maintaining that physiology deals merely with the functions of special organs, nowhere putting these organs together to get an organism, which can be tested as a whole in relation to its environment.

By redefining psychology, as a whole, to be the science of behavior Watson hoped to eliminate the ambiguities and vacillations of contemporary psychological discussions, and to provide the science with a clear problem upon which it could make consistent progress. In 1913, he wrote: [136]

"Psychology as the behaviorist views it, is a purely objective branch of natural science. Its theoretical goal is the prediction and control of behavior. Introspection forms no part of its method; neither is the scientific value of its data dependent upon the readiness with which they lend themselves to interpretation in terms of consciousness." In 1919, Watson again wrote:[137] "Psychology is that division of natural science which takes human activity and conduct as its subject matter. It attempts to formulate, through systematic observation and experimentation, the laws and principles which underlie man's reactions." Watson not only bans consciousness from the field of psychology, as the behaviorist views it, but asserts that he does not know what the word means. "The reader will find no discussion of consciousness and no reference to such terms as sensation, perception, attention, will, image and the like. These terms are in good repute but I have found that I can get along without them both in carrying out investigations and in presenting psychology as a system to my students. I frankly do not know what they mean, nor do I believe that anyone else can use them consistently."

Watson, as the leader of the behaviorists, is also probably the most extreme of them all. A close second, however, is to be found in E. B. Holt,[138] who defines psychology as the science of "specific response," the latter being described as a process of the release of energy in a system, as a mathematical function of an external object or stimulus. Psychology, according to Holt, is an objective and natural science, but has a unique subject matter which is generated by the unity and complexity of the organism as a whole. In his earlier writings,[139] Holt made use of the word "consciousness" and explained it in terms of a realistic metaphysics, as the group of objects to which the organism is reacting at any moment. But in his later writings he rejects the concept of consciousness entirely. Views similar to those of Holt are advocated by R. B. Perry,[140] a fellow Neo-Realist.

Although behaviorists such as Watson, Holt and Perry

endeavor to make out a case that behavior is a super-
physiological subject matter—so that psychology, as they
see it, is still not to be classed as a mere subdivision of
physiology—A. P. Weiss states [141] frankly that "behaviorism
is based upon the assumptions of physics." He then pro-
ceeds to develop an account of "human achievement" as a
mode of motion, using concepts and reasoning which should
prove entirely acceptable either to the modern physicist or
to an up-to-date La Mettrie. Without asserting positively
that there is no such thing as the psychical, or that his system is psychology, he nevertheless discards the psychical
concepts as futile. "Since a psychics without a physics seems
to be impossible or inadequate, behaviorism has adopted the
working hypothesis of a physics without a psychics."

Chapter II

The Definition of Psychology

Section 8

CRITERIA FOR THE ESTABLISHMENT OF THE DEFINITION

33. The Pertinency of History.—Having in the preceding chapter considered the various topics which are offered as subject matters for modern psychology, we should now be in a position to determine our own definition of the science. We may select the conception of psychology which seems to be best substantiated, or—following the style among psychological writers—may even offer a supposedly new or improved conception. However, before proceeding to this task, we shall do well to lay down the criteria by which the correctness and excellence of a definition of this kind are to be tested.

It would appear that the most general criterion of this sort is consistency with the history of the term, psychology, and its congeners. Our definition must also be consistent with the history of science and intellect as a whole. If we define psychology as the science of the stars, we do violence not only to the usage of the word, "psychology," but also to that of "astronomy." Definition is really an arbitrary matter, and a sufficiently flexible intellect could proceed to scramble all of the definitions in the dictionary without doing any real damage to truth. But the problem of defining a science means more than this. It involves characterizing in a few words the continuing purpose of an established form of human endeavor. This purpose may have operated effectively, long before it became significantly explicit, and it may also evolve so that its expressions change as time goes on. A science must not be bound by past formulations in such a manner as to impede its rational progress, but, on the other hand, a natural evolution will be governed by a principle of continuity.

Changes in the subject matter of a science may involve the addition of new topics, the elimination of old ones, or both. It may be considered legitimate to extend the definition of psychology in such a manner as to render the science more fruitful and useful. If such a thing as behavior has not already been considered by another science, and if it is intimately related to the historical subject matter of psychology, it may well be adopted. But such an act should not lead us, without due and sufficient reason, to exclude any topic which is offered to us by the history of the science.

34. Criteria of Availability.—However, it may turn out, upon close inspection, that some of the topics which are proffered by history are not actually available from a scientific standpoint. There are certain other criteria, in addition to historical consistency, which must be applied to the problems that history presents to us. In the first place, we must inquire whether these problems, as stated, are *meaningful,* or whether they are merely empty words. Can we understand what Aristotle meant by "entelechy," or what Schopenhauer intended to denote when he spoke of the "Will." What is a "transcendental ego" or a "category of the understanding"? Watson says that he does not know what is meant by "consciousness" and other familiar psychical terms. If any of the problems which are suggested by the history of psychology prove to be unintelligible, we certainly cannot include them in our definition of the science.

Assuming that a formulation is intelligible, we must next ask whether the matters to which it refers actually *exist,* or whether, perhaps, they are fictitious. We may be able to understand quite clearly what is meant by the term, soul, but if there seems to be no evidence whatsoever for the existence of the soul, psychology cannot be assigned the task of studying it. This is so even when psychology is named after the soul. Similarly, if James [142] is right when he inquires: "Does consciousness exist?" and replies in the negative, then consciousness is legitimately ruled out of the domain of scientific psychology. If history presents us with nonexistent topics, we are quite justified in paying no heed to its deliverances.

A third criterion which must be applied to the findings of historical inquiry is that of *amenability to scientific method*. Certain questions may be meaningful, may relate to existent things, but may lie wholly outside of the domain of science. This is said to be the case with the subject matters of metaphysics and of the theory of value. The most radical among the behaviorists claim that all subjective phenomena have this status of scientifically inaccessible topics. However, we should be cautious in the application of this criterion. The failure of science to make appreciable progress upon a particular problem, over long periods of time, cannot be taken as proof that no such progress will ever be made. It is necessary to adapt scientific method to special tasks. If we insist that psychology should use the same concepts as does physics, we may be stultifying rather than insuring its scientific advance.

35. Criteria of Importance.—A fourth and even more dubious test is that of *human importance*. Other requirements being met, it would appear that science should attack those problems which have the greatest practical, or at least theoretical, significance. It may be possible to devise some scheme for determining the topography of the hidden side of the moon, but this information would be of no benefit to humanity in general, and would have very little bearing upon the theory of astronomy. The difficulty of securing the information in question would certainly be tremendous. Numerous criticisms of subjective psychology have been formulated along these lines. Thus, Weiss says: "If all of the *sensations, images,* and *feelings* of all the great men in history had been minutely recorded after the manner of an approved introspective technique, it would add not one jot or tittle to our understanding of the enormous changes which man has introduced into his environment and into his own manner of living." The difficulty in the application of this criterion is obviously in being able to predict in advance what particular items of knowledge will actually prove to be quite unimportant for all time.

The majority of modern psychological writers appear to be influenced by a desire to become the founders of a new school or a new interpretation of their science. However, the actual degree of novelty which they have created is quite small. As a rule, the more radical the outbreak the less novelty is manifested. Behaviorism is as old as Parmenides. True novelty comes through gradual evolution along the fundamental and characteristic path of a science, as a consequence of the progressive synthesis of accumulating facts and principles. My own purpose in the present work is not to advocate a new definition of psychology, but to take up the science as it has been given to me, and to see if I can carry it one step further along its path of advancement. But this does not mean that we may not be able to improve to some extent upon the definitions, as well as upon the specific facts and principles, of previous writers.

Section 9

THE DELIMITATION OF THE SCOPE OF PSYCHOLOGY

36. Catalogue of Proposed Problems.—The foregoing study has revealed, for possible consideration by scientific psychology, the following problem matters:

(1) The nature and relationships of the "self" or "mind," conceived as an incorporeal entity underlying, or possessing, consciousness.

(2) A class of relations or processes, supposed to exist or to operate between an incorporeal "subject"—which in

itself is inaccessible to psychological observation—and objects. Such relations may be of various sorts, but divide themselves into two general types according as the subject acts upon objects or *vice versa.* Both types of relationship or process may be described by the term, *awareness.*

(3) The nature and conditions of *consciousness,* in the sense of *inner experience,* including such topics as thought, memory, desire, feeling, will, emotion, etc., which have been signalized by faculty theories and chapters in traditional psychologies. Consciousness, in this sense, is not explicitly regarded as a relationship or activity.

(4) The (secondary) qualities of *external* as well as of internal experience, at least insofar as they are correlated with physiological conditions. These qualities are commonly regarded as contents or objects of consciousness. They include color, musical tone, odor, taste, phenomenal pressure, hot and cold, and the like.

(5) The nature and conditions of certain aspects of the forms of combination of sensible qualities, either in external or internal experience: space, time and order in experience considered as functions of physiological variables, or as demonstrations of special psychical laws (redintegration, according to Hollingworth).

(6) The totality of concrete individual experience, regarded as a subject matter for pure systematic description, eliminating the interpreting and abstracting methods of common sense and "objective" science.

(7) The constitution of an hypothetical unconscious or subconscious mind, which stands in an explanatory relationship to certain aspects of experience and behavior, principally those supposed to demonstrate *motivation.*

(8) The *relationship* between any non-physiological components, among the topics above listed, and matter or material processes, especially organic functions and the physiology of the nervous system.

(9) Behavior, regarded as an "objective" fact, and treated without reference to "subjective" or psychical conceptions. Behavior may be viewed as an unexplained but

constant stimulus-reaction relationship (specific response, according to Holt) or it may be studied in detail as a physical mechanism of neuromuscular conduction. It may be viewed as "merely physiological" or as super-physiological.

We may now consider these proposed topics for psychological consideration in the light of the criteria which have been laid down in the preceding Section.

37. The Self.—The notion of the self, the subject or the mind as a general and necessary concomitant of all psychical reality is consistent with the early history of psychological science, but must be rejected on the ground of nonexistence or inaccessibility to scientific methods of investigation.

If the subject is regarded as a non-empirical entity which is nevertheless supposed to be logically necessary in psychological discussion, the reply must be that science is not acquainted with any logical necessities of this character. Its logical necessities are the products solely of its own methodological assumptions and the facts which it considers. The conception of the subject is logically necessary only to those who, because of prejudice or habit, prefer to define the problem of psychology so that a subject is implied. This matter has been disposed of, once and for all, by James when he says [143] that the soul "is at all events needless for expressing the actual subjective phenomena of consciousness as they appear." "The soul . . . far from making the phenomena more intelligible, can only be made intelligible itself by borrowing their form—it must be represented if at all as a transcendent stream of consciousness duplicating the one we know."

There is no difficulty whatsoever in explaining the compulsion which such writers as McDougall and Calkins experience with regard to the concept of the subject or self. If we begin a psychological discussion by laying down the requirement that the subject matter of the science cannot be regarded as a self-existent "thing," and if we insist upon formulating its problem in terms of personal pronouns and the subject-predicate relationship of everyday grammar, then there is no other logical alternative. But such an initial procedure is arbitrary and without empirical foundation.

The view of Miss Calkins that the self is a constantly present empirical fact, rather than "an indispensable hypothesis" (McDougall), is subject to the difficulty that the majority of psychologists are unable to discover it, in this status. Thus, Titchener says that if for Miss Calkins "the self-attitude is introspectively discernible in every consciousness, then I can only say that her mind must differ from mine not specifically but generically. Self-consciousness is, certainly, part of the subject matter of psychology; but it is, I think, of comparatively rare occurrence, and it would seem more natural . . . to treat it as one among the whole number of mental functions than to make it the differentia of a whole psychology." [144]

I quite agree with Titchener and other psychologists with regard to these propositions. I believe that Miss Calkins' demand for the self as a constituent of all psychical facts is due, either to a logical difficulty similar to that of McDougall in formulating these facts without the notion of a subject, or else to a misinterpretation of certain of the facts themselves. It is true that there is an empirical self in practically all concrete cases of consciousness or experience; but it is not a fundamental and unanalyzable thing, such as Miss Calkins assumes. It consists in the mass of "sensations" and "perceptions" which comprises the empirical body. The relation of this system to the phenomenal world outside of the body has been discussed with complete lucidity by Mach.[145] It is possible to rule out all of the contents of this empirical self, explicitly, and yet be bound implicitly by the fact of its constant presence. In this case we feel compelled to treat it as if it were a unique psychical entity, inexplicable in terms of more fundamental concepts.

The notion of the "mind," as an underlying explanatory system for psychological phenomena, can properly be retained if we view it merely as a useful hypothesis, and not as an essential of the subject matter of the science. The most helpful hypothesis of this sort appears to be that of the unconscious or subconscious, as elaborated by the psychoanalytic school, or even by such older thinkers as Leibnitz, Schopenhauer and Herbart.

38. Awareness.—The notion that the subject matter of psychology is a relationship or an "act," implying a subject and an object, is a remnant of an attenuated psychology of the soul. Primitive animism was an act-content theory, the soul being the actor. The hypothesis of the soul was advanced to account simultaneously for spontaneous movement and inner feeling. Although scientific criticism has succeeded in eliminating the soul hypothesis, the idea of its function has persisted—owing to the inertia of conception and language—after the functioning entity itself has vanished. The notions of subject, ego and self are mere ghosts of the ghost soul; and as such can have no scientific status. Hence we cannot accept the idea of psychology as the study of any relationship or activity which involves these conceptions.

As a matter of fact, it is extremely doubtful whether the idea of "act" can be given any intelligible meaning. Systems, such as that of Brentano, may be internally self-consistent and logically intriguing, but they may quite fail to attach themselves to any facts. The "intentional inexistence of objects" which is supposed to characterize psychical subject matter, according to Brentano, is a logical existence which is equivalent to scientific nonexistence. Logicians seem to have no difficulty in assigning "being" to nonentities, but psychologists should be wary of this type of thinking. Some "awareness psychologists," such as Stout, appear to appreciate the embarrassing nature of the situation which arises in conceiving awareness apart from the idea of a substantial subject; and sometimes the subject is identified with the awareness itself. In general, it would appear that the conception of awareness, as a form of connection between objects and an inaccessible subject, has not been rendered scientifically intelligible.

The compulsion to believe in awareness must, of course,

receive a psychological explanation. The case seems to be the same as that for the self. In nearly all actual experience there is an empirical self, constituted by the organism as given in experience; and this empirical self changes or undergoes processes which are followed by corresponding alterations in the world of external experience. A reciprocal relationship also obtains, in which the empirical self appears to be affected by factors in the external realm. Logicians and "mental philosophers" have formulated an abstract pattern of this situation, minus its concrete contents, and have been unable to escape from the notion of a transfer of influence between the abstract subject and its objects. This process of abstraction has received powerful support from the grammatical constructions of modern Occidental languages, in which personal pronouns or nouns are attached to verbs—designating action, or transition, and frequently involving objects as portions of a "predicate." This form of language is so habitually established that it constitutes one of the principal obstacles to unbiased psychological description. Its basis is to be found in the relationship of the empirical self to the remainder of experience. This relationship is of great interest to psychology, but is merely one item in, and not the essence of, the psychological subject matter.

   39. Consciousness.—According to McDougall,[146] " 'consciousness,' is generally taken to be almost, if not quite, synonymous with 'experience'; although . . . there are other usages of the word. 'Consciousness' is a thoroughly bad word, and it has been a great misfortune for psychology that the word has come into general use." However, since the term consciousness has been utilized more consistently than any other in modern times, in defining the subject matter of psychology, we cannot rule it out unless it fails to meet the requirements which we have laid down. Personally, I feel that consciousness is a thoroughly good word, and furnishes us with the key to the historical and persistent problem of psychology; and for the very reason which makes the word so objectionable to McDougall, namely that " 'con-

sciousness,' having the form of a substantive which cannot be used as a verb, allows us to forget that it stands for the fact of being conscious of something. . . ."

However, as scientific psychologists, we do not admit that consciousness has this latter implication. The real trouble with the word is that the implication in question is too common in the popular mind. Consciousness in the McDougallian sense is of course identical with what we have called awareness. It was in this sense that William James denied that consciousness exists. Conciousness as an "act," a sort of dynamic molding medium or "menstruum," as James called it, is a very dubious conception. But this is not the sense in which it is employed by the vast majority of psychologists who define their science in its terms. It is true that their concepts of consciousness are usually not very clear, but the conception is readily susceptible of being clarified and made extremely useful.

A suggestion towards a clear definition of consciousness in terms of experience appears in Titchener's statement [147] that "my 'consciousness' is the sum of mental processes which make my experience *now;* it is the mind of any given 'present' time. This section may be either artificial or natural. We may deliberately cut across mind, in order to investigate it for psychological purposes. . . . On the other hand, mind falls of itself into a series of consciousnesses, each separate consciousness being dominated by some particular group of processes." The word "process" in this context does not mean "act" but "a continued operation, a progressive change . . . which melts into and blends with operations and changes which follow and precede it."

Hollingworth says that consciousness is a word for which he has little if any use, but he states [148] that "consciousness is not a new substance appearing at some point in the evolution of a system which to begin with is exclusively matter. 'Consciousness' is made of the same stuff that comprises the rest of nature." We shall consider Hollingworth's ideas in greater detail below.

If we define consciousness, more or less informally, in

terms of its constituents—such as thought, desire, feeling, sensation and the like—or identify it with internal as opposed to external experience, we may lay ourselves open to the danger of having these constituents interpreted in terms of activity. However, we may say that consciousness consists of these and related topics insofar as they are *not* interpreted as acts or subject-object relations. We may also have to add the restriction that they must not be represented behavioristically, or in physiological terms. On this ground, can we accept the implication of Watson that such definitions of consciousness are unintelligible, so that it is impossible or even difficult to determine what they mean? I believe not. Moreover, I doubt very much whether Watson himself is quite "frank" when he says that he does not know what such terms signify. Certainly, if he is really frank in this statement, he must be conceiving consciousness as awareness and as the kind of consciousness which James says does not exist.

Surely this Jamesian conclusion cannot be applied to all current definitions of "consciousness." If consciousness is a general aspect of experience, then even a behaviorist should not be quite satisfied to deny its existence, since even "objective science" must be based upon experience. If we accept Ladd's demonstration, according to which "What we are when we are awake, and what we are not when we fall into a quiet dreamless sleep; what [149] we are as we go about our daily work, and what we are not when an overpowering blow upon the head is received—that 'is to be conscious,' " we shall have great difficulty in denying the existence of consciousness. However, Watson might be able to elude Ladd's demonstration, somehow, and construct an entirely behavioristic interpretation.

It may still be claimed that consciousness, as subjectively defined, is not amenable to scientific methods; and behaviorists indicate that this is the case by denying that introspective psychology has made any consistent progress. However, this is a matter for debate. Other critics do not concede the point. Personally, although an appreciative student of the non-psychological sciences, I do not feel that the study of consciousness has failed to make scientific progress, although I might well be in this position if I did not know what is meant by "consciousness" and its congeners. I am particularly doubtful whether behaviorism, since its inception some fifteen years ago, has brought about any great acceleration of progress, in spite of the great popularity of the doctrine. The effect has perhaps been quite the reverse, as a consequence of the resulting confusion of issues in psychology.

The answer to the question as to the amenability of consciousness to scientific method cannot be given with complete satisfaction until we have developed an unambiguous conception of its meaning. However, there can be no doubt whatsoever that demonstrable phenomena can be found corresponding to such words as thought, desire, feeling, sensation and the like. It can also be shown that these phenomena are not fully reducible to physical or behavioristic factors. Furthermore, they are not relations of any kind between a subject and objects. Thought, desire, volition, memory, etc., are data or constituents of consciousness, not differing in this respect from the objects which go to make up external experience. They are partly processes but fundamentally they are more structural than functional.

40. External Experience: Qualities and Their Configurations.—We now arrive at a proposed subject matter of psychology concerning which the questions of intelligibility and existence can scarcely be raised at all. It consists in the "sensible" qualitative components of common-sense objects, in everyday experiences which present the external world. The favorite example consists of color and spatial arrangements thereof; although the majority of common-sense properties of objects fall into the same class.

The first question which arises in connection with these proposed topics for psychology is as to whether they are legitimate property for this science. The "act" psychologists regarded them as "contents," but although for Brentano they were physical, Husserl, Witasek, Meinong and others viewed them as psychical in character. Stumpf classed them as "phenomenological," but the science of phenomenology appears not to have achieved an independent standing in the history of intellect. Consequently, it must be regarded as a subdivision of either physics or psychology, presumably the latter. As pointed out by Mach and by Avenarius, external qualities such as color seem to be of the same general character and to behave in the same general manner as internal qualities—aches, pressures, desires, etc.—and thus to have greater affinity with the latter than with the subject matters of physical science. As a matter of historical development, modern experimental psychology was founded almost exclusively upon the study of these so-called "sense data" and their physiological conditions; and the majority of modern systems of introspective psychology are explicitly based upon these same conceptions. The notion that even visual space is a subjective construct is as old as Bishop Berkeley,[150] and is a familiar tenet of all idealistic philosophies.

However, there is undeniably a great deal of confusion of thought regarding this problem. In attempting to deal with external experience, the psychologist cannot possibly avoid the adoption of some definite metaphysical assumptions. The wide discrepancies of statement and interest which exist among contemporary psychologists are largely attributable to the implicit character of their metaphysical hypotheses. If we adopt a neo-realistic point of view, such as that of Holt, Perry, Russell and others, we assign all of these qualitative entities and many of their configurations to the "real world" in such a manner that—as by a magician's touch—they vanish from the subject matter of scientific inquiry. A similar result follows from certain modern idealistic ways of thinking about experience, as if it were a universal system rather than a multitude of individual fields. It is not surprising that, under these conditions, the subject matter of psychology should become exceptionally vacuous and that the thinker should find himself back with the old problem of the awareness relation, endeavoring to under-

stand how objects or portions of the experience system get
themselves perceived, thought about, or grouped into individualized fields (cf. Holt's *Concept of Consciousness*). It
is under such assumptions that the behaviorist can glibly cast
aside the entire structure of introspective psychology without feeling that he is losing anything. But from the original
point of view of psychology, the behaviorist has been "led
into the strange delusion that none but visual-tactile events
occur." [151]

There is a type of intellect which is frequently encountered among physicists that appears to be afflicted with a
sort of *experience aphasia,* causing its thought completely to
gloss over the immediate data of experience, so as to pass
at once to the inferential conceptions of physical science.
Such an intellect, although constantly employing the experiential data as a basis for thought, never explicitly recognizes
their reality. They are intentionally nonexistent. Many of
the behaviorists appear to possess intellects of this type;
on the one hand they persistently deny the necessity of admitting the existence of consciousness in human or animal subjects which they are studying, and yet at the same time they
join with all other empirical and objective sciences in basing
their system upon the data of experience, which are after
all nothing but items in their own consciousnesses.

41. The Subject Matter of Physical Science.—Another
question, which plays a very important part in determining
our attitude towards the factors of external experience, has
to do with our conception of the subject matter and aims of
physical, as contrasted with psychological, science. From
the standpoint of such thinkers as Mach, Kirchhoff and Karl
Pearson, the natural sciences are concerned with the formulation of certain types of regularity in experience. It is not
their primary purpose to go beyond experience in the quest
of a supposedly independent universe. This positivistic view
appears to be held by the majority of modern psychologists
and philosophers of science. Unfortunately, it does not represent the actual practice of the modern physical scientist.
It would be very difficult to find any contemporary physicist

who intends to pursue this sort of program. His actual interest is in the construction, by the method of hypothesis, of an account of a universe which is quite distinct from that of experience, and which is conceived in an entirely metaphysical manner. This means that he regards it as capable of existing independently of any particular observer or conditions of observation. Indeed, he does not even consider it to be observable at all.

Physical science, as it has actually developed in the history of the subject, rather than in terms of its philosophical theory, has handed over the totality of "external experience" to psychology, or any other branch of inquiry which may be interested to adopt it. So far as modern physical thought is concerned, pure experience has been thrust out of house and home. This was not always so, since, in the beginning, the natural scientist conceived himself to be dealing directly with the "world of perception." In the earlier phases of the history of physics, only a few parts of external experience— such as the secondary qualities—could be claimed, without objection, by the psychologist. But the magnitude of the psychological moiety has tended constantly to expand, as physics itself has developed, until at the present time it comprises immediate experience in its totality.

The question as to just what this immediate experience itself comprises is one which may require considerable discussion and, accordingly, will be given careful attention in an ensuing chapter. However, we may indicate here that it consists of the entire mosaic of both inner and outer presentations, including not only the qualitative constituents of this mosaic but the manner in which they are combined. The *constitution* of experience involves both elements and their concrete configurations. These configurations embrace both space and time, as well as other modes of concatenation. Immediate experience thus embraces the "primary" as well as the "secondary" qualities and is conceived to this extent in harmony with idealistic doctrines such as that of Berkeley. However, it is a prime essential of the concept of immediate experience that it should be purified of all assumptions which lead us either to add to or to subtract from what is *actually given*. The difficulty of such purification raises one of the fundamental problems of psychological method.

Experience as thus considered can scarcely be regarded as unamenable to scientific treatment or as lacking in human importance.

42. Experience Specially Regarded.—We may now consider proposals that, in order to have a psychology, we must treat experience in some very special manner. It must certainly be admitted that the ways in which psychology deals with experience are different from those which characterize common sense or physical science, respectively. The psychological approach differs from that of common sense in being scientific, and from the physical line of attack by being concerned with *experience itself*, and not with any supposed extra-experiential reality. Is it necessary to qualify the attitude of psychology regarding experience further?

The doctrine of Mach [152] that the physical and psychical contain common elements, the components of experience being treated by the two sciences in different sets of relationships, is very intriguing; but unfortunately it is not borne out by the history of physical science. Physicists, as such, have paid practically no attention to the qualities of experience and their relations to one another, even in external space, except as symbols of supposed objective realities. One can find this attitude expressed with perfect clearness in a statement by the founder of modern physical method, Galileo, [153] who wrote: "I think that these tastes, odors, colors, etc., on the side of the object in which they seem to exist, are nothing else than mere names, but hold their residence solely in the sensitive body; so that if the animal were removed, every such quality would be abolished and annihilated." For Galileo, "the world of the senses is not its own explanation; as it stands it is an unsolved cipher, a book written in a strange language, which is to be interpreted or explained in terms of the alphabet of that language. After long wandering in false directions, man has at last discovered what the rudiments of this alphabet are—namely the prin-

ciples and units of mathematics." Of course, Galileo may
be a no greater authority concerning scientific method than
Mach, Avenarius, or Titchener, but his statements are the
most descriptive of what physicists, since his time, have actually been doing.

The Machian notion that the parts and forms of experience become psychical only when they are considered in relation to the (empirical) self or organism, was the outcome
of a very laudable attempt to provide psychology with a
substantial problem matter, and to separate its definition
from that of physics. However, the difficulty which Mach
faced was the product of an artificially exaggerated empiricism, which insists not only that all scientific inquiry should
start with experience but that it should go nowhere else.
This requirement is met by introspective psychology, but
not by physics. Although certain abstractions from the world
of external sense furnish the basis for physical reasoning, this
world is regarded by the typical physicist as being essentially
illusory. The world of sense still presents us with the astronomy of the ancients, the Copernican and approved astro-
nomic universe being a physical hypothesis which can be
brought into contact with the world of sense only at very
special points and through the medium of complex mathematics.

The scheme of Hollingworth for differentiating between
the experiential subject matter of physical and psychological
science is equally unnecessary. His system is a much more
labored one than that of Mach, and less satisfactory even on
the basis of radical empiricism. I do not wish to deny that
the distinctions which he makes are psychologically important, but only that they are essential for the definition of the
science. Hollingworth's views are based upon a naïve realism, according to which we may regard experience as being
partially in common between different individuals, and as
existing in a great mass apart from any individuals at all.
He calls such experience, "nature." He gives over to physics
those portions of experience concerning which there is an
identity of report by separate, simultaneous observers; leav-

ing the discrepantly reported or individualized aspects of experience to psychology. Here again, we can only say that modern physical science is not concerned with any part of the "nature" which Hollingworth discusses.

43. Experience as Such.—However, we may at least regard psychology as being unique in that it intends to deal with experience *per se* or "as such." This is indeed an extraordinary intention. But it is no more complicated than considering a brick, as such. Considering a brick as being merely a brick, and nothing more, would seem to be the simplest and most direct way of treating it. A proposal to consider a brick as something else from what it is might well arouse a humorous reaction. But experience seems to have had the misfortune to have been conceived habitually as being something different from itself, so that it is subject to a wide variety of "*qua*'s." Some of these are about as ludicrous as studying a brick *as a potato,* although others might be compared to regarding the brick as a building material. Nevertheless we still have the same old brick, no matter how we regard it. The same thing is true of experience. "Qua's" do it no good and no harm; it remains the same old experience, regardless of volleys of philosophical abuse and, *as such,* is the subject matter of introspective psychology.

I am aware that this intention, to adopt the Wundtian notion of psychology as the systematic description of immediate experience, may meet with objections from certain highly sophisticated psychologists of the introspective school. They will be inclined to say that although psychology aims to give a systematic account of experience as a form of existence and hence *qua* itself, psychological research can actually consider only such experience as is possible under the introspective or analytic attitude. This may be different from the experience which accompanies other attitudes or intentions. Now, while I admit the importance of the observations upon which this subtle opinion is based, I do not feel that they justify us in restricting the subject matter of psychology in the manner indicated. It would be a great misfortune if psychology should really find itself able to report only upon experiences which are distorted by the psychological attitude. The attitude exists only in the interests of describing experiences in general, and if the description —or its generating process—modifies the experience to any important degree, then certainly we are confronted with a most serious defect of psychological method, one which we must do our utmost to overcome. A psychology which can deal only with laboratory experiences is so narrowly restricted as to have very little human interest.

However, we may be forced to admit that the descriptions of certain forms of experience must be developed by a process of reconstruction, from the data of more analytical laboratory observations. There is no objection to the distortion of experience, in a process of "fractionation" of its contents or aspects, so long as we are able to utilize the knowlege thus obtained in the development, synthetically, of accounts having a more general field of application. Methods of this sort can be employed in psychology as well as in various departments of physical science, where they are the rule rather than the exception.

Hence we may conclude that the subject matter of psychology need not be defined as experience in any limited aspect less than concrete experience as a whole and as it is. However we must guard ourselves against the idea that experience is a universal system. Although such a system may exist, it is not a demonstrable subject matter for introspective psychology, which is restricted to the study of individual human fields of experience. These fields are *individual as constituted* and not because of their real or supposed dependence upon an "individual," regarded either as an organism or as a "subject."

44. The Subconscious Mind.—Although the primary problem of psychology is the description of experience, exactly as it is found, the psychologist may find it useful to employ certain hypotheses which are, strictly speaking, additions to the facts of experience. Such hypotheses are really speculative attempts to arrive at descriptions of realities which are beyond experience but which are supposed to be correlated or associated with it. The soul doctrine was an hypothesis of this sort that appears to have been of little value. This does not prove, however, that other hypotheses may not prove to be helpful in attempting to coördinate the complicated and more or less discontinuous phenomena which make up immediate experience. The most natural, and probably the most fruitful, method of hypothesis would appear to be that of an extension of experience or consciousness, itself, beyond the domain of what is actually given. This line of speculation has been followed in doctrines of the subconscious mind, in theories of psychical dispositions, determining tendencies, and the like. Such speculations are to be regarded as legitimate portions of psychological thinking, so long as they are judged by their fruits and not as logical necessities.

45. Psychophysical Relations.—If we adopt the notion of the subject matter of introspective psychology which has been indicated in the above discussion, we have obviously left out of account the relationship between the psychical and the physical. Our definition of the psychical does not rest, as in the formulae of Mach and Titchener, upon the relationship of experience to the organism. However, this is not the equivalent of denying that such a relationship exists, nor does it mean that we should refuse to admit this relationship as a further subject matter for psychology in general. The history of psychology has certainly given over the problem of the psychophysical relation to this science.

Our conception of the relationship in question obviously depends upon our definitions of the psychical and of the physical. If we view the former as immediate experience and the latter as the hypotheses of contemporary physics, then there can be no doubt whatsoever as to the existence of a relationship between these two things, and one which is worthy of study. However, the particular physical hypothesis which concerns us in psychology is that of the human organism as a mechanism or physico-chemical structure. The combined methods of introspective psychology

and physiology demonstrate that individual experience stands
in a very important relationship—of the mathematical functional type—to processes occurring in the corresponding
individual organism. The best name for the science of such
relationships appears to be *psychophysiology,* the subject
matter of the present book. This same science has also been
called "physiological psychology" and is properly regarded
as a subdivision of *general psychology,* which also includes
introspective psychology.

The amenability of psychophysical relationships to scientific method, and their human importance, can scarcely be
questioned. We shall consider their nature and means of
study in great detail in subsequent chapters.

46. Behavior.—The final possible subject matter of
psychology, which is suggested by very recent history, is
"behavior." We have seen that the behaviorists wish to
redefine psychology so that it will not be the science of
consciousness, experience or psychophysical relations, but
of certain aspects of neuromuscular adjustment. The behavioristic definition cannot be rejected on any other ground
than that of inconsistency with the history of the concepts
of psychology and those of other sciences; but this ground
is thoroughly adequate to the purpose. Although the history
of psychology makes it perfectly clear that the science in
question must deal with the relations of consciousness or
experience to matter, it is equally evident that the problem
which is envisaged by the behaviorist *is wholly a problem
in physiology,* and that psychology cannot be regarded as a
subdivision of the latter science.

Behaviorists frequently contend that physiology deals
only with the functions of individual organs in the body,
thus leaving for consideration by psychology the manner of
their interaction and coördinated functioning, in the adapta-
tions which are made by the organism to its environment.
However, the general conception of physiology, as it has
developed historically, certainly does not justify this distinction. Biology, as the general science of living matter—a
subdivision of physics in general—has been partitioned into

anatomy, the science of living structures, and physiology, the science of processes occurring within these structures. Physiology is simply the general science of vital dynamics or of biological functions. Even if we give the behaviorist's inquiry the non-psychological name, *praxiology*,[154] this latter science must be listed as a section of physiology, dealing with biological processes of a restricted kind. The notion of certain behaviorists that they can define an objective science of behavior which will not automatically fall within the domain of physiology reveals their ignorance of the history and organization of biological science.

So far as I can see, there is nothing new in the behavioristic movement except the contention that the movement in question is psychological. As a continuation of the tradition of mechanistic physiology, its positive program is wholly commendable and—in my belief—entirely workable. Since the time of Leibnitz and Spinoza, with their doctrines of parallelism and duality of aspects, there has been absolutely no need for any physiologist to make use of the idea of consciousness, or the psychical, in working out an account of organic activities. The behaviorist has made no new discovery in his proposition that the existence of consciousness should be neglected in the study of all biological functions. Even introspective psychologists have recognized that the biologist must do this to stay within his natural domain.

As a positive program for advancing the study of behavior or neuromuscular response by purely physiological methods, behaviorism should receive the encouragement of all psychologists, because of the value of the results for psychophysiology. However, as an attempt to redefine psychology, and as a system of aspersions against the science, we cannot but brand behaviorism either as a sinister propaganda or as a pitiable delusion. The making of psychology a mere branch of physiology would be justified only if no form of psychical reality existed, or if it could not be studied to any degree in a scientific way. None of these negative conditions are actually fulfilled. The reality of the psychical, as we shall conceive it in the present book, is unescapable. Its importance as a subject matter for scientific inquiry is paramount; to a race of *un*conscious mechanisms nothing would be important.

THE FORMAL DEFINITIONS OF PSYCHOLOGY AND PHYSICAL SCIENCE

47. The Definition of Physics.—We should now find ourselves in a position to formulate a technical definition of psychology and its allied sciences. In constructing such a definition, it will be helpful and perhaps necessary, to set up a corresponding characterization of physical science, since these two lines of empirical inquiry appear, in the light of intellectual history, to be mutually complementary. Empirical science naturally divides itself into two parts, and *only* two, one of these being descended from the soul concept or *psyche,* and the other from the concept of the *fusis,* in Greek philosophy. It is possible to define either psychology or physics in terms of what the other science is not.

From the point of view of the orderly development of knowledge, the definition of psychology should precede that of physics. However, historically, the reverse relationship has usually operated. Physics has defined itself automatically, while psychology—and philosophy—have had to struggle with what physics has left behind. Thoughtful students of the problems and methods of psychology have usually found that the task before them was to differentiate clearly between the subject matters of physical and of psychological science, and thus have been obliged to define them together. This applies, for example, to the ideas of Mach, Wundt and Hollingworth, which we have already reviewed.

Now, I may as well state frankly that the definition of psychology which I shall defend and employ in the present book is derived, in the above indicated manner, from what

I conceive to be the contemporary conception of physical science. According to this conception, physics is interested in the nature of a supposedly objective and universal system, no part of which is directly given in experience. This system consists of a four-dimensional space-time mosaic of positive and negative electrical particles, which are undergoing certain motions or changes, in accordance with the laws of electrostatics and electrodynamics. The task of physical science is to ascertain the exact structures of typical forms in this mosaic, and to analyze their changes in terms of electrodynamic laws. The problem of physics, as thus conceived, applies not only to electrons, protons, atoms, molecules and inorganic molar bodies of all sizes, up to and including the stars; but also to living organisms. The latter are regarded by the physical science of biology as being nothing but extremely complex electrodynamic (or static) configurations, whose forms are particularly determined by an evolutionary history. Biologists do not universally reduce their concepts to those of ultimate theoretical physics, but the notion of biology as a non-vitalistic science implies that such reduction is possible,—and necessary in all cases for a completion of the scientific treatment.

Physics is an empirical science, not in the sense that it takes any portion of experience for its subject matter, but only because it uses experience as its guide. It does not conceive—as do some forms of metaphysics—that the nature of objective reality can be ascertained by a process of pure reason apart from all experience. Moreover, physics purports to provide us with an *explanation* of certain of the phenomena of experience and, in its engineering applications, to be able to show us how to control some of these phenomena. The primary test of the truth of physical ideas lies in their consistency with experiential data. However, this test is supplemented by others, such as simplicity, generality, and formulation in terms of approved elemental concepts.

In the light of the above discussion we may offer the following definition: *Physics or physical science is the inter-*

pretation of experience, so far as possible, in terms of electricity, physical space and physical time, its experiments and observations being so devised as to assist such an interpretation.

48. Other Conceptions of Physics.—The term, physics or physical science, in the above definition, is intended to include not only mechanics, optics, and the sciences of electricity, magnetism and heat—which are ordinarily discussed in text books of "physics," but also chemistry, astronomy, geology, and biology, together with many other subordinate sciences. It is characteristic of modern scientific thought that the boundary lines among the physical sciences have vanished, so that all of these sciences appear as a single integral form of inquiry. Mechanics, optics, and chemistry are no longer regarded as having peculiar fundamental principles of their own, their conceptions and laws being merely special corrolaries of electrostatics and electrodynamics. The same is true, in a less definitely clarified manner, of the biological sciences. All of the physical sciences share in the so-called "objective method," and the lines of academic demarcation between them are significant merely of separable aspects of a single problem, the determination of the total electrodynamic universe.

From the time of Newton down to the latter decades of the nineteenth century, physicists were convinced that they could properly express all of the facts of their science in terms of space, mass and time, in accordance with the units of the famous "C. G. S." system. These are still the fundamental practical units of physical measurement. However, the establishment of electricity in place of "matter," as the basic substance of the physical universe, has displaced the notion of "mass" as fundamental. The concepts of positive and negative electric charge, dielectric capacity and magnetic permeability now appear to be more elementary than that of mass. Space and time still remain as fundamental, but relativity views, such as those of Einstein, have greatly changed their manner of conception and status. Although physical space and time may bear certain resemblances to the space and time of immediate experience, it is impossible to identify the two sets of manifolds. Experiential space, for instance, is not even Euclidean. Physical space is now also conceived to differ from the Euclidean, but not in the same manner which is characteristic of psychological space. There are numerous psychological spaces, and the notions of both space and time for physics are subject to change with the progress of the science. The physicist will always use those conceptions which yield the simplest and most comprehensive system that is consistent with his facts.

The above definition of physics is not offered in ignorance of certain modern attempts, such as those of Russell,[155] to formulate the concepts of theoretical physics in terms of direct experience. It is offered simply as a statement of what contemporary physicists are actually attempting to do, and in the belief that very few of them ever have, or ever will, read Russell and similar philosophers. Possibly, it would be in the interests of clearness of thought and the progress of knowledge if physicists would adopt some such views as those of Russell, Pearson or Kirchhoff. Personally, I doubt it. Such schemes may throw light upon the significance of physical methods, revealing some of their relationships and implicit assumptions, but I do not believe that they are profitable substitutes for a good, old-fashioned—if refined—objectivism. From the philosophical standpoint, physics must be regarded not as a science of pure experience, but as a first step in metaphysics.

The notion that the hypotheses of modern physics are merely symbolic schemes for dealing with the complexities of immediate experience, and have no valid reference beyond that experience, can be seriously entertained only by philosophers who are not conversant with the details of these hypotheses and their experiential relationships. If we cannot regard the fundamental ideas of the modern theory of "the constitution of matter" as revelations, in some way, of objective (or "ejective") truth, then we can have little hope that any such revelations will ever be possible. In spite of their admittedly inferential and speculative character, their scientific validity may vastly exceed that of any purely empirical formulation, because of the accumulation of quantitative verifications which support them. In the face of these corroborative arguments, the stoutest of "conceptualists" lose heart, and admit that, after all, there may be something apart from experience and that physics may have something to do with it. This was the eventual fate of Ostwald, who for years supported his "thermodynamic" conceptualism, in opposition to molecular and atomic principles, but finaly capitulated and admitted the validity of these and similar hypotheses.

49. The Definition of Psychology.—All of this means that physical science has now rendered unto psychology what is psychology's: the subjective attitude and data in their entirety. Perhaps it would be more appropriate to call the resulting science, "empiriology," than psychology, but we must let history be our guide in the choice of names. So we must say that: *Psychology is the systematic description of immediate experience in its own terms, and the formulation of its manner of determination by features of the physical system, or any other demonstrable factors lying outside of experience itself.* A brief, popular equivalent of this definition lies in the statement that psychology is *the scientific study of consciousness and its conditions.*

We shall consider in detail, below, the exact meaning which is to be assigned to the term, "immediate experience," together with its relationship to the notion of "consciousness." The adjective "immediate" is not employed as a synonym of "present," in a temporal sense, but merely as excluding from experience any supposed constituents which are not directly presented within it. Such constituents may be inferred from it, either intentionally or unintentionally. Considerable importance attaches to the phrase, "systematic description," in the above definition. All sciences are of course in the last analysis descriptive, no matter how generalized or mathematical their formulae may be; but description, as *a process of direct report,* is a cardinal characteristic of psychological method. Physics uses such reports—if at all

—merely as transitional steps in elaborate chains of reasoning, which lead to ultimate descriptions of non-empirical subject matters. A "systematic" description is one having a "scientific" as contrasted with a casual character, involving accuracy, completeness, generality, order, mathematical form, and other features which are well known in scientific thought and which will be exemplified further below.

It will be noted that, in accordance with our definition, psychology naturally divides itself into two sections, one dealing with immediate experience alone, and the other with its manner of determination by physical factors. The former division may be designated as *introspective psychology* and the latter as *psychophysiology*. Further subdivisions may be indicated for other possible determinants of experience, such as the subconscious mind.

50. Contrasts Between Physics and Psychology.—In comparing and contrasting introspective psychology with physical science, the following points may be noted. Physics constantly utilizes many hypotheses and assumptions, while pure psychology employs only those which are required to render systematic description possible. Psychological descriptions neither add to nor subtract from experience as it occurs, while physical accounts always do both of these things. Physics builds up a hypothetical system, discarding all portions of experience which will not fit into its scheme. Psychology deals with what is thus discarded, including the immediate experiential data upon which physical reasoning is partly based. Physics eventually abandons all data, as such, paying attention only to the inferences.

It is often said that the difference between psychology and physics is one of "point of view," but this is a very misleading analogy. Insofar as physics deals with immediate experience, its point of view is the same as that of introspective psychology. There is only one possible point of view with regard to experience, that of thought in relation to the concrete facts. The difference between physics and introspective psychology is one of purpose and method, not of "point of view." They both start with the same data, but physics considers only a limited selection among them, and these only for the purpose of inferring something which lies beyond them. Psychology, on the other hand, deals with the entirety of the empirical facts and is not concerned primarily to infer anything whatsoever on the basis of its descriptions of these facts.

Chapter III

The Fundamental Concepts of Introspective Psychology

Section 11

THE MEANINGS OF "EXPERIENCE" AND "CONSCIOUSNESS"

51. Defining "Experience."—The fundamental concepts of psychology, according to the definition which we have offered in the preceding chapter, are those of *experience* and *consciousness*. It is now our task to make the meanings of these—and other essential psychological terms—as clear as possible. It is frequently stated that "experience" and "consciousness" cannot be defined. Thus Judd says: "Psychology is the science of consciousness. . . . Everyone knows what consciousness is although it cannot be defined." It is necessary to disagree with both of the propositions which are contained in the latter sentence: very few people know what consciousness is, but it can readily be defined in a number of different ways. "Experience" is such a fundamental conception for science that it may seem to cover everything, and so be very difficult to provide with any distinguishing differentiae. However, in reality it is the most thoroughly definable of all conceptions. Psychologists who admit that they cannot define these terms are probably in the same mental condition as Watson, when he says that he does not know what they mean.

There is a great deal of mystifying hocus-pocus, in

philosophical discussion, concerning definition and "indefinables." From the dictionary standpoint, definition consists in substituting one set of words for another, but its practical purpose is to place the thinker in contact with non-verbal meanings, which can seldom be demonstrated directly in a dictionary or on any printed sheet of paper. Any discussion necessarily assumes that the reader or listener already knows the non-verbal meanings of certain words, and nearly all such meanings will have some components which are parts of experience. Two general methods of definition appear to be available for designating the meaning of the words, "experience" and "consciousness." The first is to state their *constitution:* to give a catalogue of the factors which compose them and to say how they are put together. This is an analytic method. The second scheme is to state the *conditions* under which "experience" and "consciousness" exist or occur.

Each of these methods of definition utilizes certain characteristic results of psychology as a finished science. A definition of experience in terms of its constitution is a descriptive analysis of experience, at least in synoptic form, and to develop such an analysis is the main task of introspective psychology. A definition of experience in terms of its *conditions,* at any rate in the present state of our enlightenment, will necessarily be based upon the principal facts of physiological psychology. Thus, the most thorough definitions of these fundamental concepts of the science will only be possible in a statement of all of the results of the science itself. Nevertheless, it seems permissible to anticipate some of the essentials of these results, in an attempt to clarify the fundamental concepts in advance.

If we endeavor to define experience in terms of its physiological conditions, our formula must be somewhat as follows: *Any individual experience is a distinctive system of elements and processes occurring in point-to-point correlation with the higher coördinative phases of nervous action in a waking, living organism.* Since our present psychophysiological knowledge is far from complete, we may rightly feel considerable dissatisfaction with the above definition and prefer one by the analytical method.

By this method, *experience can be defined as a structure and process involving components such as the following:* (1) the sensible qualities of objects "as we observe them," e.g., color, brightness, hardness, hotness, coldness, sweetness, sourness, odor, tone, noise, etc.; (2) the arrangement of these qualities in perceived or strictly empirical space and their manner of succession in experiential time; (3) the elements of "inner experience," thoughts, feelings, affections (pleasure and displeasure), "muscle sensations" (effort), pain, itch, "organic sensations" and the like; (4) relations between these various specified elements of any "observable" sort; (5) all "observable" changes or processes which these elements, or their manners of combination, undergo.

As above defined, experience is clearly coextensive with the inner and outer worlds of common-sense perception. It consists of all of the things which, in the "act" psychology, are regarded as objects of awareness, and comprises the actual given combination of these things. This statement, however, should not be construed as an identification of experiential and *physical* objects. For example, *color* as a part of experience is a psychological datum which bears no similarity whatsoever to those particular *wave-lengths of electromagnetic radiation* which the physicist substitutes, in his treatment, for the concrete colors themselves. Similarly, tone, a component of auditory experience, bears no similarity to the propagated sine-wave disturbances of material aggregates which the physicists call sound. The physical substitutes for the concrete items of experience are, from the psychologist's point of view, the *stimuli* of certain receptors or sense-organs with the operations of which the immediate experiential data are correlated, but it is absolutely impossible to *identify* these stimuli with their psychical correlatives.

52. **Experience As Spatial.**—It will be noted that, in accordance with the above definition, experience is inherently both spatial and temporal in structure. Many psychologists and philosophers, following the original suggestion made by

Descartes, have defined psychical reality as being essentially non-extended or non-spatial. This is a characterization which is tenable only in connection with an awareness psychology, and here apparently only because awareness does not, in point of fact, exist. As soon as we attempt to define the psychical in terms of the total experience system of any individual, we find this exclusion of extensity from the domain of the psychical to be quite untenable. Visual, tactual, kinaesthetic, auditory and nearly all other of the divisions of experience are inherently extensive; and it is only by analogy with the extensive character of these forms of experience that we are able to construct the spatial schemata which we employ in geometry and physics.

However, this explicit recognition of the spatial character of much of our experience should not lead us into the error of identifying the space of experience with that of the physical system. By hypothesis, so far as our present discussion is concerned, the entire physical system includes its own characteristic space, and lies entirely outside of any particular individual experience, so that it is quite contrary to our assumptions to suppose that these two spaces are interpenetrative. Moreover, the mere fact that there is space within experience does not imply that experience is within space. It is clear that the space within experience is finite in amount and whether this finite space of experience is continuous and interlocking with an infinite space beyond experience is a question which introspective psychology cannot answer. Furthermore, we do not need to suppose that experiential space has the same properties as are possessed by Euclidean or any other particular form of mathematical or physical space. Euclidean space, for example, is isotropic, or is possessed of the same properties in all directions, but even a casual examination of visual space will show that it is anisotropic. Visual space has some of the properties of certain image spaces in physical theory, the dimension of depth, or distance to and from the eye, being different from the other two dimensions, which are perpendicular to the line of vision.

While we maintain that experience is inherently extended in nature, this does not force us to suppose that spatial forms are the only types of structure which are observable within experience. On the contrary, experience contains *various* kinds of spaces as well as of non-spatial manifolds, compounded in both spatial and non-spatial ways.

53. The Definition of Consciousness.—*Consciousness may be defined, in terms of experience, as a cross-section of the latter taken in time, at any instant.* This technical definition agrees well with that of Titchener, but only roughly with the views of many other psychological writers However, it furnishes us with a very useful conception, and one which harmonizes as well with the common-sense notion of consciousness, and with that which has characterized the majority of psychological writers in recent times, as could be expected. Any experience is a flux; it has a time span of any defined length, a day, a year, or a lifetime. Consciousness, on the other hand, as we shall conceive it, has a zero time span. It is, so to speak, a snapshot of experience.

Having thus conceived consciousness, we may redefine experience as the sum of an infinite, continuous, temporal series of consciousness. Experience and consciousness, in other words, bear the same relation to one another that a mathematical function bears to its time derivative; the equation of consciousness is a differential one and its integral is that of experience. This analogy makes it clear that the notion of consciousness, as an instantaneous cross-section of experience, does not necessarily mean that consciousness is wholly a static entity, since rates of change can be conceived mathematically to exist at instants, as well as across finite stretches of time.

The relation between experience and consciousness may be illustrated by an analogy with the motion picture. Experience may be compared to one or more reels of pictures as projected upon the screen, the latter representing the identity and continuity of the individual experience field. A single picture on the screen—twenty-four of which are projected every second—would represent approximately a single consciousness, a succession of such pictures being required to constitute an experience. This analogy may be extended to include the entire psychophysical system, by comparing the projector which throws the picture on the screen to the organism, while the beam of light symbolizes the psychophysical relation.

It may be noted that, although experience is a broader concept than is consciousness, the latter is more closely representative of concrete reality. Strictly speaking, the only phase of experience which *exists* is the present, and this comprises a consciousness. The past and future phases of experience are nonexistent and find representation only in the present, in the form of records or prophesies. It is customary for psychologists to regard the psychological present as possessing a finite time span, but upon close analysis this notion of the "specious present" does appear to be susceptible of logical justification. It may be admitted, on a fundamental plane of analysis, that the entire conception of time as an infinite series of infinitesimal instants is an artificial construction. But if we adopt this conception of time in psychology, as we do in physics, there seems to be no reason why the local psychological instant should differ from that of physics.

The facts which lead to the notion of the specious present are really psychophysical in nature, and are concerned with the temporal relations existing between the components of any instant of experience and those of the physical time series. It is found that, as a rule, the *determinants* of a single consciousness are located, not in a single instant of physical time, but within a period of considerable magnitude in the physical system. It is this psychophysical relationship which comprises the sole significance of the conception of the specious present. Although the present consciousness is the only existing one, we do not necessarily confine ourselves to the present, but may speak of any moment of experience whatsoever, past, present or future, as constituting a consciousness. It is clear that although consciousness may be dynamic in the sense of exhibiting indices of change, it is, by description, a state and not a process; and, moreover, that any psychical *process* must comprise an experience and be describable in terms of a definite sequence of different consciousnesses.

It should be clear that a consciousness, as above defined, is an existential system—usually having a complex structure —and is not an activity or a relationship. Consciousnesses, as we find them, are *individual,* but such individuality does not mean that they depend upon an ego or subject. It is true that psychophysical investigation shows that they stand in a relation of functional interdetermination with structures and processes in individual *organisms,* so that in this sense each consciousness may be said to *belong* to a particular body. However, this is a discovery which is subsequent to the definition of consciousness as an instantaneous system of experiential components.

The majority of contemporary introspective psychologists who have abandoned the hypothesis of a "subject" approve of the term, consciousness, and employ it in their definitions and discussions. However, Hollingworth has the distinction of defining psychology as a subjective and experiental science, while frowning upon the word, consciousness. He interprets the term as standing ordinarily for experiental "events reported by another but inaccessible to me." [156] He rejects the notion that consciousness should also be held to include experiental data concerning which there is agreement between two reporting observers. His discussion of the situation is difficult to follow and not convincing. The concept of consciousness, as we shall use it in the present book, is that of the sum-total of all immediate facts which are accessible to any individual reporting process at a given instant. In Hollingworth's terminology, it comprises all "natural events" which are momentarily available to the reporting process in any individual, X. This is the X consciousness. Another such sum-total, which may be accessible at the same moment to the reporting process, Y, is regarded as another consciousness, whether or not it may have parts in common with the X consciousness.

Section 12

THE MANNER OF OCCURRENCE OF EXPERIENCE

54. Individual Experiences.—Theorists sometimes forget that the nature of experience, in itself, as viewed by introspective psychology, must be independent of all metaphysical theories concerning its external conditions, its origin, or its fate. Experience, as such, must be the same for realism, for materialism, and for idealism. Red is red. Its reality is in its appearance. A rose is as sweet by any other name, or even if regarded as a product of synthetic chemistry. If experience changes as a function of attitude, we may lose the thing we set out to study, but we are not relieved of the duty of describing it as it was before it departed.

Philosophers, and even psychologists, often speak of experience and consciousness as if they were substances uniformly spread out over the universe like the physical æther, or as if there were such an entity as experience at large or in general. Although this notion may form an interesting hypothesis, in such doctrines as objective idealism or neorealism, it cannot be adopted—at least in the beginning—by psychology. For psychology, all experience and consciousness are *individual*. Experience exists only in the form of isolated fields or foci of experience forming psychological individuals. There may be some other kind of experience than "yours," "mine," or "Smith's," but it has not yet been opened to psychological observation. Accordingly, experience must be conceived as *molecular* in occurrence or distribution, resembling the substances of chemistry or of ultimate atomic physics. Experience "in general" is either the collection of all actual isolated experience fields, thus conceived, or it is a fictitious abstraction of the common properties of many such concrete systems.

A great deal has been made in psychology, and in philosophy, of the notion of the self-identity of the personal consciousness. In formulating psychological descriptions, the use of the pronoun "I" sometimes seems to be imperative. However, as Russell points out, the sentence "I think" is more properly rendered as "It thinks in me," indicating that the mind is not an active agent but is a place or locus within which events occur more or less of their own accord. However, it may seem that in this translation we have only shifted from the subjective to the objective form, the problem of "me" having replaced that of "I." The fact which remains, however, is simply that of the concreteness and particularity of any given experience mosaic. This is a property not peculiar to fields of experience but common to all concrete forms of existence, however found or conceived. It is no more a unique property of consciousness than it is of, say, hydrogen. There is no such thing as hydrogen-in-general, but merely so many concrete hydrogen atoms, located at definite places within the physical universe. Similarly, experience is always to be found in the form of concrete isolated systems, and the account of experience is incomplete unless these particular systems are definitely and distinctively tagged.

The apparently necessary reference to self or subject in psychological description rests in part upon the fact that the direct description of any concrete experience must arise within that particular experience itself. In physics, atoms do not describe themselves but are described by the physicist. In psychology, however, the molecular units which are under consideration are forced to generate their own descriptions. Psychology, as the direct observation of experience, is clearly caught in what the modern realist calls the "egocentric predicament." However, there is no other science which is any better off in this regard, since all direct observation is that of the individual observer within his own consciousness. Psychology, as the only science which endeavors to confine itself to immediate data, naturally appreciates this egocentric situation the most keenly, but as soon as psychology decides to utilize the method of inference, which is the rule in physical sciences, it finds itself no worse off than the latter.

55. The Postulate of Other-Consciousness—Some modern thinkers, *e.g.,* James [157] and the Neo-realists, have discovered that individual experiences are not *of necessity* wholly isolated from one another. These philosophers point out that consciousnesses may conceivably overlap, or may possess common parts. This is, of course, what the man in the street supposes them to do, but a demonstration of the conceivability of such an overlap cannot be taken as a proof of its actual occurrence. Whether there is an intersection of individual experiences or not, the introspective psychologist does not know, and consequently he is compelled to treat each individual consciousness as a system unto itself. This attitude cannot lead to any fundamental mistakes, since if it should turn out that experiences in fact do overlap, it would simply mean that the psychologist had unnecessarily redescribed certain items of his subject matter.

We have insisted that, at first, psychology works exclusively within experience itself, without assumptions and without use of inference. This method is indeed characteristic of the psychological mode of approach to reality, and, if the psychologist so desires, he will find it possible to adhere strictly to such pure empiricism, always confining his thought to his own consciousness. However, in practice, psychology utilizes certain very primitive assumptions and draws inferences on the basis which they provide. These assumptions are very different from those which are employed by physics and hence the conclusions, to which they lead, form part of a system of beliefs which is quite distinct from that of physical science.

The most fundamental of these practical postulates of psychology is that of *the existence of a plurality of experiences,* in the sense of our above discussion. Every proposition in psychology is, of course, necessarily made by some particular psychologist, but he is apt to lay the proposition in question down, not only for his own consciousness, but for that of any other human being. He thus assumes the existence of consciousnesses other than his own. This assumption is suggested by the relations which exist between his own consciousness and his own organism, as he perceives the latter within this consciousness, or as he conceives it as a portion of his inferential world of physics.[158] The psychological origin of the assumption certainly does not constitute a demonstration of its validity, and it must be admitted frankly that, so far as we can see, no such demonstration is possible. Like the principle of the uniformity of nature, the *postulate of other-consciousness* is systematically ultimate, serving as a foundation for many other demonstrations, but not being itself demonstrable.

It should be noted, however, that, in a social situation, the postulate of other-consciousness is quite unescapable. So long as I confine my psychological descriptions within my own consciousness itself, not expressing them for the benefit of other individuals, I find no difficulty in maintaining a philosophy of solipsism which makes my own consciousness equivalent to the whole of admitted reality. But as soon as I converse with another psychological individual, I find that the latter has as good a claim to regard my consciousness as nonexistent as have I to look upon his consciousness in this way. The situation becomes thoroughly relativistic and symmetrical from the points of view of the two conversing minds. If these two minds are to decide the matter in concert, they must therefore feel impelled either to say that neither of the two consciousnesses exists or that both of them have reality. Since each observer knows positively that the first alternative cannot be true, both observers are forced practically to adopt the second alternative.

56. Consciousness Correlated With Organisms.—From the manner in which any one of us comes to believe in the existence of the consciousnesses of other men, it follows that the plurality of consciousnesses or experience fields, with which psychology has to deal, is conceived as point-to-point correspondent with an equal number of living, waking, human organisms. These organisms are represented, from time to time, within the consciousness of any given observer, as visual, auditory and sometimes as tactual presentations, but their most adequate representation is found in the total scheme of the physical world as worked out by geographers, ethnologists and statisticians. If these physical scientists determine that there are a billion living human organisms on the surface of the earth, the psychologist can infer the actual or potential existence of a billion individual human experiences.

It will not be possible for the psychologist to specify accurately the conditions under which he can properly infer the existence of consciousness, until he has completed his science of psychophysiology. That consciousnesses of some sort exist in conjunction with animal as well as human organisms, he has very little doubt. He may even suspect that there are vague experiences corresponding to plant forms. Practically, he assumes a consciousness in other men when they speak to him intelligibly and in particular when, as in making an introspective report, they claim to be describing their own experiences.

Adopting this criterion as a working test, the psychologist may hope, through the development of psychophysiological knowledge which is thus made possible, to arrive finally at principles which will enable him to decide definitely as to the number and variety of experience mosaics which exist in the universe at large. It seems improbable, on the basis of general analogies, that human consciousnesses are the only species of psychical system which exists. We may well deem it probable that many families, genera, species and varieties of consciousness are actually realized within the psychologist's total universe, and we may hope eventually to arrive at generalizations concerning the characteristics of these various types, dealing with them much in the same way in which the chemist treats the various atomic species that form the subject matter of his chemical science.

57. The Concept of "Mind."—Although we shall regard the terms, "experience" and "consciousness," as the fundamental concepts of psychology, there are a number of other words which may be usefully defined. The term, *mind*, is one which has been used a great deal in psychological discussions, and its exact denotation varies quite widely in various psychological contexts. In general, it appears to stand either for the *place* within which experience or consciousness is located or for the more or less permanent conditions under which it is realized. Strictly speaking, consciousness has no *location* in any sense closely analogous to that of position in space. However, the continuity of any individual experience makes it possible to define a "place" in terms of the experience itself, and "mind" can accordingly be identified with what we have already called the *field* of any individual consciousness or experience. We must be careful to recognize, however, that this field is not an actual container of consciousness, capable of being emptied of the latter, but is simply a name for the unity and continuity of any particular experiential system.

The concept of mind may be broadened somewhat if we make it include not only the experience field, but also any *psychical conditions* which may possibly be involved in the existence of this field. We do not know certainly that any such conditions actually exist, but the familiar hypothesis of the *subconscious* mind provides us with a conception of this sort. We might broaden the term even more, so that it would include also the physiological conditions of consciousness, but this extension appears to conflict too much with accepted usage. Accordingly, we may define mind as the field of consciousness, as created by the unity and continuity of experience, together with any real or supposed *psychical* conditions of the phenomena which appear therein.

58. Subjective and Ejective.—Among other words which require definition are the terms "psychical" and "subjective." By the *psychical* we mean anything which may form a part or an aspect of consciousness and, hence, of experience. The psychical is distinguished from the physical in the manner which we have already indicated. Certain conceptions of the physical may make it a particular portion of the psychical system, a set of abstractions from the world of external experience. However, we have preferred the view that the physical world lies wholly outside of experience and hence is strictly non-psychical. The term psychical is defined so that it applies to any conscious or experiential system whatever, regardless of its identity. Any system, however simple or complex, which is generally similar, in nature or substance, to a human consciousness may be described properly as being psychical. Even single atoms or electrons may have psychical entities associated with them, and the subconscious mind of man, if it exists, is just as psychical as is the introspective consciousness.

The term, *subjective,* on the other hand, may be employed to denote, exclusively, *any* unitary consciousness, *regarded from its own point of view.* Thus, *my* total consciousness is subjective for *my* thought, but is not subjective for your thought. Your consciousness, similarly, is not subjective *for me.* This use of the word, subjective, differs from that which would identify the subjective and the psychical, and also from a usage which would restrict the meaning of the subjective within any given experience to the internal as opposed to the external sections of that experience. "Things" in the common-sense world are just as subjective, according to our definition, as are thought and feeling. The correlative term, *ejective,* may be defined as the sum of all reality *not* a part of the given consciousness which is designated as the subjective. The subjective plus the ejective constitutes the entire system of existence. Subjective and ejective, according to this mode of definition, are purely relative terms, and are not significant of the nature of their subject matters. The term, psychical, on the other hand, is non-relative and is indicative of a certain general form of existence. The word, *objective,* will be used, henceforth, throughout this work, to refer to the *physical* object of response or its surrounding conditions. Its scope is much narrower than that of the term, ejective, which has general metaphysical significance.

Section 13

THE SUBDIVISIONS OF PSYCHOLOGY

It is customary, in an introduction to a psychological textbook, to enumerate the various subdivisions of the science. The two main sections which are implied in our definition of psychology are clearly those of introspective psychology and of psychophysiology, respectively. The former may be partitioned generally, as we divide biology into anatomy and physiology, into *psychostatics,* or the description of the structures and elements of consciousness and *psychodynamics,* or an account of the processes of experience. In a different plane of classification, introspective psychology and its inferential extensions may be subdivided according to the type of consciousness or experience which is under consideration. Just as biology is divided into zoölogy and botany, and these sciences are subdivided further according to the individual species which are being considered, so pure psychology will contain chapters on human consciousness, various lower animal consciousnesses, possibly plant consciousness and, conceivably, even simpler forms than those corresponding to vegetable life.

All of these varied psychic types can obviously be considered either in their typical or normal forms or in abnormal or pathological conditions, thus drawing a line between normal and abnormal psychology. It is clear that the subdivisions of physiological psychology must exactly parallel those of the purely introspective science; there will be a psychophysiology of conscious structure and also of the dynamics of experience, while each psychic species and normal or abnormal condition will have its own physiological correlatives. What is ordinarily known as *genetic psychology* will be included, for the most part, under the physiological interpretation of psychodynamics or psychical functions, with particular reference to biological evolution.

The psychology of purpose or *motives* will also be a chapter in psychodynamics, either introspectively or physiologically considered. *Social psychology,* again, of which much is being made at the present day, is another chapter in the psychophysiology of mental functions.

Chapter IV

The Methods of Introspective Psychology

Section 14

THE NATURE OF INTROSPECTION

59. Separating Psychological from Physical Data.—
Our general definition of psychology, as given in the previous
chapter, implies a division of the science into two logically
distinct parts, introspective psychology and psychophysiology.
Introspective psychology is the science of the constitution and processes of immediate experience, a science of
elements, structures and changes. Psychophysiology, on the
other hand, is a science of special relations, of the laws
which connect the data of introspective psychology with
those of physiology, the latter being a purely physical science.

We have defined introspective psychology as a systematic
description of immediate experience in its own terms.   This
definition, as we have seen, demands that pure psychology
should not reduce experience to anything which it does not find
directly within experience. All of the methods, criteria, units,
standards, etc. of introspective psychology must be subjective
for any psychological observer, i.e., they must borrow nothing, except possibly by analogy, from physics or any other
inferential science. Practically, in the laboratory, nearly
all of our observations or experiments involve an integral
combination of introspective and physiological methods, but
it is essential that these two lines of attack be kept logically
separate. If this logical separation is not strictly followed
it becomes impossible not only to establish a strictly
psychological psychology but also to develop a clear-cut

physiological psychology. Since the concepts of the two sciences—psychology and physiology—are inherently different, it is requisite that we should separate them clearly in all of our intellectual operations. Such a separation—functional and behavioristic psychologists to the contrary notwithstanding—is perfectly feasible.

The distinctive method of psychology is usually described by the word *introspection*. Although we shall retain this term, it will be necessary for us to define it carefully, and our final conception of its nature may differ quite radically from that which has been adopted by many psychologists and philosophers. The classical psychologists regarded introspection as a peculiar reflexive relationship or process, in which consciousness turns upon itself somewhat like a dog chasing its own tail. In "inspection," or physical observation, they asserted, we are conscious of objects, but in introspection we are conscious of being conscious, or of the manner in which we are conscious. This notion of introspection is clearly derived from the idea of psychical phenomena as being relations between subjects and objects. Since, for our present purposes, we have quite abandoned this idea, it is necessary for us to revise our conception of the nature of introspection. If the subject matter of psychology is experience as a whole and is not a hypothetical relation of awareness, and if experience is a unified dynamic structure of qualitative elements, then it is clear that the science of experience cannot be limited to a method as obscure and slippery as that described by the classical psychologists.

60. The Nature of Description.—The primary problem of psychology, as we have seen, is that of the *description* of experience. In order to understand the essential psychological method, therefore, it seems necessary to recognize clearly the nature of description. As we shall see, description has many, and some very complicated, phases but it consists essentially in the process of utilizing verbal symbols; the substitution within consciousness of a word for that which the word means. In a highly systematized science, this process of substitution may have a very elaborate technique, with complicated rules which must be carefully followed. The foundation of all such rules, however, is established by the process of *definition*, which is the reverse of description: the substitution within consciousness of a meaning for a symbol which has been adopted to stand for it.

Definition depends upon a fiat, upon an arbitrary act of thought; but once a definition has been established, description is determined by the nature of what is to be described. Thus we define the word r-e-d as the symbol for a definite visual quality or color, and thereafter, if we adhere to our definition, we are forced to reproduce this word whenever the color in question appears as part of an experience which is to be described. The word "red" is a description of the color in question; the words *rot* and *rouge* are equally good descriptions within the two definition systems which we call the German and the French languages respectively. It may seem that to call a certain color, "red," does not constitute a description of this color, but a moment's reflection will show that, in the case of an absolutely simple quality like a color, no other form of description is possible. More complicated factors of experience, as we shall see, may be given *analytical* descriptions, and it is symbolic accounts of this sort which are commonly regarded as being adequately descriptive in nature. Analytical descriptions, however, are simply concatenations of symbols which, individually, are descriptive by a simple reference to a single characteristic meaning. All descriptions, no matter how analytical or complex, ultimately find their roots in such elementary symbols and their definitions.

61. Introspection as Pure Descriptive Report.—A complete understanding of the process by which descriptions arise within consciousness has not as yet been attained by psychological research. What is known positively concerning this process will form a portion of later chapters. (See Volume III.) It is sufficient for our present purposes to be convinced of the possibility of the process in question. The generation of descriptions appears to be one of the principal functions of human consciousness, as we know it.

and in the beginning we take this function for granted and adopt it as the main instrument of psychological investigation. It would appear that, given the requisite definitions, one ought to be able to describe anything which occurs within his experience. We might even be tempted to define consciousness or experience as the sum of all immediately describable things.

However, if appropriate definitions do not exist—as they certainly do not in connection with many psychological topics—description will be impossible even if the characteristic experiences are quite perfectly realized. It would be absurd to suppose that a thing cannot exist in experience until we have a word capable of symbolizing it. In a similar way, we must recognize that much of our experience never gets described at all, for itself, even when appropriate words exist, the experiences being interpreted directly as symbols of physical or other non-experiential factors. The phenomena of aphasia, which we shall consider in detail later, show that profound derangements of the mechanisms by which descriptions are evoked may occur without serious damage to the remainder of experience.

Now *introspection,* from our point of view, is identical with the process of description itself, provided only that the meanings of the symbols which appear in the description are completely given as parts of the experience within which the description arises. This provision may seem to be one which is easily realized, but unfortunately such is not the case. The majority of common-sense, as well as of scientific, descriptions are couched in terms referring to a great many things not contained within the given experience, things which are either parts of other associated experiences or are merely hypothetical in character. Nearly all of the conceptions which we find in everyday language suffer from this defect, when we try to employ them as instruments of psychological research. We therefore find it necessary to define new terms or to redefine old ones so that they shall be capable of referring exclusively to given components of experience. Persons naïve in psychological observation almost inevitably describe their experiences in terms which are largely physical or metaphysical in their significance, and *training in introspection* consists largely in developing a vocabulary which excludes inferred and associated meanings. The failure to use such a vocabulary leads to what James calls "the psychologist's fallacy" and to what Titchener designates as "the stimulus error."

It may seem that the identification of introspection with the mere process of describing experience in its own terms leaves out the primary activity which is involved, for ordinarily we regard the description or report as a secondary result of the act of observation. However, as a matter of fact, we do not find it possible, in introspection, to separate any such process of observation from the generation of the description. It is, of course, true that we place ourselves in a certain mental attitude that is determined by the problem which has been set for us, but this is merely one of the factors determining the descriptive activity. In physical science, on account of the metaphysical leanings of physics, observation may perhaps be considered to involve something which is definitely accessory or supplementary to the description. For physics the process of bringing a thing into consciousness and holding it there is ordinarily regarded as a part of the act of observation. But for psychology the thing is already there or it does not exist. It would seem, therefore, that nothing remains except to find the words which properly describe it. When we train an observer in introspection we are not sharpening his organs of sense or showing him how to enrich and expand his perceptions; to do this, as is done in education in physical science, would be to change the individual's experience, and this is exactly what we wish not to do in psychology. Our actual task is simply to provide the introspective observer with the proper verbal symbols and to train his associative functions so that they will be aroused by his experiences in a delicately accurate and reliable fashion.

62. Introspection as Analysis.—To say "experience" is completely to describe the subject matter of psychology, but such a description, just because of its completeness, is of little value. Useful descriptions must record an *analysis* of the thing described, or, at least, must serve to differentiate it from other things. If the experience which we are considering is simple in constitution, containing no differentiable parts, the best that can be done is to assign to it a name which shall be indicative of its peculiar quality, or other characteristic attributes which it may possess. In the vast majority of cases, however, any concrete experience will be found to be *complex in constitution,* so that an enumeration of its components, together with a specification of their structural combination, becomes possible. Moreover, if we are considering, not simply a moment of experience (or a consciousness), but an experience having a finite duration, we can form descriptions of the *successive* consciousnesses which make up the experience in time, thus recording a *temporal analysis* of our subject matter.

The purpose to *describe* a thing leads naturally to *analysis,* as is shown by the common impression that an unanalytic description is not even a description, although it would be possible to describe all of the different complexes which appear in experience without analysis, if we wished to assign a name to each differentiable complex. The methods of the modern *Gestalt* psychologists tend in this direction. However, carried to the extreme, such a procedure would lead to an absolutely unwieldy terminology, analogous in nature to the written Chinese language, which in principle has a separate character for each separate idea. Practically, since there are many less elementary constituents in experience than there are distinctive experiential aggregates, we can effect an economy of terminology by describing all such aggregates in terms of their components. This, however, is not the only reason for the use of an analytic method of description, for such a method provides us with materials, on the basis of which we may hope to make comprehensive generalizations regarding the constitution of experience. Such generalizations, again, should lead to further economy of description and enable us to reduce our symbolic results to a system.

It should be noted that the descriptive analysis of experience, if thorough, cannot end simply in a catalogue of elements, but must formulate clearly the *relations* which exist between the elements in the given concrete mosaic. No structural or combinational aspect of the latter can be neglected, if the description is to be complete. The relations of the psychical elements in space, in time and in all other existent manifolds, must be taken into account. Moreover, if the elements are partially fused together and if there are general attributes or qualities of the experiential complexes as wholes, these features must not be omitted from the description.

A careful study of analytical descriptions of experience shows that at least three different kinds of analysis may be involved. These consist of (1) analysis by parts, (2) analysis by aspects, and (3) analysis by phases. The first type is concerned with an actual structural complexity in the psychical subject matter. It deals with the constitution of consciousness in terms of components which may be conceived as a being separable from one another. The adjacent constituents of any space pattern, such as a color mosaic, can be regarded in this manner. We may designate analysis of this sort as *structural*. Analysis by aspects deals with *attributes*, rather than with parts. It does not imply any actual structural complexity in the subject matter, but only different modes of comparison between separate subject matters. Since such "modes" can be established only on the basis of such comparison, attributive analysis must be regarded as logically subordinate to analysis of the structural type. We shall consider its foundations in greater detail, below (*cf.* pages 120 *ff.*). Analysis by phases involves the descriptive establishment of arbitrary demarcation boundaries along the time dimension of experience. Here, again, we are not dealing with actual parts, but only with a convenient method for describing changes. As a matter of fact, only one instant of the temporal series actually exists, namely, the present, so that temporal analysis is really only a special method of verbally *recording* psychical events. We shall discuss this problem, also, in greater detail below (*cf.* pages 196 *ff.*).

63. Criticisms of Structural Analysis in Psychology.— The application of descriptive analysis to psychological problems has been severely criticized by numerous modern thinkers. Among these are the French philosopher, Bergson,[159] and the German school of *Gestalt* psychologists. The criticisms which have been advanced by Bergson and such representatives of the *Gestalt* school as Köhler,[160] refer to rather different aspects of experience, but are essentially of the same character. The attack appears to be primarily upon analysis of the structural and temporal types, description in terms of attributes or aspects being allowed as a necessary method. For Bergson, psychical life consists in a relatively inscrutable inner flux which is not subject to intellectualization. In order that it should be understood, it must be "intuited"; we must know it directly and not by "description." Köhler, on the other hand, is interested primarily in perception, or phenomena which appear in portions of the world of external experience.

The specific objections which are raised against structural analysis seem to be as follows. (1) An analytical description falsifies experience by making it appear to be a mere aggregation of ununited parts. (2) The descriptive attitude or method actually changes the experience while it is being described, so that it is no longer representative in character. (3) An analytical description implies that the parts are logically or naturally prior to their combinations, whereas the opposite is the truth. (4) Complex psychical states or processes have properties which belong only to the whole, and cannot be deduced from the parts, and such properties are lost in an analytical description.

Now, so far as Bergson is concerned, I will say that his general psychological doctrine appears to me to be essentially mystical and explicitly to rule out of the domain of psychology any subject matter which can be discussed fruitfully. However, I quite agree with his contention that in order to know the nature of experience, we must "intuite" it—which merely means: *have* it. No description or intellectualization of experience can have any meaning, save as it can be carried back into contact with the actual experience to which it refers. There is nothing in a description, *per se,* which reveals the experience or its properties. But this is not a unique characteristic of what Bergson calls "pure duration," or the supposed centrally mental flux; it is equally characteristic of the most objectified and physically conceived facts. The meanings of "red" and "square" can only be given by an exhibition of these facts themselves. The process of "intuition" is therefore not an alternative to that of description, but is a necessary foundation of the latter in all cases. However, if we leave out the description, we have neither science nor philosophy, but only bare experience.

Bergson's contention that the analytical treatment of mind, as a structure, is quite illegitimate can only be taken to mean that he conceives consciousness to be perfectly simple. In this case, it could be described adequately by means of a single word. Bergson himself devotes a very large number of words to the subject, but the analysis which this seems to imply is apparently of the attributive sort. For Bergson, consciousness has no parts, but it can nevertheless be compared in many different ways with other things. Consequently, it would seem to possess a considerable number of attributes, which can be separately designated, but, according to Bergson, even such a description in terms of separated aspects cannot reconstitute the original reality. This latter proposition is of course obvious, since any description is merely a system of signs pointing back to its actual subject matter.

The *Gestalt* school, as represented by Köhler, Koffka and others, has made many important positive contributions to psychological progress. However, as in the case of behaviorism, the vigor of the movement seems to be expended largely in an attack upon accepted concepts and methods.   Köhler criticizes the traditional structural psychology partly on the ground that it is based upon a mistaken analogy with physics.   He points out that modern physical science does not regard the world as being made up of a vacuous mosaic of atom grains, but rather as an electrodynamic fabric, in which each component is an active determinant in the equilibrium form or motion of the total configuration.   In this he is quite correct, but he becomes guilty of serious overemphasis when he neglects the outstanding fact that—in spite of electrodynamics and statics—physical systems *are* conceived as being made up of individualizable constituents.   Although there is more continuity in the conception of the physical world to-day than there was at the time of Dalton, there is also much more atomism.

Pure introspective psychology is, of course, not under any necessity of basing its methods either upon Daltonian or upon modern physical ideas.   The problem is simply that of formulating a detailed description of immediate experience exactly as it is given.   As given, it ordinarily shows parts which can be named individually.   These parts are never one hundred per cent isolated from one another; the boundaries between them are always more or less indistinct, as is the case, also, with the parts of physical configurations. Certain psychological systems may have tended to overindividualize such psychical parts, but this should not cause us to jump to the opposite error of under-individualizing them.   The situation in psychology happens actually to be similar to that which exists in physics; if we are to make progress we must pay attention simultaneously to the elements and to their forms of combination.   The latter include various degree of fusion or true integration.

64. Precautions to be Used in Introspection.—One of the primary precautions of psychological method must evidently be to render its descriptive technique capable of handling intelligibly all of the forms of experience which it is forced to consider.   Where analytic description is actually impossible, on account of the apparent simplicity of the subject matter, description must be confined to a mere process of designation by means of single symbols. But wherever parts can actually be discriminated within the experience, psychology will be justified in employing a complex symbolic system to designate the whole. The underlying cause of such criticisms as that of Bergson is to be found in the tendency, which philosophers exhibit, to identify a description with that which it describes. The similarity between analytical descriptions and the systems for which they stand is very slight, indeed. Regarded as a series of visual or auditory perceptions, a description is essentially broken up or articulate in structure, but we should not allow this characteristic of our symbolic material to imply, in our thought, the existence of a similarly disintegrated constitution in the experiences to which the description may refer. These criticisms of introspective analysis rest upon an over-interpretation of the psychologist's method of work.

However, it appears to be an actual fact that, in certain cases, the introspective attitude does bring about a change in the subject matter which it purports to describe. This may be considered to be due, in part, to the presence of the description within the same integral conscious system which contains the thing to be described, so that there is an interaction between them. However, critics of scientific, and particularly of analytical, psychology have very frequently overestimated the magnitude and importance of such changes. We are not justified, just because a slight modification occurs, in saying that the new status is "totally different" from the original one. It is doubtful whether the phrase "totally different" can legitimately be applied to any actual pair of facts. We have already considered this situation in its general bearing. In particular, if the analytical attitude generates experiential parts where they did not exist before, or if it over-individualizes parts which are actually there, then we must seek some method of correcting the description so that it will conform to the facts as they exist apart from this attitude. If this is impossible, it is also impossible for us to know that any such over-individualization actually occurs. Of course, the supposedly over-structured consciousness of the trained introspective psychologist is itself a perfectly legitimate subject matter for introspection, its principal defect lying simply in its alleged failure to represent the average human experience.[161]

The question as to which is prior, the parts or the whole, is irrelevant from the purely methodological standpoint. Introspection takes experiences as it finds them and, as found, they are complex wholes. As a rule, the descriptions of such experiences which are most readily produced are in terms that refer to the wholes or to complex aspects, rather than, in detail, to the parts.[162] However, this does not preclude the possibility that the parts, also, are given; but there can certainly be no meaning in the statement that they are given prior to, or in any more fundamental manner than the whole. Consequently, the question does not appear to be nearly as sensible as that of the much-ridiculed priority dispute between the hen and the egg. Where we are concerned with actual psychodynamics, and not merely with descriptive technique, we are as likely to find wholes breaking up into parts as to discover parts combining to form wholes—at any rate, if we argue by analogy with the processes of the world of physics.

The objection to analysis on the ground that it neglects certain over-all qualitative characteristics of complex experiences, is valid only with respect to particular analytical descriptions which are actually negligent in this respect. There appears to be no reason why an analysis in terms of parts should necessitate neglect of any feature of the whole. Such a neglect should only arise if we assume that all of the properties of the whole can be explained in terms of those of the parts and their relationships. This assumption may be correct, but it is not necessary to the descriptive method. The latter must verbally specify every discriminable aspect of the experience with which it has to deal; and it is a problem of systematization to prove that the properties of the whole are functions of constitution.

The above rebuttal of the *Gestalt* attack upon the analytical method in psychology is not intended to imply a rejection of the constructive proposals and demonstrations of the *Gestalt* school. (*Cf.* Volume III.) I am inclined to regard the assault of Köhler and Koffka upon structural psychology as a polemic aiming at a shift of emphasis in psychological work, rather than as an attempt to displace structural analysis. In general, the history of science suggests that analytical description is indispensable to intellectual progress, and confinement of such description along restricted lines—such as dealing with attributes and stimulus characteristics, to the exclusion of the part-whole relationship—is to be feared as a stultifying influence.

Section 15

THE ELEMENTARY COMPONENTS OF CONSCIOUSNESS, AND THEIR TREATMENT

65. The Nature of Psychical Elements.—A thoroughgoing application of the analytical method in introspective psychology leads naturally to lists of psychological "elements," or ultimate components of experience. Psychical elements can be regarded in two rather different ways, first, as structurally unanalyzable parts of psychical wholes whose full nature is demonstrable directly to introspection, and, second, as hypothetical constituents which are used to explain the formation of consciousness by a supposed process of synthesis. Even the most radical *Gestalter* can scarcely deny the existence of elements in the first sense. Some experiences have parts and others have no parts. Experiences of the latter kind are elements. Now, the notion of a psychical element in this sense might have very little value if various experiential wholes did not exhibit *similar* parts, but it is a fact that the same kinds of parts can be discerned in many differently compounded wholes. Thus, the elementary colors, red and blue, are capable of forming an infinite number of different color patterns. The properties of such colors, or other elementary qualities, may vary slightly from one context to another, but their similarities are much more marked than are their differences, under such conditions.   These similarities enable us to designate any psychical element, such as *red,* by the same name, regardless of its context.

Many of the psychical elements are identical with certain properties of common-sense things, as given in external experience.   Warm, cool, green and yellow are examples. Other elements constitute what the layman ordinarily calls "sensations," e.g., pain.   Psychologists, on the other hand, have frequently applied the term, sensation, to all or nearly all of the elementary qualities.   In the present book, however, we shall reserve the term in question for a special psychophysiological meaning (See Volume II).   In common-sense descriptions, concepts of quality are ordinarily employed as adjectives, but in psychology they tend to play the rôles of substantives.

The notion of a psychical part, whether or not elementary, encounters some difficulty in the fact that such parts are usually not sharply separated from one another. The concept of the part itself cannot conveniently be defined so as to include this feature, particularly since the latter is variable in degree.   Consequently, we are compelled to treat the part, verbally, as if it were an entirely clear-cut individual, and then add a statement of its degree of overlap or fusion with adjacent parts.   It is this situation which frequently leads the psychologist to overestimate the distinctness of his elements.   However, no harm can come of it if we realize that descriptions are incomplete unless the boundary conditions between the elements or other parts have been specified.   Leaving out this feature in the description would be like neglecting to state one of the equations in a group of simultaneous equations which is required to determine some physical process or structure.

Nevertheless, the situation under consideration tempts us to consider the possible significance of the second interpretation of the concept of a psychical element, suggested above.   It is easily conceivable that the parts of psychical wholes may actually be capable of separating from one another, without losing their existence or identity, and without suffering any very radical change in nature. It is conceivable, furthermore, that psychical wholes may really be created by the coming together and union of preëxisting parts. Philosophers of the absolutist persuasion believe that the whole is constitutive of its parts, but common sense and physics find it more helpful to think in terms of the reverse relationship. Introspection gives us the parts and the whole at one blow, and it would seem to be merely a matter of convenience in theorizing, as to which we regard as substantially prior.

In the interests of such theorizing, we may require that all psychical elements shall be capable of being regarded as logically self-sufficient. Elements should not be selected or defined so that they presuppose the existence of other facts or conditions. In this way they differ radically from *attributes,* which are explicitly derived from an intercomparison of many facts, and are obviously abstract in character. The color, *red,* can properly be regarded as an elementary quality, in this way, whereas saturation, an attribute of red, cannot. Although red is ordinarily given as a part of a much more complex experiential mosaic, there is nothing about the red which seems to demand any such accompaniments, and the latter may be of any possible kind. However, it is apparently impossible to exemplify the meaning of the word, saturation, without at the same time displaying concrete colors having other attributes, such as brilliance and hue. Moreover, we define saturation technically in terms of the system of all known colors, but we can give meaning to any individual color name merely by picking out the given color from all of its contexts and treating it in isolation.

These views are intended to establish a definite compromise between a radical mental atomism, such as that of Herbart or even of Titchener, and ostensibly unanalytic methods, such as those of Bergson and of the *Gestalt* school. The question at issue is not whether we shall have ultra-analysis or no analysis at all, but one of striking the proper balance between attention to the properties of parts and those of the whole. There is danger in an overemphasis upon either aspect, but for the purposes of psychophysiology, a neglect of structural analysis in introspection will probably entail the greatest interference with progress. Since it is the problem of psychophysiology to correlate psychical with physical factors, we shall do well to follow the plan of physical logic, when no good reasons appear for a contrary procedure. In general, modern physics explains the properties of wholes in terms of those of the parts, rather than the reverse, but it lays the greatest emphasis upon the ways in which the parts are put together.

66. The Classification of Psychical Elements. — Although the elements which are found by the psychologist are logically similar to those conceived by the chemist, they are vastly more numerous, and there appears to be very little hope that their number will be reduced by any purely psychological method. Each new psychological research tends to make contributions, swelling the list further. The simplification of such a subject matter must therefore be logical, depending upon classification and systematic arrangements. Two methods of attacking the problem of classification among psychological elements may be suggested. The first is based purely upon introspective data and consists in grouping the various elements together in accordance with their inherent resemblances or differences, a process thus resting entirely upon the intrinsic nature of the elements in question. Such a classification, along lines similar to those which are established in the biological sciences by conceptions of genera and species, is the first step in the systematization of the general results obtained from introspective analysis. It is made possible by a purely subjective process of discrimination and comparison.

The second method of attack is psychophysiological, resting upon a knowledge of the relations existing between the elementary qualities and their physiological conditions. It is only by the use of this second method that we are able to discriminate between sensory elements, imaginal elements, volitional elements, etc.   In all probability, the classification of the constituents of consciousness in terms of their relations to physiological conditions will prove of more use than a classification based upon purely subjective considerations. However, this question cannot be settled in advance of an actual comparison of the two methods, and it is probable that we shall find it necessary to employ both methods in order to secure a maximally valuable result.   If we are interested in the establishment of true psychophysical laws, the use of a purely subjective method of systematizing the data of experience would seem to be imperative.

67. Quantitative Series of Qualities.—The classification of experience elements on the basis of their general resemblances and differences leads to the formation of distinctive groups of qualities such as the visual, the auditory, the gustatory, the tactual, the kinaesthetic, the visceral, etc.   Many, if not all, of these groups prove to possess characteristics which lend themselves to a further refinement of the systematizing process, consisting in the arrangement of the members of the group into *quantitative series*.   All of the members of a single group, of course, resemble one another to a certain degree and yet at the same time, in order to be separately considered, they must *differ* definitely from one another.   The differences among the members of the group are therefore quantitative, or are subject to a judgment of "more or less."   This quantitative aspect of the differences between similar qualities is utilized in the production of quantitative series, generated according to the following rule.   *The members of the group must be arranged in such a fashion that the sum of the differences between all neighboring members of the arrangement shall be a minimum.* This is the condition for the consecutive number series: 1, 2, 3, 4, 5, etc.   Experiment will quickly show that the sum of the differences between adjacent components of such a consecutive series is less than the similar sum for any other possible succession of the same numbers.

If we apply this rule to such a group of qualities as the

achromatic colors or grays, we obtain a linear or uni-dimensional series, beginning with black and running through a succession of grays which constantly increase in brilliance and finally reach white. The group of auditory *tones* develops a similar linear arrangement, represented by the musical scale, when subjected to this rule for a quantitative series of qualities. Other groups of experience elements, such as the chromatic colors, require two-dimensional or three-dimensional systems, and there is no reason why the same criterion may not lead to qualitative series having any number of dimensions. The number of dimensions in the system must be increased until a minimum of total internal differences, or of internal discontinuity, is realized.

The systematization of groups of elementary qualities by this method is analogous to that which is employed in biology, when various genera and species are arranged in an evolutionary scale or order. All quantitative schemes ultimately root back into the same fundamental conceptions. Some philosophers, for example Bergson,[163] have claimed that quantitative ideas cannot be applied directly to psychical realities, the quantitative aspect being restricted to physical or geometrical subject matters. It seems, however, that, although quantity is most clearly represented by geometrical or spatial constructions, it is fundamentally attached to the *fact of differentiation,* judgments of difference or of similarity, wherever they apply, being subject to modifications in *degree.* Geometrical and physical quantities fall under this general principle as clearly as do the quantitative aspects of psychological topics. Spatial magnitudes and positions can be regarded as differences, and their quantitative ordering can be developed in terms of the differences and degrees of difference which obtain among them.

68. Properties of Quality Systems.—The attempt to construct a quantitative series out of any group of elementary qualities varies in success according to the particular group which is selected. The visual qualities which we call colors are very readily arranged into a system of this sort.

The auditory qualities called tones also submit readily to this scheme, but those which we designate as noises prove to be less amenable to quantitative arrangement. Olfactory, gustatory, and tactual qualities can be arranged into respective series in order of the intensities of a number of subsidiary modalities, but the system is much less continuous than it is in vision or audition. Other qualities, such as the kinaesthetic, have thus far proven quite refractory under our attempts to arrange them in quantitative order.

Each one of the numerous groups of qualities appears to be separated from the other groups by unbridged qualitative gaps. We find no qualities which are capable of filling in the difference which exists between any color and any tone. It is not inconceivable, however, that such qualities, intermediate between colors and tones or between tones and tastes, should be capable of existing, so that ultimately we may be able to include all of the elementary qualities of experience in a single continuous quantitative system, but one having, in all probability, a very large number of dimensions. It is clear, even in our present state of knowledge, that certain groups of qualities are closely affiliated, in resemblance, while others are radically different from one another. For example, the gustatory and olfactory qualities are so closely similar that they can easily be conceived as a single class, whereas the visual and the auditory qualities are so very different that bridging the gap between them seems almost inconceivable.

The qualitative gaps which exist within, as well as among, the different species of experience elements may conceivably be filled in by new discoveries or by hypothetical intermediaries, properly chosen. It is clear that, in general, there can be more than one line of qualities between any two markedly different experience elements, and it is quite conceivable that an infinite number of such connecting series is possible. This appears to be true, for example, in the color system, between any two different colors which we may select. However, within any such system, and probably for any two qualities whatsoever, there will be one series of intermediaries which will represent a minimum amount of difference and which will form the analogue, in this scheme of psychical quantities, of the straight line in geometry.

Section 16

ATTRIBUTES AND THEIR MEASUREMENT

69. The Nature of Attributes.—The elementary qualities, of which we find consciousness to be built up, often appear to be endowed with complex systems of attributes. For example, all of them are said to possess the attributes of quality, intensity, and duration. Those elements which Titchener classifies as "sensations" have also, according to him, the attribute of clearness.[164] Colors possess the three attributes of hue, saturation and brilliance. As already noted, attributes form a category which is radically distinct from that of elementary qualities, the qualities being considered capable of existence in their own rights, whereas the attributes of any element cannot be separated from one another and from the concrete reality in which they are said to inhere. The simplicity of an elementary quality is not in the least impugned by its possession of a multiplicity of attributes.

In order to understand the actual meaning of these statements concerning attributes, and thus to see how they can be true, we must recognize that the definition of any attribute presupposes the construction of a quantitative series, in accordance with the principles which we have above laid down. If we arrange all of the colors into a system such that the sum of all of the differences between neighboring terms is a minimum, we find the resulting configuration to be three-dimensional. This tridimensionality is a normal consequence of the inherent nature of the colors, combined with the logical principle which we have adopted to govern their arrangement. It does not, however, indicate a trifold constitution in any individual color, any more than the tri-dimensionality of geometrical space implies that the points of which it is built up have a triadic constitution.

Having constructed the color solid, however, we naturally give the three dimensions of the solid three characteristic names, and we specify the position of any particular color in the system by separate references to each of the given three dimensions; the color has a position in the hue dimension, in the saturation dimension and in the brilliance dimension. Simplification of our methods of description, or symbolism, leads us to speak as if these three positions were inherent within the color itself, instead of simply representing three directions of similarity which a color exhibits with respect to all other colors. Thus, we come to say that any color possesses a hue, a saturation, and a brilliance, so that these characteristics are *attributed* to every individual color. It is clear, however, that such attributes are not elements of the members of the system, but merely represent different modes of variability, or of systematic relationship to other members.

The same general principles, which we have just illustrated in the case of color, apply to all other quantitative systems of elementary qualities. Such systems may have any number of dimensions, as required by the fundamental logical principle which underlies their generation. The qualities which enter into any system will be said to possess as many attributes as there are dimensions in the system. In no case, however, will the possession of a multiplicity of attributes, in this sense, necessarily imply that the element which possesses them has any inherent complexity. Ultimately, when we are seeking for an explanation of specific attributes, or in other words are endeavoring to understand the differences in inherent nature which exist between the various elements of experience, we may be tempted to interpret the attributes in terms of the constitution of the elements. Such interpretations, however, will be, for the most part, hypothetical and metaphysical, and will not belong to our directly empirical system of psychology.

70. Units for Series of Qualities.—In order that a quantitative series of qualities, as above defined, should provide the basis for actual mathematical reasoning, we must adopt a unit of measurement within the series. Since the quantitative aspect of any such series rests entirely upon the differences between the various members of the series, the unit in question must be a *unit difference.* If we are to adhere to our requirement that the system shall be throughout subjective in its definition and methods, we cannot appeal, for the establishment of our unit, to any physical or physiological considerations. It must be a unit which can be applied immediately to experience as we find it, without hypothesis or inference. In physical science any arbitrary quantity may be selected as a unit, and this unit is supposed to be invariable in all of its applications, so that all instances of the unit are exactly equal. Consequently, the physicist is obliged to specify, for each type of unit, a *criterion of equality.* In the case of units of length, such as the centimeter, the criterion in question is that of superposition in space. In the case of a unit of mass or weight such as the gram, however, the criterion is quite different, namely, the establishment of a condition of balance on an equal arm lever.

In attempting to measure the differences which exist between various pairs of experiential qualities, we may select as a unit *any arbitrary difference,* obtaining between any arbitrarily chosen pair of qualities. We shall be forced, however, to add a criterion by means of which to test the equality of the difference between any other pair of qualities and that between the standard pair. Such a criterion should not be regarded as resting upon a discovery of the conditions for actual equality, but rather as *defining equality* in terms of certain convenient tests. The most obvious suggestion for a criterion of this character is that the two differences should *appear* equal. We find, however, that, in practice, this criterion is a very difficult one to apply, because the direct comparison of differences usually requires an undue refinement of our powers of discrimination and judgment. There is also a serious objection to adopting as a unit the difference between some particular pair of qualities, on account of the fact that such qualities are not permanent entities like a meter-stick, which can be stored away in a vault for purposes of standardization and reference. The reproduction of standard qualities must rest for its security either upon memory or upon a reproduction of stimulus conditions. Although both of these methods are workable, they involve considerable uncertainty.

With these considerations in mind, we may feel well justified in choosing, as our unit in psychical measurement, that degree of difference between the elementary qualities in any scale or series which can be most readily established and reproduced. The quantity which fulfills this requirement appears to be what is called the *differential threshold* or the "just noticeable difference" (j. n. d.). This is the minimum difference which can be detected in any region of a given series of qualities. It forms the natural unit of measurement within such a series because, if the series is complete, it will contain all differentiable qualities of the given species and, in accordance with the law of such systems, these will all be separated from their neighbors by a just noticeable difference. There will be no members separated by a difference less than this amount. Any such members would be judged as exactly similar and hence, systematically, would constitute a single member only.

If we consider a scale of qualities which, in this sense, is composed of the necessary and sufficient aggregation of qualities, the successive members in each dimension can be assigned numbers, in order of their positions within the dimension in question. These numbers will serve to designate unequivocally the position of any elementary quality within the several dimensions, and hence may be said to comprise the *measures* of the several attributes which are possessed by the qualities under consideration. The numbers thus assigned may be regarded, if we desire, as indicating a purely ordinal relationship. However, we are not necessarily restricted to this later interpretation, since it appears quite legitimate to regard any such number as constituting a true

measure of the amount or *degree of difference* which sepa-
rates the given elementary quality from the quality which
is designated as number zero in the series.

This latter interpretation, it is true, rests upon the assumption that all just noticeable differences, no matter where
they are found within a system of qualities, are equal. There
has been a great deal of argumentation, since the time when
Fechner [165] first proposed the differential threshold as a fundamental unit of psychical measurement, as to whether these
liminal differences are equal under all conditions. It is
impossible to settle this question unless we possess a general
definition or criterion of equality which is applicable to all
psychological magnitudes. As already indicated, above, it
would appear feasible to select the differential threshold
itself to satisfy this demand, thus sidestepping entirely the
interminable argument which has centered around this problem. In adopting this standpoint we shall be in harmony
with higher criticism in modern physics, which doubts the
validity of all *prima facie* demonstrations of equality. From
this point of view, the question as to whether equal-appear-
ing differences are actually equal will be answered fundamentally by comparing the number of differential thresholds
which they separately comprise.

71. The Meaning of Psychical Measurement.—If we
adopt the above conventions and interpretations, the way
would appear to be paved for a thoroughgoing mathematical treatment of the elements and processes to be found
within immediate experience. This treatment will be quite
independent of all physical or physiological considerations.
It is true that, in practice, convenience may lead us to employ the *physical or physiological correlates* of various members of a qualitative scale as indices of the respective
qualities. We may also have to rely upon standard conditions of stimulation in the attempt to reproduce the fundamental reference or zero point of our qualitative system.
The utilization of such auxiliaries, however, does not vitiate
the essential subjectivity of the system of measurement which
is involved. In practice, the realization of the varieties of

experience involves definite correlations with physiological processes, and it is impossible to exemplify any of the elementary qualities, without simultaneously setting off specific physiological activities. Nevertheless, our logical system is entirely independent, in its conception, of these physiological conditions, just as the physicist's system of units is independent of the concrete conditions which surround the actual manufacture of weights and measures, or of things which are to be weighed or measured.

There has been considerable discussion as to whether the ordinary mathematical operations of arithmetic and algebra are legitimately applicable to the results of psychical measurement in terms of threshold units. It has been asserted that such numerical designations cannot be added, subtracted or multiplied to yield any intelligible results. It would seem impossible, for example, to add together two grays, to obtain an integral gray, represented by the sum of the values for the two combined qualities. It is, indeed, obvious that such an operation is unintelligible in the absence of further elucidation. In order that the statement should become significant we must tell *what we mean* by the addition of grays. We must demonstrate experimentally that the actual consummation of some specified process yields a third gray, the psychical measure of which is equal to the sum of the psychical measures of the two added grays. If, by the addition of grays, we mean the superposition of their stimuli upon a single retina, then the data already at hand indicate that the resultant gray has a psychical measure equal not to the sum of the measures of the two component grays, but to the logarithm of the sum of the antilogarithms, to an appropriate base. If, on the other hand, we mean by the addition of the same grays, the simultaneous application of their appropriate stimuli to corresponding areas of the two retinas, respectively, then data already at hand indicate that the resultant gray has a measure approximately equal to the arithmetic mean of the measures of the two component grays.

From the illustrations just given, it should be clear that

the nature of the mathematical operations which we carry out upon psychical measures will be indicated wholly by expediency and the fruitfulness of the results. Since the qualities of experience, as such, are not subject to manipulation, actual operations upon these qualities can rarely, if ever, be carried out. In the present state of psychological science, at any rate, we are forced to confine our operations to the physiological, and mainly to the physical stimulus, correlatives of the experiential factors. However, it is often desirable to express the consequences of such physiological operations in terms of the concomitant psychical factors or events. In doing this, we are justified in operating mathematically upon the psychological phases in any manner whatsoever, provided such operations yield truthful results. If we regard the numerical designations of experiential qualities as indicative of varying degrees of difference, it is clear that an *addition* of these numbers is expressive of an *addition of differences*. Hence the sum of the numbers for two grays necessarily represents a third gray which has a difference from the zero or reference gray, equal to the sum of the differences between this same reference member and each of the two added grays. Whether or not an operation of this sort will prove to be of any value in psychological science must be decided entirely by a survey of accumulated introspective and psychophysiological data.

72. **Extensions of Psychical Calculation.**—Up to the present day in psychology, the application of Fechnerian methods of measuring experience has been limited mainly to the formulation of psychophysical laws or equations, having, on one side, mental measures and, on the other side, physical quantities. It is by no means certain, however, that in the future we may not be able to formulate purely psychical laws, in which the terms of consciousness enter into both sides of the equation. If we adopt the philosophical standpoint of *psychical monism* (*vide* Volume IV), we must believe that all reality is psychical in nature, so that ultimately all laws, mathematical and otherwise, must refer to a psychical subject matter. The nature and processes of human intro-

spective experience appear to be determined, for the most part, by factors lying outside of that experience, and thus far we have learned very little concerning any factors of this sort with the exception of those considered by physiology. However, the rapidly advancing hypothesis of the subconscious mind provides us with conceptions of psychical systems lying outside of introspective experience, and yet determining its structure and activity. It is quite conceivable that, eventually, we shall actually realize the program of the Herbartian [166] psychology, which aimed to predict all of the phenomena of consciousness by mathematical calculations, on the basis of a theory of the subconscious psychical system.

It should be noted that the construction of quantitative series of qualities, and the application to such series of the just noticeable difference as a unit of measurement, provides us with a means of designating introspectively *unknown* psychical elements. The construction of a series of qualities establishes, by virtue of its one or more dimensions, what we may describe as *psychical directions,* and just as soon as we have adopted a unit for measurement along any such direction, we are in a position to specify possible qualities which may lie outside of the range of qualities which were originally employed to establish the direction in question. For example, we can easily conceive, by this technique, of a white which is any number of threshold differences brighter than the brightest white which we have ever actually had in experience. In the construction of the color triangle, as we shall see, we can make use of conceptions of primary colors which are more saturated than those of the spectrum or even than colors which we can realize by any experimental technique.

If we are so sanguine as to conceive of the possibility of a comprehensive, many-dimensional, continuum which includes all of the elementary components of human introspective consciousness, we shall see the possibility of designating, in terms of its dimensions and subjective units of measurement, a great variety of possible qualities which are not included at all in the human introspective system. Some of these qualities will be represented as filling in the gaps which exist within the human scheme, while others will depend upon extrapolation rather than upon interpolation, on the basis of the given system. If we combine a scheme of this sort with the fundamental data of physiology, by means of the correlations observed to exist between the components of experience and those of the physiological mechanism, we may ultimately find ourselves in a position to describe in purely psychological terms the experiences which comprise psychical systems other than the human, for example those of lower animal consciousnesses. In other words, if we properly systematize the data of human experience, the latter may provide a base line, with reference to which—by a sort of psychical triangulation—we may eventually be able to explore a much more comprehensive psychical domain.

Section 17

THE DESCRIPTION OF PSYCHICAL CONFIGURATIONS AND PROCESSES

73. **The Terminology of Psychical Form.**—A discussion of the component qualities of experience, and of their arrangement into quantitative systems, forms an important part of introspective psychology, but it should not be permitted to overshadow the study of the *forms of combination* of such components. In order to complete its task of describing experience, introspection must deal with the structural constitution of each consciousness and with the manner of succession of consciousnesses in total experiences. The notion of structure or configuration must be distinguished very sharply from that of the components which enter into the given structures, although it is impossible to have structures without components, and in practice we never find the components in isolation.

The word, structure, is commonly used to stand either for an abstract set of relationships between components, or it may represent a concrete compound of elementary parts, including the latter. For example, consciousness, as a whole, may be said to *possess* a structure in the former sense and to *be* a structure in the latter sense. The term, structure, is best employed in the abstract meaning, while the word *configuration* is available for the more concrete one. Used as a translation of the German word, *Gestalt*, "configuration" implies that the properties of the parts are modified by their relation to the whole.[167] The "configurationists" tend to deal with experience more concretely than do the "structuralists," whose methods they combat, and yet their literature is by no means free from structural abstractions.

The word, *form,* may perhaps be reserved for a meaning which is more general than that which attaches to "structure," including all consequences or aspects of the combination of psychical components. As we shall see, psychical systems may sometimes be intricate, without revealing a clear structure. Structuration may be replaced by a "fusion" of parts and a characteristic over-all "form-quality." [168] Just as the same component qualities may combine structurally in many different ways, so, conceivably, they may "fuse" in a variety of distinct fashions, yielding correspondingly different forms. From one standpoint, which we shall develop later in detail, both quality and structure can be regarded as special cases of *form*.

As we have already noted, in our definition of the term, experience, the majority of structures which are found in consciousness are spatial in nature, although in general they are non-Euclidean. We shall regard the spatiality of consciousness as being essentially a structural phenomenon. This means that we shall not postulate an empty subjective space within which experiential components are arranged, but shall consider that experiential space is nothing more than the arrangements themselves. However, this view does not prevent us from assuming qualitative elements, in special instances, which have an inherently spatial nature, so long as an arrangement of these elements is required to yield a spatial manifold.

The recognition that consciousness may contain spatial structures should not lead us to the extreme of supposing that no other forms of combination exist therein. It is certain that many non-spatial structures, as well as fusion forms, are given in experience. These must be described in their own terms, and not reduced to any symbolic spatial pattern. The various spaces, visual, auditory, tactual, etc., which are found within experience are themselves combined in the total psychic mosaic, and we shall have to consider whether this combination of spaces is itself spatial or non-spatial in character.

74. The Description of Psychical Processes.—Since we have defined consciousness as a cross-section of experience in time, taken instantaneously, it follows that the analysis of consciousness will deal primarily with static elements and forms. As we have previously recognized, this does not mean that any single consciousness cannot be inherently dynamic, or be possessed of definite rates of change, but merely that a description of consciousness cannot involve a *succession* of states. When, however, we come to consider an *experience*—which must have a finite duration—such a succession of different consciousnesses or experiential mosaics becomes possible. Not all experiences involve change, but the vast majority of them possess this characteristic. Consciousness is very unstable in time, one constellation of qualities replacing another, often with great rapidity. Consequently, in the description of an experience, we must take into consideration a third fundamental and categorical aspect of the psychologist's subject matter, *viz.*, that of *process*.

Some psychologists, such as Titchener, tend to designate all psychical components as processes, being led to this mode of expression by the instability and fugitivity of psychical phenomena. However, if we adhere strictly to the distinction between consciousness and experience which we have made in our preliminary definition, it would appear impossible for a *consciousness* to contain a process. Moreover, it is logically impossible to conceive a process without at the same time conceiving of something which is undergoing the process in question. A process is essentially a change or a variation in some quantity or quality, which latter in itself cannot always be some other change. It is true that there are processes of various orders, corresponding to the various successive derivatives of a mathematical function. For example, a velocity is a change in position, while an acceleration is a change in velocity, but none of these hierarchically arranged processes is conceivable apart from some fundamental term which is not itself a process.

Consequently, in spite of the fugitivity of the aspects presented by experience, we are forced to think of them as static as well as dynamic. None of the elementary qualities, into which consciousness is analyzed, can be regarded legitimately as a process; red, middle C and pain are static entities.[169] Although red is not a process it may *undergo* a process, but such an event necessitates that the given quality should cease to be red, becoming, for example, a purple or a pink. A process, in other words, must always consist in a replacement of one static component of consciousness by a different one, whether this replacement be continuous or discontinuous in nature.

Even *experiences* are not necessarily characterized by process, since it is conceivable that a given structure of consciousness should endure for a considerable period, and in case an experience exhibits no change it cannot properly be said to comprise a process. However, in the case of the majority of interesting experiences, where changes do occur, the specifications of these changes is required in order to make an introspective analysis complete. The most convenient way in which to describe any such experience, analytically, is to regard it as a succession of different consciousnesses, which are to be described separately in the proper temporal order. Theoretically, if a consciousness is an instantaneous snapshot of experience, any experience of finite duration must consist of an infinite series of consciousnesses, and to describe individually all of the members of such a series would obviously be impossible. Practically, we divide up any experience into a relatively small number of successive phases, within any one of which the change is negligibly slight. Our description of each phase then refers to the average constitution of all of the consciousnesses comprised by this finite division of experience. In case the aspects of the experience in which we are interested happen to be describable in quantitative terms, we may be able to symbolize the experience in its entirety as a continuum, by the use of a mathematical equation which represents consciousness as a certain function of time; or we may have recourse to graphical representation, in which the given aspect of consciousness is plotted with reference to a time axis. Even in cases where this is impossible, quantitative estimates of the duration of the successive phases, into which the experience is conceived to be broken up, will assist us in completing our analytical account.

75. "Fusion" and "Creative Resultants."—It would seem that a description of any experience analytically, in terms of its components and their arrangements in coexistence and time, would inevitably prove to be exhaustive. However, there are certain peculiarities of psychical syntheses which appear to render necessary an amplification of such analytic descriptions, in the majority of cases. These characteristics have been discussed in many works under the general caption of "mental chemistry," [170] and depend upon the fact that psychical compounds possess qualitative attributes which are inseparable from the compounds as such (thus not being true elements), and yet are not reducible to terms of structure. These over-all modifications of conscious complexes are usually called "form-qualities," [171] because they are qualitative characteristics which seemingly depend upon the *constellation* of the elements within the complex.

Associated with the existence of such form-qualities, is another characteristic of psychical compounds which we have already noted and which requires special treatment. This consists in the fact that, as a rule, the union of psychical elements is not simply a matter of mere juxtaposition, but involves *a real fusion or integration*. We may suppose, hypothetically, that specific form-qualities are the *fruits* of fusions into which definite elements enter in definite ways. The form-quality which is generated is, so to speak, a compensation for, or a conservation index of, the partial losses of identity which are sustained by the elements. This interpretation of the relation, existing between form-quality and fusion, is corroborated by the observation that those portions of experience which exhibit the greatest degree of fusion also manifest the greatest qualitative differentiation of the compounds with respect to their components.

It is clear that psychical fusion is a matter of more or less, and does not operate on the "all or none" principle. In fact, we may suppose that all psychical compounds require a certain degree of fusion and that the total absence of fusion would imply a complete psychical separation of the elements which are concerned. In other words, the coherence of a set of elements to form a single consciousness or experience is, itself, a form of fusion. However, the quantitative difference between the type of fusion which is required to produce a clearly structural configuration, such as a visual "perception," and that which accompanies (say) organic experiences must be very great. Psychical complexes of a distinctly spatial type have sometimes been designated as *colligations*,[172] and have been set over in contrast to fusions. But, in all probability, all experiential configurations must fall into some place in a continuous linear series of possible psychical compounds, arranged in order of the degree of fusion of their respective components. Just as, at one end of this series, we have entire absence of psychical coherence, so, at the other end, there would be a complete absence of structural complexity within the compound. In this latter condition of *complete fusion,* the individuality of the combining units would be totally lost, the result being a distinctly new psychic individual having a quality all its own. This process, by which combining elements—sacrificing their individuality—generate novelty, has been called by Wundt "creative synthesis." [173]

76. **Various Interpretations of Qualitative Unity.**—Philosophers, such as John Stuart Mill,[174] have endeavored to throw light upon this principle of creative resultants by comparing it with the phenomena of chemical change. They point out that the combination of such substances as hydrogen and oxygen to form (say) water involves the disappearance of the characteristics of the first two substances—which are gases—and the generation of a new body—a liquid—having altogether different properties. Now, this comparison may have a very definite psychophysical significance—not contemplated by Mill and other adherents to the idea of "mental chemistry"—but it does not appear to be very pertinent in the light of modern notions regarding the nature of chemical change. The analogy is convincing only when we confuse the chemical *phenomena* with their physical explanations.[175] The phenomena are simply psychological facts. There is certainly a true qualitative transition in experience between a gas and something which is wet, but from the physical standpoint there is no real qualitative modification, and also no difficulty in explaining the properties of water in terms of those of hydrogen and oxygen, in combination.

When atoms of these two elements combine, they form a new and characteristic geometrical arrangement having a special configuration of electromagnetic force fields, the whole process being reducible to a spatial rearrangement of essentially immutable physical units. The only ground upon which we can claim that physical science provides us with an analogy for the process of creative synthesis is to hold that differences in geometrical form are qualitative. This requirement holds even if we grant that the old idea of matter as a crowd of isolated particles can no longer be accepted, and must be augmented by the notion of definite contours of electrical and magnetic force fields which unite the particles into a dynamically unified and equilibrated whole. Geometric continuity and dynamic balance have no *obvious* relationship to quality.

The concept of creative resultants, as applied to the method of introspection, should not be interpreted psychodynamically. As a mere matter of the description of consciousness, we are not concerned with the *origin* of form-qualities or other over-all characteristics of complex consciousness or experience. From the descriptive standpoint, the principle merely states that, after we have given an exhaustive account of the subject matter in terms of its parts and their relationships, we may still find something more to be said, and that this something applies to the whole rather than to the parts. It may also apply to certain groups of parts, less than the whole. However, such descriptions certainly imply that *if* actual synthesis occurs, there must be a creation of such over-all characteristics and that, with actual analysis or decomposition, they must disappear.

In any event, there appears to be no reason why analytical descriptions should neglect either form-qualities or the degree of fusion of the parts in any conscious structure. If reference to these characteristics of the compound is omitted, the description cannot be regarded as complete. Fusion is a concept which is evidently susceptible to quantitative treatment, so that degrees of fusion may be specified in differential threshold units, in accordance with the general principles which we have already outlined above. It is to be presumed that form-qualities will also prove to be susceptible to arrangement into continuous series, and to quantitative treatment. If all psychical processes are law-abiding, we may hope to establish definite relationships between form-quality and constitution, which will enable us to predict the former from a knowledge of the latter.

Such laws of the production of form-qualities will presumably involve the exact *manner of fusion* of the elements in question, as well as their identity. This "manner of fusion" may be regarded as comprised by the structure or the specific arrangement of elements which exists at a moment just prior to the fusion, and which disappears as a result of the fusion itself. This, of course, involves a hypothetical genetic treatment of the synthetic complex and there would be nothing except a unitary quality within the complex, as finally formed, to represent the structure which has disappeared. However, it is likely that, in many cases at least, the reverse process of disintegration or defusion would take a course that exactly reverses the series of events which led to the original production of the compound. In this case, we might regard each fused and qualitatively modified complex as containing *potential* structure, although we should be obliged to admit that this potential structure is not an existent feature of the compound, save as it may be represented by the actually given form-quality, but merely stands for the future or the past of this particular psychological entity.

Some philosophers, for example, Bergson in his doctrine of creative evolution,[176] have felt that the development of true novelty—such as would be implied by the principle of creative synthesis—is a process which transcends scientific formulation. They have thought that, if novelty were regarded as predictable in accordance with any known scientific law, it could no longer be regarded as being novel, for then it would already be preëxistent within the law. However, in the light of our foregoing analysis of methods in introspective psychology, such conclusions would not appear to be warranted. A scientific law, regarded merely as a symbolic description, cannot be supposed to contain within itself anything whatsoever of its subject matter. In practice, it is very seldom that we actually contemplate a scientific law alongside of its actual meaning and, in the case of laws which are represented by mathematical equations, there is an infinite number of conceivable meanings out of which only a finite number can ever actually be realized. In our previous discussion we have seen how, by means of psychological quality systems, we may conceivably extrapolate our descriptions of psychological quantities so that they reach beyond the scope of actually given data. We may thus be able to write appropriate descriptions for forms of experience which have never been exemplified within our own minds, and, furthermore, we may be able to incorporate these descriptions in general laws which will state the conditions for realizing the novel experiences in question.

77. Psychological Atomism.—The conception of the complete fusion of psychical elements suggests an hypothesis known as *psychological atomism*. If it is possible for a plurality of psychical elements to combine to form a single new and different element, then it is conceivable that the great variety of related elementary qualities, which we now find in experience, have actually been produced by the complete fusion, in various proportions and ways, of a much smaller number of more ultimate qualities or psychical atoms. The qualitative diversity of the elementary qualities which we actually find would be referable to differences in the mathematical combinations and permutations of the ultimate units, in accordance with principles already suggested above. This doctrine of psychological atomism is based, of course, upon an analogy with the system of chemical elements in relation to their compounds. It may also be compared with the scheme of modern atomic physics, in which two units—the proton and the electron—are supposed to combine in a considerable variety of different ways to form atoms of many different species, as recognized by the chemist.

Although it is quite conceivable that we may ultimately be able to work out a system of this sort, we should bear constantly in mind that the significance of such a scheme in psychology will be radically different from that which holds for physics. In physics, as we have seen, combination is merely a matter of structural condensation, involving no true synthesis, whereas in the psychological case the structure must be conceived actually to disappear, being replaced by the synthetic resultant. Psychological atomism, therefore, can have a genetic or prophetic significance only;

although a system founded upon such considerations may assist us enormously in simplifying our discussion of these fundamental matters.

In addition to form-qualities, there may be other attributes of total consciousnesses or experiences—or of non-elemental components of the latter—which will require description. Such characteristics of complex psychical states or processes as affection and clearness probably cannot be regarded as elements, in the sense that they can be separated from the concrete psychical configurations in which they inhere. Consequently, if we were to confine ourselves to a formulation of the actually separable components, together with their structural and temporal interrelations, we should miss these essential characteristics of the experiences as wholes. It is highly probable that—as the program of introspective analysis advances—we shall find other peculiarities of experience which will not fall under any of our present rubrics. When these appear, we should meet them by expanding our present system of concepts, rather than by feeling that the system must be thrown into the discard in its entirety.

PART TWO

THE NATURE OF THE PSYCHOPHYSICAL RELATIONSHIP

Chapter V

A General Analysis of the Psychophysical Problem

Section 18

THE PROBLEM OF THE CONDITIONS OF CONSCIOUSNESS

78. The General Problem of Psychical Determinants. —In accordance with the definition which we have laid down in preceding chapters, psychology is the science of immediate experience and its *conditions*. These conditions are conceived as factors or variables which are external to the given experience but, nevertheless, determine its nature or processes. In the chapter just preceding, we have analyzed the fundamental principles and methods of *introspective* psychology, which deals with the first and essential portion of psychology's subject matter—experience itself. It is now our purpose to consider the general conceptions and principles that are involved in the second section of the psychological problem, the investigation of the manner in which experience is correlated with other actual or hypo‑thetical things.

If the science of the *conditions* of experience or consciousness is to be regarded as a system of knowledge not contained within but purely supplementary to introspective psychology, it is clear that these conditions must be so defined as not to lie within the given experience itself. Insofar as consciousness or experience is self-determining, or is controlled by laws holding between various components or aspects of itself, the problem is wholly one in introspective

psychology.   The mere fact that we have characterized the
method of introspective psychology as being purely descriptive does not prevent the science in question from developing
general laws which interrelate combinations of psychical
variables.   All such laws are simply condensed descriptions
having a complicated logical technique.   If introspective
psychology describes all of the data which it finds, and if it
systematizes its descriptions to the utmost, it will necessarily
formulate all of the correlations which exist between given
experiential factors.   Now, there can be no doubt whatsoever that, as emphasized by Yerkes,[177] some of the determinants of certain aspects of experience are to be found
within experience itself.   For example, the elimination of
an unpleasant image from consciousness may be attributed
directly to its unpleasantness.

However, if we attempt to work out a coherent determinative or causal scheme, by the use of which we may hope
to predict all of the changes which occur in experience, we
find that this cannot be done on the basis of the immediate
experiential data alone.   Our experience behaves as if it
were only in part determined by itself and were in large
measure dependent upon something lying completely outside of it.   If we accept the general principle of cause and
effect, according to which all changes, and even states, must
be conceived to have determinants located outside of themselves, we are forced to believe that experience possesses
such external conditions, for it does not constitute within
itself a closed and self-sufficient causal system.   In respect
to causal coherency, it resembles a chopped-up picture puz-
zle, the majority of the pieces of which have been lost.

If the conditions of experience lie, in this way, largely
outside of experience, it is evident that, from the point of
view of any particular individual, such conditions must be
mainly hypothetical or inferential.   For a *group* of psychical
individuals, however, they might be concretely demonstrable,
since the conditions of the experience of any one individual
might be found, in part, within the experience of some other
individual in the group.   A situation, approximately of this

sort, appears in the so-called "psychological experiment," [178] in which two individuals are involved. One, the observer, is required to introspect, while the other, the experimenter, notes certain constituents of his own experience which he conceives as forming some of the conditions of the observer's experience.

Numerous hypotheses concerning the determination of psychical states and events have appeared in the history of science, the most prominent among these being that of the soul, which was explicitly conceived as the determiner of sentiency. The disappearance of the soul from psychology has naturally been followed by the introduction of other conceptions, perhaps equally hypothetical but more useful, which attempt to solve this same problem. At the present time, two genral hypotheses of this character are entertained. One of these is the doctrine of the subconscious mind, which in effect localizes certain, if not all, of the conditions for the introspective consciousness in a secondary and ejective psychical system. There is nothing inherently improbable or absurd about this conception, since our belief in the reality of consciousnesses belonging to other human organisms involves an assumption of exactly the same character.

79. The Organism as an Hypothesis.—The second hypothesis in question is that of the *physical organism*. It may seem strange to classify this conception as an hypothesis, but if by the physical organism we mean a complicated structure of molecules, atoms or electrons forming an integral part of the universe as discussed by theoretical physics, then it seems quite necessary to acknowledge the hypothetical character of the notion. If, on the other hand, what we intend to designate as the physical organism consists of the "perceptions" which form parts of the experiences of biologists when they are at work, we are clearly referring to psychological data and are restricted to a study of the interrelations existing between certain concrete minds.

Although we are compelled by frankness to admit the hypothetical character of the physical organism, as conceived by mechanistic physiology, this does not force us to rank the ideas of the organism and of the subconscious mind as of equal scientific validity. On the contrary, in spite of the inferential character of all modern physics, including physiology, the results which are attained by these sciences must command the utmost intellectual respect, because of the definiteness and precision of the methods of reasoning which are employed. The fundamental inferences, on the basis of which we construct our notion of the physical universe, are supported by experience at a thousand different points, and the methods of work which are utilized by all physical scientists are substantially so similar that, in the end, practically all careful and honest investigators arrive at identical conclusions.

As we have already noted, many thinkers would not only admit the hypothetical character of the notion of the physical universe, but would deny that the system of physics has any significance apart from immediate experience. They would say that our ideas of physical space, the molecule, the atom, the electron, etc., are merely convenient concepts in terms of which to symbolize complex combinations of experiences. According to these so-called *conceptualists,* the actual significance of all physical ideas is to be found within experience itself. Nearly all physicists, on the other hand, would confess to a belief in the *reality* of the physical system, as they conceive it, while admitting that it cannot be demonstrated within experience. The final answer to this question must depend upon a metaphysical study which does not belong properly within the domain of psychology, although it borders upon the latter. We shall consider some possible answers in Volume IV of this work. For the present, it is sufficient to indicate that, whatever may be the final disposition which is made of the physical world as conceived by specialists in various branches of physical science, the problem of the relations of this world (as conceived) to consciousness must remain before us. The simplest conception of the psychophysical relation rests upon a working assumption that the physical universe, including all physiological organisms, lies completely outside of all concrete fields of experience, human or otherwise.

Although the hypothesis of the subconscious mind is of great utility to psychology in certain lines of investigation, by far the greater portion of our systematic knowledge concerning the conditions of consciousness consists of a statement of the relations which it sustains to the physical world and, in particular, to living organisms. The behaviorist's wish to restrict psychology wholly to the study of certain aspects of organic activities is reflected in the constant attention which the introspective psychologist is compelled to pay to the physiological conditions of consciousness. In the study of these conditions he finds many, if not all, of the factors which he needs as supplements to the data of introspection and to render psychology a coherent system, capable of explaining and of predicting the course of experience. Why this should be true, or just what it means philosophically, is a problem in metaphysics, but in the face of existing evidence we can not doubt it as a practical fact.

Section 19

PSYCHOPHYSICAL VERSUS COSMOLOGICAL RELATIONS

80. The Functional Relation of Consciousness and Matter.—Among the possible relationships which may exist between "body and mind," we can distinguish two types which are fundamentally interesting, although quite different in character. One of these, which we may call the *determinative* relation, is of a *functional* sort and comprises the problem of psychophysiology or "physiological psychology." The other, which we may designate as the *cosmological* relation, is of a *structural* nature and constitutes the subject matter of that part of metaphysics which attempts to *explain* the determinative connections between the physical and the psychical, as discovered by psychophysiology. Let us consider in some detail the nature of these two sets of relationships.

Psychophysiology—as a subdivision of the search for the conditions of consciousness—is our name for the science which starts with the facts learned by introspection, and seeks their determinants in the physical structures and processes of biological organisms. Its problem is solely that of determining the formal laws, or mathematical functions, which hold between various respective aspects of consciousness and of living matter. Psychophysiology may be regarded as a subdivision of a more general science, called *psychophysics,* which is concerned with the determinative interrelations of the psychical and the physical at large. Since we find our human consciousness to be related primarily to the activities of living matter, psychophysiology must be studied prior to a general psychophysics, furnishing the data for the latter if it should prove, upon panpsychic postulates, to be possible at all. The term psychophysiology is preferable to "physiological psychology" because of its more adequate connotations as well as its superior brevity. The science which deals with the laws linking electrical with chemical phenomena is not called electrical chemistry but electrochemistry. Strictly speaking, "physiological psychology" should be synonymous with "behaviorism," although the term may perhaps be reserved for the *method* of studying consciousness by the aid of physiological experimentation.

The problem of psychophysiology can be schematized in mathematical form if we adopt the symbols, ψ and ϕ, to stand for the psychical and the physical systems, respectively. These symbols may be conceived to represent, as mathematical variables, any psychical and any physical factors. The task of psychophysiology consists wholly in determining the exact form of the function: $\psi = f(\phi)$. This use of the functional relation is helpful because it defines the problem very clearly, ruling out all unnecessary assumptions and collateral philosophical questions. The functional relation symbolizes pure determinism or interdependency, without any regard whatsoever to the mechanism which may be responsible for the interrelations in question. This statement of the psychophysiological problem is equally consistent with all philosophical doctrines concerning the cosmological connections of the psychical and the physical. It is as consistent with interactionism as with parallelism, or with idealistic as with realistic views; it neither assumes an existential connection between ψ and ϕ nor the absence of such a connection.

Moreover, as we shall conceive the problem to be stated, either ψ or ϕ may be taken as the *independent variable*. The logical relation between them is quite symmetrical so far as our preliminary assumptions are concerned. We may find, later on in our cosmological investigation, that mind is an epiphenomenon of matter or *vice versa,* but this will not affect the validity of the laws which describe their correlated changes. The statement of the problem of psychophysiology by means of the mathematical functional relation reduces the whole question to a matter of interpredictability; all that is required is the discovery of formulae by the use of which, given the psychical, we can ascertain the accompanying physical condition or *vice versa.* It is, of course, evident that in actually working out the concrete form of the function, $\psi = f(\phi)$, this general schematic relationship must be broken up into a large number of minor equations, expressing the psychophysical laws which govern the many different aspects of psychical systems.

81. The Cosmological Relation of Consciousness and Matter.—As previously suggested, the problem of the *cosmological relation* between consciousness and matter is created by the demonstration of their functional interdependency. The structural hypotheses of modern physics are attempts to explain the principles which have been demonstrated by physical experimentation, and cosmological theories, like the hypotheses of physics, are structural in character. They offer general diagrams of different ways in which consciousness and matter may be conceived to fit together in the formation of a universal mosaic involving them both. Consider, for example, Leibnitz's analogy [179] in which body and mind are compared respectively to two clocks which run in exact synchronism. This relationship is explicable on three different hypotheses corresponding sev-

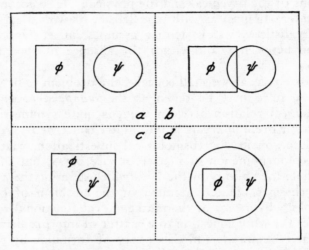

FIG. 1.   SCHEMATA TO REPRESENT VARIOUS COSMOLOGICAL RELATIONS OF THE PHYSICAL AND THE PSYCHICAL WORLDS.

Figure *a* shows the physical and the psychical as mutually exclusive; *b*, as partially overlapping; in *c*, the psychical is wholly contained within the physical, while in *d*, the reverse relationship obtains. The physical world is represented in the figures as a square area, whereas the psychical is symbolized by a circle. See text.

erally with mechanical linkage, human supervision, or perfect accuracy of the horological mechanisms.

Different theories of the structural interrelation between the psychical and the physical worlds are given by such philosophical doctrines as idealism, realism, parallelism, psychical monism, etc. Practically all of these doctrines can be symbolized by means of areas or circles, representing ψ and φ, respectively, placed in various relative positions. For instance, parallelism would set ψ completely outside of φ, while materialism would place it completely inside of φ; idealism, on the other hand, would locate φ completely inside of ψ. The cosmological problem, accordingly, can be defined as that of *the place of consciousness and matter in the universe as a whole*. The solution of this problem, however, may not constitute the entire content of cosmology, since it is conceivable that the universe in its entirety may contain some constituents other than consciousness and matter. But in the present state of our knowledge we have no appreciable evidence for the existence of any such further entities, so that psychophysiology may be regarded as furnishing cosmology, a branch of metaphysics, with its most important data. We shall return to a more detailed consideration of certain specific cosmological theories in Volume IV.

Chapter VI

The Fundamental Concepts of Psychophysiology

Section 20

THE DEGREE OF CORRELATION OF THE PSYCHICAL AND PHYSICAL

82. Is Psychophysical Determination Complete?—The fundamental conceptions which are involved in psychophysiological reasoning must be determined by the facts which the science encounters in its actual researches. A detailed analysis, or even a comprehensive general formulation, of the psychophysiological relationship, would presuppose all of the special knowledge which we are to present in subsequent chapters. However, it is in the interests of clearness that we should anticipate here some of the more important ideas and principles which are involved. This is particularly desirable on account of the necessity, which we shall be under, of recasting many notions which have been employed in classical discussions of the psychophysical problem. The majority of such discussions have been influenced in a definite manner by specific cosmological theories of the relationship of mind to body; and it is essential that psychophysiology or psychophysics, as sciences, should employ logical instruments which are quite free from all such implications.

The sole assumption of psychophysiological research is that the psychical can be represented as a function of certain physical variables or *vice versa*. It presupposes the existence, between component variables in the two systems, of *a finite degree of correlation,* which can be represented by means of a correlation ratio greater than zero. This assumption is supported by very simple arguments, based upon everyday experience, and finds additional corroboration in each new research which appears in the domain of experimental psychology. The correlation ratio is a well-known index of the degree to which variations in two factors are systematically related, as if one depended for its magnitude upon the values of the other. Given a set of corresponding values of the two factors, the formula for the correlation ratio enables us to compute a definite numerical value for the latter. The formula is of such a nature that complete lack of interdependency yields a value of zero, while perfect determination is represented by unity.

One of the first questions concerning this association of the psychical and the physical has to do with the *perfection* of their determinative interrelationship. Suppose that, as in the customary formula for the calculation of the correlation ratio, we represent absolute dependency of mind upon matter or *vice versa* by unity, and complete absence of such interdetermination by zero. Then, although we are forced by everyday knowledge to recognize that the correlation value cannot be zero, we are not necessarily compelled to assume that it is equal to unity. Psychophysiologists, however, as a rule, work upon the hypothesis that the value actually *is* unity, although this hypothesis can only be verified by the perfection of all of our psychophysiological sciences, in the form of a completely coherent deductive system wherein every item of experience is represented as a function of some physical variable. The adoption, by the psychophysiologist, of *the assumption of complete psychophysical determinism* may be regarded as an expression of an optimistic hope that the consummation of such a scientific body of knowledge is at least theoretically possible.

In the present state of our knowledge, however, we are forced to admit that the existence of a perfect psychophysical interdetermination has not been proven, so that, from the philosophical standpoint, other suppositions may legitimately be considered. The principle of free will, which has been advocated so passionately by many sentimental philosophers, must be regarded, in certain of its formulations, as implying a psychophysical correlation index less than unity. According to this view, which is allied with the "tychism" of James and Peirce,[180] the psychical events comprising the subjective aspects of volition, are not representable as rigid functions of any concomitant physical variables. Various interpretations of this supposed situation are possible. We might assume that, although the processes of volition do not depend uniformly upon physical events, they are nevertheless completely determined by *psychical* factors other than themselves, thus being predictable by means of purely psychical laws, in which case the entire psychophysical system would be completely deterministic, even in the absence of complete fixity in the psychophysical relationship.

83. Doctrines of Psychical Freedom.—Another interpretation of psychic freedom would make the individual factors in the conscious processes *self*-determinative. However, unless this means that their spontaneous changes are periodic and hence representable as functions of the time, there is no formal difference between such a state of affairs and a partial chaos to which no law whatsoever is applicable. Still a third interpretation may be suggested, according to which the psychical changes which show no correlation with physical events depend upon characteristics of the "self." By the "self" may be meant the subconscious mind, a system of psychical variables generally similar to but separate from the introspective group of experiences, or the "self" may stand for a transcendental entity such as the soul. In the latter case the problem of determining the laws which are operative would appear to transcend the methods of scientific inquiry.

In general, doctrines of psychical freedom may be grouped into two classes, according as they imply (1) either that there are certain items in experience which are completely undetermined or (2) that experience is representable as a function of the physical only in combination with certain other variables.   The latter class of doctrines would make the psychical thoroughly determinate as a whole, but would imply that the partial correlation between the psychical and the physical is represented by an index less than unity.   Certain cosmological theories, such as that of Berkelian subjectivism and psychical monism (*vide supra*), deny the reality of the physical universe in its totality.   These philosophical doctrines, of course, cannot avoid or reject utterly the psychophysical laws which are developed by the methods of physiological psychology.   However, since the physical system is actually a hypothetical construction, it is possible to reinterpret the psychophysiological results in terms of some ejective system which is substituted for the physical scheme of things.   In Berkeley's philosophy [181] this surrogate ejective reality is identified with God, while in psychical monism it is conceived as an intricate psychical system, different in inherent nature from the physical, but having the same formal properties as the latter.

Section 21

THE REGION OF DETERMINATION OF CONSCIOUSNESS

84. Definition of the Region of Determination.—A second, very general aspect of the psychophysiological problem is concerned with what may be designated as the *region of determination of consciousness* in the physical world. This corresponds approximately with the classical problem of "the seat of consciousness" or of "the seat of soul"; but in any clear-minded analysis we must be very careful to avoid the absurdity of assigning to consciousness a seat or location within the physical world.   Even apart from this absurdity, the problem of the localization of consciousness must be regarded as cosmological rather than as psychophysiological in nature.

The region of determination of consciousness can be defined technically as *that portion of the physical universe which contains the variables of which consciousness is immediately a function.* The term, function, is used here, of course, in the mathematical and not in the physiological sense. It is to be presumed that each individual consciousness or experience will possess a separate, or at least a partially separate, region of determination. The problem of localizing the region in question for any given consciousness may be attacked by starting conceptually with the entire physical universe and narrowing the system down gradually, or in stages, until the essential determining factors are demonstrated. We know that almost anything in the physical world is capable of getting some sort of representation in consciousness, but it is also evident that some portions of the physical scheme are much more important for our immediate experience than are others.

85. Environmental and Organic Factors.—The same facts of everyday experience which demonstrate a certain degree of dependency between the psychical and the physical also indicate approximately the portion of the universe upon which consciousness "depends." The most evident correlation is that which exists between external perceptions, such as those in vision, audition and touch, and the physical objects which lie in the vicinity of our organisms. The objects of physical science are in the first instance direct substitutions for these external "perceptions." We have already seen that, although common sense tends to confuse these two classes of things, this cannot be justified scientifically. Colors cannot be identified with radiant energy of different wave-lengths, nor can tactual impressions be reduced, actually, to configurations of electrical particles. Even the space, the time and the mass of the physical system are *substitutes* for corresponding components in experience, rather than being identifiable with the latter. The items which the physicist thus utilizes to replace the concrete "perceptions" that make up our external experience, turn out, in many cases, to constitute the respective physiological *stimuli* for the experiential components in question. The correlation which is thus established between the physical and the psychical systems is that between constituents of consciousness and certain physical factors lying in the environments of our organisms.

However, there are portions of experience for which the ordinary physicist substitutes nothing, for example, images and affections. Even such a gross difference in experience as that existing between indifferent and painful contact, in the domain of cutaneous sensibility, is not regarded by the physicist as significant of any differentiation between physical objects. But in this connection, the physiologist—who must, of course, be regarded as a special physical investigator—may have something to say. He may point out that the difference between pain and touch represents the distinction between injurious and non-injurious distortion of the skin, thus linking these particular differentiations of consciousness with specific organic conditions, rather than with the environmental situation. In this comment, however, the physiologist is playing the rôle rather of a psychophysiologist than of an objective or physical biologist, for the latter would study various degrees of skin distortion by a method mainly visual in character, or involving the experiences of some individual other than the one whose skin is under consideration. When we turn our attention to even more inward experiences, such as those which constitute kinaesthetic imagery and some kinds of thinking, the physiologist again may suggest a correlation between these psychical factors and physical processes occurring in the *central nervous system*. But here, once more, his point of view is psychophysiological rather than strictly physical, since the nervous system of any individual can, at least theoretically, be studied by any other individual through the medium of visual and possibly tactual perceptions. Such perceptions form a more reliable basis for physical inference than do images or affections.

86. Response Necessary to Determination.—In order to arrive at clear conceptions regarding the psychophysical relation it is necessary to consider the situation, not for all psychical individuals simultaneously, but *for any single individual*. This is because the portions of the physical world which are correlated with one individual experience are, in general, separable from those which are correlated with any other such experience. The most vivid way in which to establish this point of view for a reader is to employ the second person.

Following this plan, it appears from what has been said above that common-sense physics and physiology demonstrate a relation of interdetermination between *your* experience and the physical objects and energies which surround and influence *your* organism. Your organism is defined as a physical mechanism which you, as a physical physiologist, substitute for a certain focal system of external perceptions which you call your *empirical* body. This empirical body differs from other living bodies, which you perceive in vision, audition, or touch, in that it occupies a unique position in your total consciousness, always remaining substantially the same in location and bulk, no matter how much the rest of consciousness may change.

Your *physical* organism, however, cannot be identified with this empirical body, any more than a physical dust particle can be identified with the speck of luminosity which represents it in your experience. The dependency of certain, if not all, portions of your external experience upon the system of physical energies, which is conceived to surround your physical organism, is a fundamental postulate of common sense as well as of physical science. The philosophical vagueness of both of these ways of thinking has permitted a pragmatic identification, in many instances, of the empirical and the inferential items which are involved in the situation. The cosmological doctrine known as natural realism subscribes to this identification on a metaphysical plane. The psychologist, however, must carefully avoid a confusion of this sort, and not being a cosmologist, can only determine and state the laws that connect his experience with the constitution of the environment in which his organism is placed.

In analyzing the given situation, however, the psychophysiologist soon finds that, if the physical objects or energies surrounding his organism are prevented from acting upon the latter, they have no representation within his consciousness. Thus, although your visual "perception" which you call "a tree" lies in your experience at a distance from your empirical body, this percept will be wholly blotted out if the physical tree does not radiate energy of appropriate wave-lengths which is picked up by the pupils of your eyes and focused upon your retinas. Further investigation shows that, not only is action of some sort upon the organism required, but that it must be specifically upon the nervous system, a small portion of the total mass of the organism. A still more detailed study indicates that, in order to find representation within your consciousness, the train of influences which emanate from a physical object must be transmitted to your *central* nervous system or brain, mere action upon peripheral nerves completely failing to evoke a representation in experience. The central nervous processes are *en route* to, and are closely linked with, the muscular reactions of your organism and these, in turn, affect the objects or the environment itself.

These general considerations, therefore, show that the "region of determination" of your consciousness is to be found in *that portion of the physical world which is comprised by your neuromuscular system and the surrounding objects or energies which affect or are affected by it.* A certain group of such physical factors comprises what may be called your *response system.* For a clear understanding of the possibilities involved in the psychophysical relationship it will, therefore, be necessary to have before us a general analysis of *response,* regarded as a physical process.

Section 22

THE NATURE AND STRUCTURE OF RESPONSE

87. Response as a Form of Propagation.—The term, *response,* is often used to denote simply the muscular or glandular effects which result from the application of a stimulus. However, a broader meaning is frequently assigned to the term and makes response embrace the entire neuromuscular process, beginning with the stimulation of a sense-organ and ending (say) with a muscular contraction. This usage of the term makes it analogous to that which is current for the word, "reflex," according to which the latter designates the sensory as well as the motor mechanisms which are involved in the given nervous process as a whole. A *response arc,* according to this mode of conception, would be any nervous mechanism constructed on the general pattern of a reflex arc, but being in almost all concrete instances far more intricate than the latter.

In the present book, however, we shall employ the word "response" in an even broader sense than the one which has just been designated, and shall include within the response not only the sensory, central, and motor phases of the activity but also, on the afferent side, the object and stimulus, and, on the efferent side, the action of the motor or other effector changes upon the environment. The reason for thus extending the concept of a response lies in the physical continuity of the successive events which are involved. There appears to be no inevitable reason why we should locate the boundaries or termini of the response process exactly at the superficies of the organism, and a general understanding of the situation will be favored if we include in response the environmental factors which are the principal causes and effects of the process. (See Fig. 2.)

Response, thus defined, is a special example of a rather general physical process known as *propagation,* and shares certain characteristics with other instances of this type of process. Every propagation may be regarded as being composed of a chain of causally associated events which are successively displaced in space and in time. Thus, an event, *a*, located at a point, *p*, and occurring at a time, *t*, gives rise to a second event, *b*, situated at an adjacent point, say *p'*, and occurring at a subsequent time such as *t'*, this process being repeated until the propagation comes to an end. The constituents of any propagation, thus analyzed, may be described as *stages*, and the chain of such events, depending ultimately upon a single initial event but successively displaced with respect to the latter both in space and time, may be called *corresponding stages*.

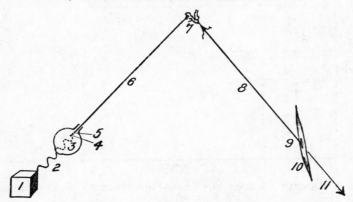

FIG. 2. SCHEMATIC DIAGRAM OF THE RESPONSE ARC.

The figure represents a simplified visual response arc, showing eleven successive stage *positions,* corresponding to the following events: (1) the object, (2) the stimulus, (3) the sense-organ process, (4) the receptor process, (5) the afferent nerve excitation, (6) the afferent nerve conduction, (7) the central adjustor or synaptic process, (8) the efferent nerve conduction, (9) the end-plate process, (10) the effector or muscular reaction, and (11) the effect upon the organism or the environment.

It is clear that there will be as many such chains of corresponding events as there are conceived to be initial events to give rise to them. The space-time position of any chain of corresponding stages can be represented by a continuous line, as in Fig. 3, in which the ordinates represent space and the abscissae, time. The slope of this line at any point represents the speed of the propagation at the instant,

or at the position, represented by the point in question.   The dependency of each stage in a propagation
upon the just preceding corresponding stage may be regarded as a characteristic case of the causal relationship, as
ordinarily conceived.   However, it seems preferable, on the
whole, to formulate this relationship in terms of the functional notation which we have utilized in stating the general

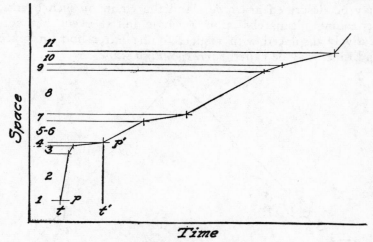

FIG. 3.   DIAGRAM TO SHOW THE SPACE-TIME RELATIONS OF CORRESPONDING
RESPONSE STAGES.

The figure shows, symbolically, the mutual displacement in space and
time of the disturbance set up during a single instant of the response propagation. Successive stage positions (See Fig. 2) are represented numerically along
the space coördinate. Variations in slope represent relative speeds of propagation in different stages.

problem of psychophysiology, although in the present case
both variables in the function are physical or physiological.
Accordingly, we may assert that any stage of a propagation
is representable as a function of the just preceding corresponding stage.   For example $b = f(a)$, $c = f(b)$, etc.
Each of the stages of a propagation is therefore at least
indirectly a function of any other stage.

88. Response Stages and Complications.—In some specific examples of propagation the division of the entire
process into successive stages may be largely an arbitrary

affair, because of the homogeneity of the process. This is
true, for instance, of the propagation of energy, as sound
or as radiation, through a homogeneous spatial medium.
It is not true, however, for other cases of propagation such
as those involved in X-ray tube phenomena or in neuromuscular response. In some forms of propagation, the energy involved in any stage is received from the preceding
one and can be traced back entirely to the initial event, but
in other instances energy is liberated in various successive
stages. The propagation of radiant energy in free space
is an example of the first sort while response furnishes a
case of the second type.

   If we examine response as an example of physical propagation, we find that its inherent heterogeneity leads to the
following analysis into successive stages: (1) the physical
object, (2) the stimulus, (3) the sense-organ processes,
(4) the receptor process, (5) the afferent nerve stimulation,
(6) the afferent nerve conduction, (7) the central synaptic
or adjustor process, (8) the efferent nerve conduction, (9)
the end-plate process, (10) the effector process, (11) the
effect. Each of the successive stages of response is dependent upon the just preceding stage and is therefore representable as a function of the latter.

   However, on account of the heterogeneity of the various
stages, these functions are all different, and we must assign
to each stage certain constants which represent the characteristic features of the stage in question. Each stage of
response also, of course, has individual variables of its own,
that is, the characteristics of each stage which are subject
to determination by the preceding stage are not ordinarily
duplicated within such preceding stage. This may be illustrated by an example taken from visual response, in which
we note that the image, which is formed upon the retina
by the refractive mechanism of the eye, consists of radiant
energy of various intensities and wave-lengths, but determines an activity within the retina which is photochemical
and must therefore be described in quite different terms.
Moreover, although the photochemical process is governed
by the radiation which is incident upon the retina, it also

depends upon the inherent constitution of the retina itself. This example serves to show that the functional interrelations of successive stages are not necessarily simple or expressible by means of a single equation, since in the case which we have cited the factors of intensity and of wavelength must be treated separately. The characteristic constants of any stage in the response may be called the *parameters* of that stage.

The general analysis of the response system which we have above indicated reveals a rather complicated mechanism. However, the case which we have considered is as simple as possible, since it represents the so-called *simple reflex,* which is ordinarily regarded in physiology as a mere abstraction from systems that are far more complex in structure. The more complex mechanisms, however, may be viewed as built up of a certain number of reflex arcs, operating either in parallel or in series, although usually such combinations involve a condensation in which some of the reflex elements are deprived of certain of their characteristic stages.

The combination of a plurality of response arcs in *parallel* leads to a system involving some new analytical aspects such as that of the *pattern of the response,* or the manner of distribution of activities over the several parallel lines, in a cross-section taken at any desired stage. The combination of response elements *in series,* which may result from the interpolation of further nerve conductors and synapses between the afferent nerve stimulation and the end-plate process, leads to the notion of various *levels of adjustment* or of synaptic transfer, such levels being arranged, in general, into a hierarchy, in which one is superior to all of the rest. As an example of a response pattern, at the receptor stage, we may consider the distribution of excitations over the retina of the eye, as determined by a given "retinal image pattern." As illustrations of different levels of adjustment, or synaptic transfer, we may mention the ganglia of the spinal cord, the mid-brain and the cerebral cortex, respectively.

Section 23

DIRECT AND INDIRECT DETERMINANTS OF CONSCIOUSNESS

89. The Test for Direct Determinants.—When we reflect upon the nature of the response system, as above depicted, we realize certain difficulties which must be met in establishing, within this system, the exact location of what we have described as the region of determination of consciousness. Although common sense, and the considerations which have led to the so-called motor theory of consciousness, show that your experience is determined by your responses, these simple considerations do not prove that the *whole* of the system is directly involved in the psychophysical relationship.   For example, consciousness might con-

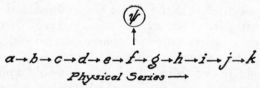

FIG. 4. DIAGRAM TO REPRESENT THE DIFFERENCE BETWEEN DIRECT AND INDIRECT DETERMINANTS OF CONSCIOUSNESS.

The lower line of letters represents a series of corresponding response stages.   Of these, only one, viz., *f*, as indicated by the vertical arrow, is directly determinative of the psychical, ψ.

ceivably be determined by a *single* stage in the response activity, but *appear* to be a function of any and all stages, because of the serial causal dependency of them all.   In this situation, it is clearly necessary to distinguish between the *direct* and the *indirect determinants* of consciousness. This distinction can readily be symbolized by means of a diagram as in Fig. 4, but in order to understand its significance thoroughly a rather subtle analysis is required. Such an analysis may consist of an attempt to devise tests, by the application of which we may hope to tell whether a given determinant is direct or indirect.

Since psychophysiology is not concerned with the structural interconnection of consciousness and the response system—this being left to cosmology—we cannot define a direct determinant in terms of a direct structural linkage such as we have represented in Fig. 4, but we must employ conceptions which are immediately relevant to the functional relationship, $\psi = f(\phi)$. The notion or test which proves to be most readily applicable to this relationship is that of *degree of correlation*,[182] which we have employed above in our discussion of psychophysical determinism. If we adhere to the psychophysiologist's assumption that this determinism is perfect, when consciousness is considered in relation to all relevant physical factors, it becomes possible to define the direct determinants of consciousness as consisting of *those physical factors which, in the proper logical combination, show perfect correlation with the corresponding factors of consciousness under all circumstances.*

It may seem that if the direct determinants of consciousness are strict functions of so-called *indirect* determinants, then the correlation between consciousness and the latter should also be perfect, so that the test which we have suggested would prove to be of no value. This would indeed be true if the various stages of the response, with their constituent internal factors, were themselves *perfectly* correlated with one another, or if such a correlation could not be broken down by any artificial means. However, as a moment's reflection will show, such an inviolable correlation between the various response stages does not in point of fact exist. Disease or injury, and even experimental manipulation, may serve to cut off the various stages of the response from one another, either wholly or partially, so that the correlation existing between the various response stages is not, under all circumstances, perfect and representable by an index of unity. It is this fact which renders our formal definition of direct determination practically significant, permitting it to be employed as a basis for actual tests in psychophysiological research.

If it should turn out that the psychophysiologist's as-

sumption of complete determinism between consciousness
and response is not valid, it would be necessary to modify
the foregoing definition of a direct determinant by substituting the term "maximal" for "perfect." Even if we do
not accept the view that consciousness has a chaotic factor
or is determined in part by some non-physical agency, we
have still to combat the lack of precision in our psychophysical measurements, which will always tend to reduce our
correlation measures below unity, even if the actual variables that we are measuring are in reality inviolably correlated. Consequently, in practical work, the search for the
direct determinants of consciousness will consist in an
endeavor to ascertain which components of the response
system show the highest correlation with the introspective
data.

Of course, the actual computation of a correlation measure presupposes the existence of a technique for measuring,
or at least for arranging, psychical as well as physical factors; and on the psychical side great difficulty will sometimes
be experienced in constructing appropriate series of psychological items. As already noticed, however, it is at least
conceivable that all of the components or aspects of experience should ultimately be subject to such treatment. Nevertheless, in all purely psychological or subjective classifications
we are liable to gross errors in the recognition of our facts
or in assigning to them the proper descriptive labels.

90. Alternative Forms for the Determinative Function.
—The complexity of the data which we have before us in
psychophysiology necessitates a corresponding complexity in
our definitions and methods. It would be very satisfying if,
at the outset of our discussion, we could assume consciousness to be determined by some single constituent, or even
by a single stage, in the response system. Although we shall
advocate the view that only a single stage actually is operative in this situation, it is not legitimate to involve this
assumption in our definitions. Consequently we are obliged
to recognize the possibility that consciousness is a function,
simultaneously and directly, of more than one, and possibly

all, of the stages of response.   As we shall see, a considerable number of current psychophysical theories employ this
supposition, whch can be represented in symbolic form by
the equation $\psi = f(a, b, c, d)$, where the various letters
on the right-hand side of the equation represent different
stages in the response.   A relationship of this sort between
the psychical and the physical may be described as *polyphasic,* because it involves a plurality of stages which are
simultaneously and directly operative as determinants of
consciousness.   A relationship, on the other hand, such as
that of traditional physiological psychology, which makes
consciousness depend upon a single stage in the response
series (e.g., the brain process), may be described as a *monophasic* relation, since only a single stage is involved.

A study of the mathematical relationships which are
inevitably concerned shows that, if we attempt to compute
the correlation between ψ and any selection of variables from
the response, the result which we obtain will depend as
much upon the manner in which we combine these variables
as upon their identity.   In other words, the function $\psi = f(\phi)$ must be given a definite form, before we can determine whether or not we have picked out the direct deter-
minants for which we are seeking.   In pratice, therefore, we
shall be obliged to experiment not only with different selec-
tions of response components, but also with various logical
combinations of the later.   This is true even in a monophasic
theory, since even a single variable can be placed in an
indefinitely large number of functional or equational forms.
For example, according to Fechner, the intensity of a sensation is proportional to the logarithm of the intensity of
the corresponding brain process, $S = k \log R + K$, and, if
this represents a relationship of direct determination, the
correlation between S and $k \log R + K$ will be perfect; but
if any function of R other than the one stated were employed, the correlation would be represented by an index
less than unity.   In practice, we may find that psychophysical functions are very simple in form, and can readily be
detected in the relationships between psychophysical data as

we accumulate them, but we must be prepared theoretically to deal with any conceivable set of relationships.

Our definition of direct and indirect determinants of consciousness suggests a situation in which consciousness is, in some sense, *identified* with its direct determinants. However, to explain the relationhip which obtains between consciousness and its direct determinants is wholly a problem in cosmology, to which psychophysiology makes contributions, but the solution of which it cannot presuppose. The word, "determinant," as we employ it, does not imply even that the response factors are logically prior to those of experience, or that they should be regarded as the independent variables in the psychophysical equation. We assume nothing but the possibility of establishing, by scientific methods, the validity of certain formal relationships which receive their ideal expressions as mathematical equations.

The "region of determination of consciousness" will evidently consist of those parts of the response arc in which the direct determinants of consciousness are located. A monophasic theory would imply that this region is a single continuous spatial volume, whereas a polyphasic theory might render it a plurality of discontinuously bounded regions.

Chapter VII

More Specific Relationships Between Experience and Response

Section 24

THE MONOPHASIC CEREBRAL-ADJUSTOR HYPOTHESIS

91. An Experimental Method for Finding the Direct Determinants.—As we have previously noted, the final specification of the region of determination of consciousness must depend upon all of the data of psychophysiology, so that we cannot identify it positively in advance. However, in order to obtain a clear view of the problems of psychophysiology, it is desirable to have some definite working hypothesis concerning the location of the region in question. Without such an hypothesis, we shall have great difficulty in systematizing the various facts and problems which must be considered. Now, it happens that, although extant data do not permit us to fix the region of determination of consciousness absolutely and beyond peradventure, nevertheless these data do point very definitely toward a particular hypothesis, which is consistent with all facts thus far adduced. This corresponds with the classical view that the "seat of consciousness" lies exclusively in the "brain."

We must first examine, a little more in detail, the kind of reasoning from the facts which is required in order to ascertain the region of determination or the "direct determinants" of consciousness. We have said that these determinants must show a perfect, or at least a maximal, correlation with the corresponding factors in experience, although in order to apply the correlation test, the factors in question must be combined into the proper functional or equational form. But, if there are any portions of the response mechanism which are wholly indirect in their determinative relationship to consciousness, their correlation with the latter should be zero, *when they are causally isolated from all of the direct determinants.* The psychophysical correlation measure of the latter, however, will not be influenced by such an elimination of indirect determinants. The concrete values or conditions of the direct determinants may be radically affected, but their relationship to experience or consciousness should remain unchanged.

A method of investigation which embodies these theoretical requirements in practical form may be outlined as follows. Suppose that we start with the first or "object" stage of the given response system, and eliminate or radically modify this and later stages, successively; and at the same time employ artificial means which maintain the next succeeding—and hence all other subsequent stages—in an unaltered condition. At each step in this series of experiments, we note what happens in consciousness. Any component of the response system which can be varied under these conditions, without any correlated changes occurring on the psychical side, is ruled out of the "region of determination," or is an *in*direct rather than a direct determinant thereof.

It is to be noted that, in order to establish the essential irrelevancy of a given factor, it is necessary not only to show that the given form of consciousness can be reproduced perfectly in its absence, but that the values of the remaining and operative factors are exactly the same as they would be in the presence of the excluded factor. For example, it is not sufficient to demonstrate that a particular "perceptual" consciousness can be aroused exclusively on the basis of neural activities, in the complete absence of the normal environmental objects or conditions. If it turns out that the required nerve processes are changed, under such conditions, we may still be compelled to include the environmental factors among the direct determinants of the normal perceptual consciousness. It is always conceivable that the elimination of one among a number of direct determinants can be compensated by a change in some other determinant; although whether or not this is actually possible must depend upon the form of the function into which they all enter.

The problem of the "region of determination" presents different aspects, according to the exact kind of consciousness which is under consideration. It is entirely conceivable that the regions for different species of experience should be separately located. For example, if we accept the views of Henry Head,[183] the affective aspect of experience is especially correlated with processes in the thalamic section of the brain, whereas "sensory" and intellectual aspects relate particularly to activities in the cerebral cortex. The form of consciousness which seems to require the most careful examination—and which may therefore be taken as the most complete illustration of general principles—is that of visual presentations. We may enlarge upon our previous brief consideration of the psychophysiology of such presentations, by analyzing the facts in some detail.

92. The Non-essentiality of the Object.—The common-sense persuasion that the visual thing in consciousness is identical with the physical object which is before the eyes may be regarded, technically, as locating the region of determination of the experiential "thing" in the first or "object" stage of the response. As soon as we become familiar with what physics has to say about the object, we realize that the attempted identification is absurd, and that the realistic assumptions must be stated in the form of a correlation or interdependency between such things as electronic vibration frequencies and colors. A superficial conception of the interrelationships of visual and physical space may permit us to regard the perspective form of the visual thing as in some sense coincident with its non-perspective physical shape, in a single spaced system.

However, if we perform the experiment of extinguishing the source of illumination of the physical object, we find that the corresponding visual consciousness is radically modified, so that the visual thing is no longer present. A similar result ensues if the rays which leave the physical object are intercepted before they impinge upon the corneas of the eyes, as can be shown by the simple test of closing the eyelids. These observations show that the visible radiant energy which enters the eyes must be added to the object of the response, in our list of determinants of the visual consciousness; but in order to demonstrate that the object itself is wholly an indirect determinant, operating exclusively via the stimulus, we must eliminate the object and reproduce the exact pattern of rays which it normally sends through the pupils. No practical physicist or psychologist has any doubt that under these conditions the visual experience would be unmodified. In other words, if it were feasible to deliver at the entrances of the pupils of your two eyes, the same bundles of rays which are now arriving there, but to do this without there being any physical objects in front of you, your so-called perception of these objects would continue exactly as before.

It is true that this conviction is usually not based upon completely rigid and thoroughgoing tests. It is founded, rather, upon the fact that all experiments which have actually been made have been consistent with the assumption in question. If we replace the physical object or objects by a picture, the resulting experience is very similar to the original. If stereoscopically related pictures are presented simultaneously to the separate eyes, a still more realistic impression is produced. If motion pictures in natural colors are employed stereoscopically, the illusion becomes nearly perfect, and what imperfections may remain are all explicable in terms of the technical failure of the means which are employed to reconstitute the stimulus.

Now, it is to be acknowledged that such experiments do not eliminate response objects altogether. We are still forced to use photographs, screens, projectors, etc., in order to mould the stimulus into the required form. However, there has been a radical modification of the object stage of the response system, without any corresponding change in the accompanying consciousness. If the experiment is adequately performed, the consciousness does not represent the projectors or even the photographs but, instead, the object which these instruments are used to depict.

The physicist's notion, that the visual things in consciousness achieve correlation with the physical objects only through the medium of the stimulus, is further strengthened by the fact that all distortions of the latter are represented by corresponding changes in the form of the visual consciousness. If we place a regularly reflecting surface before the eyes, objects are represented in consciousness behind the mirror, and their apparent positions are determined by the directions of the rays, as the latter enter the eyes, and not by any other external factors. If the reflecting surface departs from a plane, the things in consciousness are correspondingly distorted, their forms being predictable from the differential changes in direction which are suffered by the rays. Similar propositions apply to the effects of refraction by transparent bodies, which may be interposed between objects and the eyes.

Of course, the physicist or the physiologist may regard it as *a priori* obvious that visual experience must be determined exclusively via the pupillary rays. However, this is due to the tacit and wholly unjustifiable supposition that the consciousness resides in the brain.[184] Ancient physicists entertained quite a different view. They believed that the eyes emitted a sort of flux which reached out into the environment and came into direct contact with external objects, but modern physical research has been unsuccessful in demonstrating any such effluvia, the actual process being entirely in the opposite direction.

93. Eliminating the Stimulus Stage.—The next logical step would be to eliminate or to modify the stimulus stage of the response, while maintaining the sense-organ process unaltered. In our visual example, this would amount to generating the rays at the surfaces of the two corneas, so that their courses within the eyes would lead to the formation of the two retinal images, just as if the external ray stimuli were still present. Practically, no enlightened student of physiological optics can doubt that, if the two retinal images were perfectly reproduced, the accompanying visual experience would be an exact reproduction of the one which characterizes the natural series of events. Here again, even more than in the case of the elimination of the object stage, the persuasion of equivalency is based upon the fact that all extant data are consistent with this hypothesis and that there seems to be no good reason for adopting any other view.

Unfortunately, we are not acquainted with any experimental method for creating retinal images, or directed patterns of rays, wholly inside of the eyes; but a multitude of considerations in physiological optics indicate the intimate correlation which exists between the two retinal images and the constitution of visual experience. As the rays pass through the media of the eyes, they receive the impress of numerous peculiarities of the ocular tissues; and these yield corresponding modifications in consciousness. Thus, the "rays" which are such characteristic features of stars, or other bright points in the visual field, are attributable not to the physical luminaries, but to the striated structures of the eye lenses. Halos, surrounding such bright points, are due to the scattering or diffraction of light by cells in the cornea. The "muscae volitantes," which may move across a white paper or open sky area, are representations of tissue fragments floating between the vitreous humor and the retina. Darting and sparkling points, seen against bright backgrounds, correspond with the blood corpuscles which pulse through the retinal capillaries. Under violet illumination, the complex branching formation of the retinal blood-vessels becomes clearly visible. These and many other "entoptic phenomena" demonstrate that changes in rays patterns within the eye can bring about corresponding modifications of consciousness. Such facts strengthen our belief that the consciousness is adequately determined by the retinal images, without reference to preceding stages of the response.

Certain phenomena of binocular vision also contribute to this conviction. If one of the eyes is pressed out of its normal position, the visual pattern in experience is doubled. A similar effect is noticeable in the case of objects upon which the eyes do not properly converge. In these instances, the stimulus conditions external to the eyes are essentially unmodified, but the normal interrelations of the two retinal images are disturbed. It appears that the two retinas do not act as a physiological unit but as separate systems, whose products must be combined in a definite manner in order to yield normal visual experience. If we interchange the optical viewpoints of the two eyes, by means of the "pseudoscope," visual things are turned inside out; what was originally near becomes far, etc. A careful study of these and a multitude of other related facts provides us with no reason for supposing that stages of the visual response, prior to the retinal images, are directly determinative of the visual consciousness. If the two images are reproduced, the experience also will be repeated, regardless of possible irregularities in preceding stages.

94. The Effectiveness of the Receptor Stage.—The next step in the experiment should obviously be to eliminate or radically to modify the refractive processes of the eyes, and yet to maintain the exact pattern of excitation of the retinal receptors (the rods and cones). Here, again, no physiologist or psychologist doubts that if this could be done, the visual experience would be exactly as before. Nevertheless, it must be acknowledged that here we are arriving upon somewhat more slippery ground. We are even lacking in positive conceptions as to the exact nature of the receptor processes which are in question. However, there is no difficulty whatsoever in demonstrating that these receptor activities must be included among the determinants of the visual experience, whether or not *prior* stages can be eliminated from the class of direct determinants.

In the first place, there are certain aspects of retinal

structure which find representation in special types of normal visual consciousness, if not in all cases of the latter. These include the maximal visual acuity and the "night blindness" of the center of the visual field—related to the cone structure of the retinal foveas; the respective blindspots of right and left monocular vision—corresponding to the absence of receptors at the exit points of the optic nerves; the color-blindness of the peripheral visual field, etc. However, abnormal conditions of the visual response apparatus provide the most convincing evidence. Destruction or degenerations of the retinas result in total or partial blindness—or failure of objects to receive representation in visual experience—such failure frequently having definitely restricted localizations in the visual field, corresponding to local retinal injuries. In cases of retinal detachment, the visual objects in experience are correspondingly distorted, and may even be doubled or tripled where the receptor layer is folded over upon itself.

However, we can go further than this and show that the excitation of the retina, by means other than light, yields corresponding results in the visual experience field. Thus, pressure produces patches of brilliance, electrical currents yield color patterns, and an alternating magnetic field generates a luminous haze. Experimental technique in this connection has not yet even remotely approached the ideal of accurately reduplicating complex patterns of retinal excitation, such as occur in normal vision as consequences of the optical stimulation. However, this may eventually be accomplished, and the details of our present knowledge provide us with a fairly safe basis for predicting that such an experimental procedure will be entirely successful in bringing about a perfect reproduction of the corresponding visual consciousness.

A study of the temporal relationships of visual experience and the correlated response processes furnishes us with some natural demonstrations of at least one form of independence with respect to all stimulus and sense-organ activities. We find that practically all visual experiences continue for a finite time after their stimuli have been cut off, this effect being known commonly as "persistence of vision." Under circumstances such as those of motion picture projection, this persistence is measured in fractions of a second, but other conditions can be found where the effect runs into minutes or even hours. Dr. Swindle [185] has studied some of these latter conditions in great detail, and has shown how to produce so-called positive after-images which have all the reality of an original perception. Now it is true that we cannot absolutely demonstrate that these effects are due primarily to the persistence of a purely retinal, as opposed to other neurological, processes; but it is reasonable to suppose that the retinal reactions have some degree of inertia, not ceasing immediately the stimulus is cut off. If the visual consciousness persists after the object, stimulus, and sense-organ stages have been removed, these stages would seem to be of minor importance. The main flaw in our proof here lies in the fact that we have no reliable evidence that the persisting physiological processes are identical with those which accompany normal conditions of visual stimulation. However, their temporal continuity with these normal processes strengthens our belief that there is at least an approximate identity.

95. Consciousness from Afferent Conduction Processes.—If we are satisfied that the visual consciousness can be controlled by the retinal receptor processes, without any necessary coöperation of preceding stages in the normal response, we may next consider the elimination of the receptor stage, with an accompanying preservation of the conduction processes in the optic nerves and tracts. The structure and general physiology of the optic nervous mechanism lead us to believe that, for each characteristic pair of retinal images, there are equally definite patterns of excitation among the optic nerve fibres. Any serious interference with the functioning of these fibres is accompanied by corresponding depressions of visual consciousness. Moderate pressure upon the nerves may produce only amblyopia, or dimness of vision, but their destruction brings about a blindness which is just as complete as that which goes with loss of the eyes or the retinas. Localized changes within the cross-sections of the nerves yield spatially limited modifications of the visual consciousness. It is therefore evident that the optic nerve processes must be included in the list of determinants of visual experience.

However, it must be admitted that, at the present juncture, we have no conclusive proof that reduplication of the optic excitations, in the complete absence of the receptor processes, will suffice to bring about a regeneration of the given visual consciousness. Nevertheless, the majority of psychologists assume that such a regeneration would occur under these conditions, and we shall adopt this assumption as a working hypothesis. We can at least say that there is no evidence which is contrary to the proposition in question.

The next step in our investigation should evidently be to eliminate or radically to modify all of the afferent conduction processes of the visual response chain, and then endeavor to reconstitute the central or adjustor stage in their absence. Now, the line of demarcation between the central and the afferent stages is not entirely clear-cut. There are a number of different levels of transfer of optic excitation from the afferent to the efferent sides of the nervous system, and there are also several sub-stations along the line of afferent conduction to the highest nerve centers. Thus, after the in-going currents have passed through the crossing of the optic nerves at the chiasma, and have entered the optic tracts on either side of the head, they divide along two paths, one of which leads to the so-called external geniculate body and the other to the anterior quadrigeminate body. The first line of conduction is continued through the "central visual tract" to the visual projection areas of the cerebral cortex. The second group of currents is carried along a separate route to the nuclei of the third cranial or oculomotor nerve. These nuclei also receive currents, via the "tegmentum," from the visual cortex.[186]

A thorough analysis would demand that we should

examine separately the correlations of these various components with consciousness.   In practice, we are unable to determine the exact nature of the processes which occur in these several nerve tracts and centers; so that we are compelled to employ the method of hypothesis.   However, the facts of brain pathology have made it evident that the quadrigeminate branch of the optic nerve path is not included within the region of determination of the visual consciousness.   Injuries to this portion of the system have no representation in consciousness.   However, if the central visual tracts are damaged, the effect upon the psychical field of vision is the same, in principle, as that which results from optic nerve disorders.   Consequently the processes in these tracts must be included among the determinants (direct or indirect) of the visual experience.   At the present time we have no artificial means for rearousing in these tracts or at their terminations, such processes as occur within them under normal conditions of vision.   But there is no evidence which contradicts the proposition that such a process reproduction would suffice to regenerate the original visual experience, in its entirety.

96. Consciousness Due to Isolated Central Factors.— We may next consider the question as to whether the processes in the central or cortical stage of the visual response chain are included among the determinants—direct or indirect—of the visual consciousness.   This question receives a very positive answer from observations upon cerebral pathology, which show that lesions of the occipital cortex can produce a wide variety of disturbances in visual experience, ranging from slight amblyopia to complete blindness.   Relatively small, localized degenerations yield restricted scotomata or blind-spots while the remainder of the visual field may be substantially unaffected.   However, if the destruction of cortical tissues is *very extensive,* the loss of visual experience may include, not only perception, but also visual memory, imagination and thought.   In this respect, the cortical stage of the response appears to be more perfectly correlated with consciousness than are any of the preceding phases; since the complete destruction of the optical sense-organs and inward conduction processes does not necessitate the disappearance of visual imagery. On the contrary, blindness due to such peripheral causes may be favorable to a wealth of imaginative representation in visual terms. At a later point in our discussion, we shall consider further details concerning these correlations between the cortical processes and various aspects of visual experience.

Suppose, however, that we eliminate all of the inward conducting tracts and their way-stations, and all subcortical levels of transfer; and then restore the cortical processes to their original status. May we expect the visual experience to reappear in unmodified nature and form? It is not entirely inconceivable that a psychophysical experiment of this sort may actually be performed in the not far distant future. The cerebral cortex, like other nervous tissues, is subject to excitation by electrical impulses, and Cushing [187] has already made numerous tests by this method upon conscious patients. I have not found any record of such experiments upon the visual cortex, but in the case of the somaesthetic area there is a fragmentary reproduction of the corresponding tactual consciousness. Although the greater part of the visual area is tucked away within internal folds of the cerebral surface, the most important region—corresponding to the central part of the visual field—is exposed on the occipital pole of the cerebrum. It would therefore appear to be merely a matter of refined technique, to excite this area in a pattern formation, in cases where a brain operation exposes it in a conscious patient. In such an experiment, we might hope to obtain a reasonably clear-cut visual experience, having a form corresponding to that which is impressed upon the cortical processes. The first results would of course be crude, as in the case of early experiments in television and similar projects, but eventually we might hope to develop a technique which would regenerate a consciousness or experience having complete perceptual reality. In order to make the demonstration conclusive, as to the irrelevancy of the preceding afferent stages in the response system, it would be necessary to show that the electrically aroused processes were identical with the processes yielding the same experience in the presence of normally flowing afferent nerve currents.

Now, nature apparently carries out experiments of this general character, and does it much more perfectly than we shall be able to for a long time to come. The principal difficulty with nature's experiments is that we have not been able to ascertain exactly what is happening in the visual centers of the cortex in such cases. All that we know positively is that there is a centrally generated disturbance in these regions and that the accompanying visual experiences are frequently very complex, vivid and convincing. In some cases, the afferent sector of the response system is intact but is presumed not to be functioning; while, under other circumstances, it may be seriously damaged or cut off from the centers. Sometimes, the centrally generated effects are simply *added* to those due to the afferent nerve currents. The phenomena which appear under such circumstances include dreams, hallucinations, memory images, images of imagination, and less perceptually organized experiences such as scintillating scotomata, erythropsia, etc. It is quite common for degenerative changes in the visual region of the cortex not only to cut off the latter from afferent nerve influences, but to provide the irritant to centrally aroused activities. Thus, in certain forms or stages of cortical blindness, hallucinatory experiences appear in the visual field, and under these conditions we can feel quite certain that they are exclusively determined by central stage factors.

The phenomena of normal dreaming are almost equally convincing since, although there may be some excitation of the optic nerves, the usual conditions of darkness and closure of the eyelids prevent any significant influence of the external environment. The almost complete lack of correspondence between the dream experiences and the environmental facts is a further indication of the central source of the dream energies. However, we must acknowledge that there is no positive physiological evidence for the existence

of central activities during dreaming, nor have we any means
for demonstrating their exact nature, if they do exist. The
central processes in this case are inferences from the fact
that experiences are given, without evident peripheral
foundations.

Hallucinations, such as occur in hysteria and other functional disorders of the brain, have a status somewhat similar
to that of the dream experiences, although the hallucinatory
effects are usually more vivid and, ordinarily, merge with
factors having a true sensory basis. Images of memory
and imagination in normal waking life, are also lacking in
verified cortical concomitants, but it seems unreasonable to
deny the probable existence of the latter, as well as their
immediate independence of concurrent processes in the
afferent arc.

97. The Bearing of Association Area Processes.—Discussions of the central foundations of visual experience are
usually limited to a consideration of the visual projection
areas and immediately outlying zones. However, the total
cerebral process which is based upon the optic nerve currents
is far more comprehensive and complex than this, and involves activities in the association and motor areas of the
cortex. It does not seem legitmate to treat the cortical
stage of the response as a unit. We are logically compelled to divide it up into a number of sub-stages, and to
examine the correlations of each of these with consciousness
separately. A convenient subdivision of this sort is into
sensory projection, sensory association, motor association
and motor projection stages, respectively. The "sensory
association" phase is concerned with the combination and
organization of concurrent afferent impulses; while the
"motor association" division is concerned with the unified
control of the outgoing efferent currents. These two association stages may be combined conceptually in order to simplify the discussion.

The evidence of pathology shows that very extensive
damage to some of the associative regions of the cerebral
cortex is possible with little or no modification of conscious-

ness. However, we should be cautious in concluding from
these observations that the association regions are wholly
or even relatively unimportant as determinants of consciousness. The anatomical sequences of the nerve conductors
in the cortex, between the visual and the motor projection
zones, are such that a current starting from any point in
the visual area can spread out, fanwise, as it progresses in
the direction of the motor region; or it may make a choice
between a large number of alternative paths. Consequently,
it is extremely difficult, in the present state of our knowledge,
to trace the paths of the currents which constitute any given
visual response, after they have left the sensory projection
areas. Some authorities, such as Lashley,[188] believe that the
entire system of associative fibres is involved in every response. Others, such as Herrick,[189] prefer the view that
any particular response utilizes certain fairly restricted lines
of conduction, while another response, based perhaps upon
the same sensory field (e.g., vision) may select quite a
different path.

It is a corollary of either of these conceptions that
limited lesions of the associative substance will not necessarily bring about any serious interference with the response
or the accompanying consciousness. If one path becomes
impassable, another equally effective one can easily be found.
If such notions as to the manner of operation of the associative cortical mechanisms are valid, we cannot expect to get
any very clear-cut experimental evidence concerning the
dependency of consciousness upon the activities of these
mechanisms, unless we employ methods of study which can
isolate the exact paths which are followed by the response
of the given moment.

However, we are by no means lacking in evidence to
indicate a positive determinative relationship between consciousness and certain association area processes. Thus, on
the afferent side, lesions in Wernicke's sector bring about
a loss of meaning in heard or seen words, and similar consequences follow for objects perceived through touch, when

the parietal association regions are damaged. However, the most powerful correlation with consciousness seems to be manifested by the functions of the so-called frontal association areas,[190] particularly in the left hemisphere of a right-handed person. Lesions and pathological conditions in this region may be accompanied by radical changes in nearly every aspect of consciousness, but more particularly in those aspects which are concerned with the higher organization of personality. When the disturbance is sufficiently intense, consciousness is badly befogged or may disintegrate entirely, so that the patient lies in a stupor. Such facts make it highly probable that the proper functioning of some part of the frontal lobe areas is essential to the existence of the introspective consciousness. We shall discuss these facts in greater detail in our chapters on cerebration, Volume III. The frontal lobe processes appear to lie at a point in the response propagation which is subsequent to the parietal and temporal association activities and prior to those of motor control.

98. The Irrelevancy of the Efferent Arc.—Leaving the association stage for the time being, let us pass on to consider the relationship between the motor control mechanism and consciousness. In any full-fledged case of visual response, the voluntary muscular innervations, which emanate from the so-called motor region of the cortex, may be regarded as sections of a continuous flux of nerve currents, having their origins in the two retinas. *A priori*, it is just as conceivable that consciousness should be correlated with motor stages in this propagation as with afferent or sensory ones. However, the facts indicate that there is no direct correlation between the cortical motor control processes and the psychical field. Lesions in the motor areas result in paralyses of the voluntary neuromuscular system, which are localized in accordance with the position of the destructive changes; but they are not reflected by any significant diminution or distortion of consciousness, either visual or non-visual. Electrical stimulation of the motor cortex in a conscious subject produces movements of corresponding portions of the body, but no relevant sensory or perceptual consequences in consciousness.[191]

The word, "relevant," is necessary because, under ordinary conditions, bodily movements affect the relation of the organism to its environment and thus may change the stimuli which are acting upon the sense-organs. All movements are ordinarily registered on the afferent side through the medium of the so-called proprioceptors, yielding kinaesthetic "sensations" or "perceptions" in consciousness. Consequently, any motor reaction or failure to react will have a psychical concomitant. Obviously, if an individual is muscularly paralyzed, the normal course of his experience will undergo serious modifications. However, it would be a manifestation of extreme naïveté to confuse this sort of correlation with the kind which we are here considering.

The fact, thus indicated, that the complete destruction of the whole muscular control system of the motor cortex would bring about no concomitant change in visual or other consciousness, necessarily rules out these stages of the response from the "region of determination." If we perform the typical experiment of eradicating all prior stages, and then reconstitute the motor control operations, the result will be normal behavior but complete unconsciousness. Exactly similar propositions apply to all subsequent stages of the response on the efferent side. The destruction of the pyramidial fibres, or of more peripheral motor conductors, is not accompanied by any significant changes in experience. Lesions in or ablation of the cerebellum are likewise without psychical consequences. The functions of this organ apparently lie entirely on the efferent side of the response arc which passes through the cerebrum. The modifications which are actually observed can all be traced to consequent alternations of sense-organ stimuli. In other words, if we were to employ artificial means to maintain the stimulus patterns in all of the sensory fields, interruptions of the motor process would have no bearing whatsoever upon the accompanying consciousness. Let the muscles be paralyzed or destroyed; and let the active behavior of the individual cease entirely; yet his experience would continue exactly as before, if all sensory processes were maintained or engineered along their customary courses.

It may be noted that this conclusion seems to conflict with the general tendency of the so-called "motor theory of consciousness," which emphasizes the importance of efferent expressions for the understanding of consciousness, making behavior and motor functions the principal justification for the existence of psychical states and processes. However, as shown clearly by McComas,[192] there appears to be not a scrap of technical evidence in favor of a formal linkage of consciousness with the efferent side of the response arc. The actual basis for the motor theory of consciousness, and allied doctrines, is to be found not in the nature of the psychophysical relation, in its refined technical aspects, but in the fact that the normal response mechanism as a whole is *functionally directed* towards the control of motor activities, finding its biological utility wholly in this relationship. The formal association of experience with the central and, possibly, some of the afferent stages of this mechanism therefore connects it in a practical way with behavior, and makes possible an interpretation of consciousness with reference to motor activity, by the use of biological or teleological methods of reasoning. Such ways of thinking, although they may prove useful in many philosophical or even psychological debates, should not mislead us when we are considering the technical problems of psychophysiology.

99. Forms of the Cerebral Monophasic Hypothesis.— A detailed analysis, similar to that which has been presented above for the case of visual response, can be carried through for responses based upon other sensory mechanisms, such as hearing, touch, taste, etc. Although we are far from having entirely satisfactory evidence in any field of response, nevertheless the indications, so far as the data go, are the same as in the visual instance. However, we should not rule out the possibility that important differences may eventually be found among separate departments of receptive control or diverse aspects of consciousness. The evidence, as it now stands, is to the effect that *the direct determinants of the human introspective consciousness lie exclusively in the central or adjustor stage of the response.* This places them somewhere in the region which is intermediate, in the conduction path, between the sensory and motor projection zones of the cerebral cortex. The exact demarcation of the determinative region, within this general domain, is largely a matter for speculation at the present time, although it seems highly probable that the frontal lobe process occupies a very central position in the total determinative activity.

There are a number of fairly distinct hypotheses which are about equally consistent with the facts. According to one view, which we may designate as Hypothesis A, the region of determination of consciousness simultaneously involves the sensory projection areas and subsequent associative stages. The so-called sensory aspects of consciousness are conceived to be correlated directly with the primary projection or cortical-receptive processes. So-called perceptual elaborations of the sensory material are determined by subsequent cortical stages, which are nevertheless located closely adjacent to the projection activities. Visual images may rest upon a further step in the efferent direction, in the so-called visuopsychic region. Such features as meaning, associated ideas, and relations to other sensory fields (incorporations of factors from numerous fields in perceptual wholes, etc.), and general organization into personality form, may be determined directly by processes in the more remote association areas.

A second view, which may be designated as Hypothesis B, would regard certain portions of the final associative stage, presumably in the frontal lobes, as containing the sole direct determinants of consciousness in its entirety. According to this doctrine, all of the projection area activities could be eradicated without harming consciousness, provided the integrative processes of the association mechanism could be retained intact and unmodified. It may, perhaps, be impossible to specify reliably the exact location of this critically important associative focus, because its position presumably fluctuates from one moment to another. Nevertheless, at any instant, it should be confined within some definite and well-restricted section of the total association region. The reason for the physiological existence of such a focus is to be sought in the necessity for *integrating* the data obtained from all of the receptive fields of the organism, and for bringing the results of such integration to bear upon a maximal number of effector fields.

Hypothesis B does not seem to be definitely demonstrated by the experimental facts which we have thus far examined, although it is entirely consistent with these facts. However, it has the advantage over Hypothesis A of providing a view which facilitates a very clear formulation of the interrelations of consciousness and matter, both from the psychophysiological and from the cosmological standpoints. It presents us with a definite physiological basis for the total conscious field, with its characteristic unification of peripherally initiated, but centrally molded, components. We shall develop both of the hypotheses in greater detail in our subsequent discussions of concrete problems. (See Volume III.)

Either Hypothesis A or Hypothesis B may be regarded as providing us with an approximately *monophasic* theory of the region of determination of consciousness. "B" is more strictly monophasic than "A." Either hypothesis may be said to attribute consciousness to the cerebral adjustor stage of the response as a direct determinant. Hence the conclusion which we have reached may be characterized as the *monophasic cerebral-adjustor* theory of the direct determinants or region of determination of consciousness. Although this general theory is well supported by facts, it cannot be regarded as conclusively demonstrated for all cases. Consequently, although we shall employ it as an aid to the systematization of data and concepts, we shall not be bound to base all of our reasoning upon it.

100. Pre- and Post-Determinant Stages, etc.—It should be noted that, although the afferent and efferent stages of the response are both excluded from the region of determination, their *indirect* determinative relationships to consciousness are radically different. Under normal conditions of response, both of these series of stages are correlated with experience, but under such circumstances, the elimination of the efferent series is not accompanied by any significant change in consciousness. However, if the afferent series is modified, there will almost always be an important alteration of the psychical system. This is obviously because the efferent sequence is *post-determinant,* while the afferent one is *pre-determinant.* Ordinarily, the central processes are controlled by the afferent chain of events, so that anything which happens to this chain will modify the central activity and, hence, will receive representation in consciousness. The efferent series of stages, however, is not a cause but rather an effect of the central process, so that its elimination or alteration will have no direct influence upon the latter.

Another way of formulating the difference between these two species of indirect relationships is to say that, under normal response conditions, consciousness is a *mediate* function of afferent processes, in which the latter can enter only as *independent* variables. The efferent processes, on the other hand, are mediate functions of *consciousness,* and cannot be expressed as independent variables, of which consciousness may be a function. However, in the case of the direct determinants, we conceive that it is just as legitimate to regard consciousness as the independent variable as it is to treat the direct determinants in this manner. Of course, in practice, if a standard sequence of events in the response arc is given, we can deduce the consciousness from the efferent as well as from the afferent factors; but any modification of the former which does not depend upon the cortical adjustor operations will become a source of error in such inferences.

It will be noted that the tentative conclusions which we

have reached above correspond with the classical doctrine that the "seat of consciousness" is in the higher centers of the brain. However, the reader should continuously bear in mind that our formulation of the facts is carefully designed to avoid any implication that consciousness, or any thing, actually *resides* at any point in the response system. The factors which have a "seat" in the brain are the direct determinants of consciousness; consciousness, itself, has no "seat" anywhere in the physical world. The persuasion that the psychical structures and processes must be located in the cerebral cortex, because their determinants are there, is due to a sort of logical short-circuit, which has been aided by the vagueness of meaning of psychological terms. When consciousness is defined as a temporal cross-section of immediate experience, we see at once that it cannot possibly be located in the physical brain.

The monophasic cerebral-adjustor theory of the direct determinants of individual experience is evidently consistent with Johannes Müller's classical principle of "specific nerve energies," [193] according to which the "sensation," evoked in consciousness, depends only upon the identity of the nerve channel which is set into activity, and is independent of the character of the stimulus. Modern interpretations of this principle admit that certain features of the nerve process (such as impulse frequency) may be determined by the stimulus, but the process is primarily an expression of the intrinsic nature of the nervous tissue, and not of that of the stimulus.

THE CORRELATION OF PATTERNS BETWEEN CONSCIOUSNESS AND RESPONSE STAGES

101. Changes in Pattern During Response Propagation. —The foregoing study of the relationship which may be conceived to exist between consciousness and response has taken into consideration only the analysis of the latter into successive stages.   As we have already noted, practically any concrete instance of response involves the simultaneous action of a large number of parallel response paths, and a cross-section taken perpendicularly to the line of propagation of the response at any stage will reveal a definite pattern of excitation or of structure.   The excitation patterns of successive stages are, in general, different from one another, changing progressively under the influence of the differing arrangements and connections of the numerous nerve elements, or other components which are involved.   The structural pattern of the conducting elements, concerned in any particular stage, may be designated as "the stage field pattern," while the distribution of activity among these elements or units may be called the "excitation pattern" for the stage in question.

Changes in pattern from one stage of the response to another must depend in part upon the specific interrelations which exist between the field patterns of successive stages, but must also be determined—if we are to understand the actual facts in the case—by the momentary excitation pattern, as well.   All sorts of pattern changes of this nature can be conceived, but there are several types which have particular interest.   Among these may be mentioned the changes which bring about a *convergence* of nerve currents or a condensation of the excitation pattern from one stage to another.   Such convergence is characteristic of propagation in complex response systems which are spread out on the afferent side over nearly all of the receptor fields of the body, but which may be focused on the efferent side upon a very limited group of muscles. The neurone system controlling such a limited effector mechanism has been called by Sherrington a "final common path," upon which many different lines of nerve flux converge and where they may either combine or conflict with one another.

Although the convergence of nerve currents or the condensation of excitation patterns is perhaps the most characteristic type of pattern change which is undergone in a complex response propagation, we are forced to believe that the reverse process, or a *divergence* of currents, also occurs. Not only do we find that all of the receptor mechanisms of the body can contribute to the regulation of a very limited group of effector mechanisms but, on the other hand—if the occasion demands—all of the effector systems can be controlled with respect to processes occurring within a very limited receptor field. Single neurones are provided, as a rule, with a large number of collecting branches or dendrites but with only a single axon or distributing branch. However, we find that, in many cases, the axon possesses subsidiary branches, called collaterals, which are capable of distributing the excitation of a single neurone to a group of more efferent neurones (see Fig. 5). This collateral arrangement is particularly in evidence on the efferent side of the response arc. At this place, it permits a centrally unified nerve activity to bring into action, in a coördinated fashion, a plurality of muscle cells or muscles.

102. Relations Between Psychical and Response Patterns.—It seems likely that streams of nerve energy, passing from receptor fields through the cerebral cortex to the effector fields of the voluntary musculature, exhibit maximum condensation in the cortex, being more complex in pattern on both the afferent and the efferent sides of the latter. If this is true, the cortex may be regarded as containing a sort of *focus* of concomitant nerve activities, these activities converging upon it like the light from a lens to a focal point, and diverging away, just as does the light from such a focal position at which the converging rays cross. The general structure of the cerebral conduction paths suggest that, if such a focal point exists, it probably lies in one of the

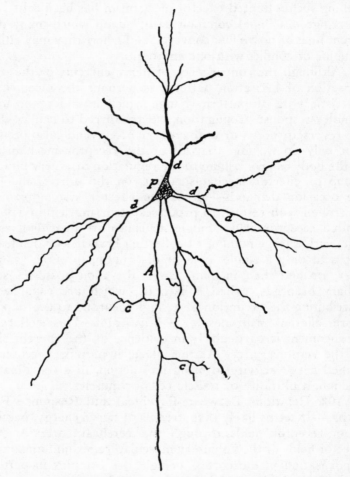

FIG. 5. A NEURONE, WITH ITS DENDRITES, AXON AND COLLATERALS.

The cell-body or perikaryon is represented at *P*. *A* is the axon, while dendrites and collaterals are designated by the letters, *d* and *c*, at various points.

so-called association areas of the cortex, standing approximately midway between the sensory and the motor projection areas. If we accept a monophasic cerebral theory of the determination of consciousness, it would seem plausible that the region of determination of the latter should lie exactly in this cortical focal point, which synthesizes to a maximal degree both sensory information and motor control. This supposition is plausible, not only because of its logical simplicity, but because consciousness appears to represent exactly such an integrated system of afferent and efferent tendencies.

This becomes evident when we consider the structure of consciousness in relation to the pattern of response, a general psychophysical association which is of the utmost psychological, and also metaphysical, interest. In general, it appears likely that the *structure* of consciousness will be determined by the spatial form of the process within the region of direct determination of consciousness. This is by no means a logical necessity, since we can readily formulate hypothetical functional relationships, between consciousness and response, which express a dependency of qualitative aspects of consciousness upon structural characteristics of the response or *vice versa*. Indeed, when we are considering the fine structural details of components in the response, it appears absolutely necessary to believe that the minute material structure in the nervous system determines qualitative rather than structural differences in experience. The grosser anatomical or histological features, involving units not smaller than the single neurone, would seem, however, to have mainly a structural significance for consciousness. We are forced to conceive of these units and their excitations as possessing a definite distribution or arrangement in space, and it seems very improbable that the determinants of consciousness should be restricted— even within a single stage and on the monophasic theory— to the activities of a single neurological unit. Since we find it possible, in general, to divide consciousness up into elementary components, we are naturally led to seek separate neurological determinants for each of these components. Should we succeed, thus, in establishing a "point-for-point" correspondence between consciousness and the nerve elements which are involved in its "region of determination," we should most certainly expect to find that the mode of interconnection of the nerve units determines the associative form of the psychical elements.

However, even if this expectation should be realized, it would not be a necessary corollary that the pattern of the response should be the *same* as that of consciousness. All that would be required would be a "point-to-point" correspondence of elements on the two sides, and some sort of functional dependency between the respective forms of combination of the two sets of elements, a formula by which we could deduce the structure of consciousness from the pattern of response in the region of determination. Actual data, already in our possession, indicate very clearly that a pattern correspondence must exist between consciousness and certain cortical activities, but these same data render it very doubtful whether this correspondence can involve a close geometrical similarity between the two patterns.

103. Visual Patterns As An Example.—Some of the conceptions which have been developed in the present Section will be made clearer by means of a specific example, which may be drawn most readily from the case of visual response. In vision, the relevant patterns of the first stage in the response propagation, viz., the object, consist of an arrangement of surfaces in three-dimensional space. From these surfaces are reflected the various streams of radiation which constitute the second stage, or the stimulus. It will be noted that although the distribution of these streams of radiant energy in space, between the object and the eye, depends upon the form of the object, it is by no means identical with the latter. At every point in the stimulus stage, there is a complete representation of all points in the objects which are visible at the given stimulus point. Upon striking the cornea of the eye and entering the third or sense-organ stage of the response, the distribution of radiation is subjected to radical changes, as a result of the refractive influences exerted by the ocular media, so that it arrives at the retina to constitute a new and different pattern. This somewhat resembles the pattern of the object, but is nevertheless not to be identified with the latter, since it is much more nearly condensed into a single geometrical surface, and the latter is roughly spherical in form in coincidence with the shape of the retina.

In the next subsequent stage, the receptor process, involving the simultaneous activities of many millions of rods and cones, the response pattern becomes broken up into a vast atomic mosaic roughly coincident in space with the retinal image but having a dot structure like a half-tone engraving screen. In the next stage of the response, the afferent nerve stimulation, this dot structure is reduplicated at least approximately, but in the following stage, the afferent nerve conduction, the distribution of the atomic excitation in space is subject to a rapid and radical modification, involving immediately a very extensive condensation, owing to the fact that many receptors are connected to a single conductor of the optic nerve. In passing along the nerve fibres of the retina through the papilla and along the optic nerve, the distribution of elementary excitations in space is so modified from that which obtains in the retina as to become quite unrecognizable.

Still further changes must occur at the optic chiasma and in the several intermediate nuclei through which the optic impulses pass along two different channels, on either side of the head, before they arrive at the sensory projection areas of the cerebral cortex. At the cortex, representing the central or adjustor stage, the distribution of corresponding activities must again be radically different from that which obtains in the retina. However, the data which we actually possess indicate, beyond any doubt, the existence of a point-to-point or at least a part-to-part correspondence between the excitation patterns in the visual projection areas, and those of the retina. The same evidence clearly demonstrates a similar general form of correspondence between the structure of the visual consciousness and that of either the cortical process or the retinal activities.*

* For a more detailed study of the visual conduction process see Volume III.

All of these patterns, therefore, are linked together in a functional way, but this linkage does not imply geometrical similarity. As a matter of fact, although it is quite clear that the psychical pattern is determined more directly by that of the visual projection area process than by the pattern either of the retinal activity or of the object, nevertheless, there is a greater degree of resemblance between the conscious pattern and that of either of the two last-mentioned stages than there is between the structure of the visual consciousness and the structure of the brain process.

If we attempt to trace the pattern evolution of visual response, beyond the cortex, on the efferent side, we find that the changes which occur vary greatly with special conditions, including not only the general set of the central nervous system but also the particular excitation pattern which is impressed upon the retina, and hence upon the cortical projection areas. We may not only direct the eyes towards or away from the given objects in the response but may react with movements of any portion of the body whatsoever. It would appear that the correlation between afferent and efferent patterns is a very labile one, depending to a marked degree upon special conditions.

Even a cursory examination of the structure of the visual consciousness in relation to the excitation patterns of successive stages in visual response shows that this structure is determined by the afferent stages, having practically no constant relationship to the efferent stages. However, it would not be perfectly accurate to assert that no correlation whatsoever exists between the psychical configuration and the form of the given efferent activity. The modicum of definite interdependency which actually obtains here, however, is traceable to two secondary influences, first, the fact that the central visual process is organized functionally to control certain motor reactions and, second, that these alter the relation between the organism and its environment, thus changing the stimulus and modifying subsequent phases of the central stage in the response, by an afferent mechanism. (As we shall see later in our specific psychophysical discussion, extant data from practically all the fields of sensation substantiate the view that the structure of consciousness is determined wholly by the pattern of the central stage in any complex response, this central pattern being governed by a combination of afferent and central factors.) Efferent patterns are determined by central ones but have no point-to-point representation within consciousness. The nearest approach to such representation is found in the domain of kinaesthetic sensation, but here we find that, in reality, it is not an efferent but a special afferent system which reflects the processes in the effectors.

104. Difficulties of Psychophysical Pattern Correlation. —The notion of a point-to-point or part-to-part correspondence between consciousness and response patterns seems to be inevitable in any attempt to conceive of the relationship obtaining between these two systems. However, it is a notion which is by no means free from difficulties. One set of difficulties arises from the fact that the components of response which apparently correspond to single elements of consciousness are not themselves elementary, being made up of an enormous number of ultimate physical units. Another allied set of difficulties lies in the tendency of psychical components to fuse partially with one another to yield characteristic form-qualities. The system thus generated has some resemblance to that of the absolute idealist, in which each constituent is to a certain extent actually constitutive of the nature of other constituents.

It would seem as if this type of organization could find no counterpart in a physical mosaic. However, as we shall see later on, a careful examination of the attributes of physical systems will reveal characteristics which are analogous to the apparent idiosyncrasies of psychical configurations. The ultimate electrical units of the physical universe, although conceived to be immutable and individual, are nevertheless surrounded by mutable and interpenetrating fields of force, which vary widely in intensity and continuity. It will be easy to show that, if we include these distributed energies of the physical system in our psychophysical equation, we can arrive at formulations which will be consistent with all of the properties—analytic as well as synthetic—of psychical manifolds. (See Volume III.)

Section 26

THE TEMPORAL RELATIONSHIPS OF EXPERIENCE AND RESPONSE

105. Time An Abstraction from Change.—Both experience and the response system possess temporal aspects. Response exists and occurs not only in physical space, but in physical time. The succession of consciousnesses which we have called experience, also takes place in a dimension which may properly be designated as *psychical* time. However, we have no reason, at the outset of our discussion, for identifying these two temporal manifolds. Just as physical and psychical space are distinct systems, so also may be physical and psychical time.

An analytical study of time, either from the physical or the psychological standpoints, indicates that such an identification would be devoid of meaning unless its conditions were carefully specified. Modern physical science no longer regards time as a universal and homogeneous dimension. It is, rather, a logically complex method for coördinating events which occur in different places. Each point or system in physical space is said to possess its own "local time," which can only be brought into correspondence with the time which is characteristic of another point or system by means of some concrete method of intercommunication between the two places. The notion of an eventless or empty time, analogous to empty geometrical or physical space, does not commend itself to intelligent thought in any domain of science. The schematization of time in terms of space as a linear series of instants, is purely diagrammatic and would have no actual facts to represent if the universe were completely static. The fundamental fact underlying the notion of time is therefore that of *change*.

Change, in any realm, may be defined as *the generation of difference*. The concept of change is thus subordinate, logically, to that of difference; but it nevertheless involves a unique characteristic which can only be appreciated in immediate experience. It is this characteristic which leads to the idea of time in the abstract. Difference can *coexist* between *separate* facts, but when it appears *within a single fact*, or entity, we have a case of change. Any such instance of the generation of difference, without intercomparison, can be treated as a temporal succession of separate different things, each of which occupies its own private niche in time. However, as a matter of concrete existence, only one of these supposed, temporally successive things can be real, namely that one which is located in the particular portion of time known as the *present;* and the present is instantaneous and timeless. These principles apply equally to the physical and the psychical domains, although the superior immediacy of the latter renders time a relatively more abstract concept in psychology than in physics.

106. The Specious Doctrine of the Specious Present. —However, something which at least corresponds with time manifests itself in experience as a concrete phenomenon. It will be recalled that Bergson [196] finds the essence of the psychical in "pure duration," and the concept of the "time sense" plays an important rôle in traditional introspective psychology. "Duration" is listed by Titchener [197] and his followers as one of the attributes of "sensation" and other psychical components. According to Kant,[198] time is a fundamental category of the "understanding," which necessarily impresses itself upon all experience. The paradoxical doctrine of the "specious present" purports to represent successive moments as in some sense coexistent in a single consciousness. This classical notion of psychological time is exemplified by the following quotation from Ladd.[199]

"(1) All the contents of consciousness, in order to be known as related in time, must be somewhat prolonged *processes* rather than instantaneous events. All conscious states actually take time to form themselves. For this reason we object to the favorite term, 'the specious present,' to indicate the unit of psychological time. It is just this present which *is* real—the actual 'time-grasp' of consciousness. It is the mathematical present which is specious and unreal. The real present is never a non-enduring 'now.' (2) The consciousness of time, whether of the endurance of a state or of a succession of states, is itself a process. The apprehension of time is itself a time-experience. (3) Conscious states, as considered by themselves, all have an aspect or quality, which we may call 'endurance'; and when compared they stand in a relation which we may call 'succession.' (4) Attention, as stimulated by emotional accompaniments and effects, is directed to this aspect, or quality; and in connection with this focusing of attention, all the activities of the intellect are called out in forming and developing the conception of time."

Now, it is clear that the definition of consciousness which we have adopted for the purposes of the present book is inconsistent with many of the above statements. From our standpoint, the psychical present is to be considered as being just as instantaneous as is any physical or kinematical moment. But this act of definition cannot rule out of consciousness anything which is actually existent within it. Neither does it prevent consciousness, as defined, from enduring or changing. The present consciousness must be considered as moving continuously along the temporal dimension, changing smoothly without any absolutely sudden transitions, and yet never embracing more than a single instant. Moreover, there can be no denying that within each instant of consciousness there will be found the records and accumulations of many instants which are past. Within each consciousness, also, are realities from which future consciousnesses will be formed. But to say that the present contains the past and the future, as such—and not merely identical contents with the past or future—is obviously to destroy the idea of time completely.

107. Time as a Fact in Experience.—The doctrine of the "specious present" is a very typical example of what James [200] calls "the psychologist's fallacy," in which the psychologist confuses "his own standpoint with that of the mental fact about which he is making his report." The difficulties which psychologists have had with this problem are due to their tacit assumption that empty or abstract time is a real manifold within which consciousness must be placed, and which is capable of limiting the nature of psychical reality. Consciousness is entitled to any properties which it actually possesses, and it cannot be robbed of any of its possessions by conceptually confining it within the compartments of the temporal sequence, however minute these compartments may be. There seems to be no reason why the memory of a past event should not be regarded as a proper portion of the instantaneous present. If it were still in the past, it would not be a memory. Placing the present consciousness within a mathematical instant does not make it discontinuous with the past or future, nor does such a condition deprive consciousness of any of the effects of the past or its causal relationship to the future.

Another source of confusion lies in the idea that, if time is not included as a finite span within the supposedly instantaneous consciousness, then it cannot be known within the latter. There are a number of different ways of meeting this alleged difficulty. One way is to say that time, as an abstract system, is non-existent, and hence does not need to be known. From another standpoint, we may regard time as an intellectual construction, within the instantaneous consciousness, and based upon certain very evident facts of the latter, namely its content of memories, recognitions, expectations and related phenomena. From this standpoint, we know all there is to be known about time, because we have created it according to our own arbitrary plans. Or, again, we may point out that, although the present consciousness cannot contain the past or the future, nevertheless, it is a dynamic or changing reality. Every mathematical physicist is familiar with the fact that time-derivatives, as indices of rates of change, have finite values at *instants* and do not require a span of time. From a still different angle, we might abstract from our definition of consciousness as an instantaneous entity and say that, although consciousness can contain no demonstration of time as a temporal period or length, such a demonstration can certainly be given in *experience;* where the concept of time may as well be utilized as in the ideally instantaneous consciousness.

James [201] and other psychologists have thought it significant of the nature of psychical time that the process of making an introspective report is not instantaneous, so that when the report is completed, the facts to which it refers may have vanished. However, this situation should not lead us into an attempt to prolong the described facts conceptually, so that they are conceived to last as long as it takes to describe them, even when their actual duration is less than this. In general, there can be no legitimacy in the demand that all consciousnesses which are described should last forever, in order that their descriptions should remain valid. If we are seriously embarrassed by the evanescent character of certain psychical phenomena, we may be impelled to design conditions under which they will last at least as long as it takes to formulate them. But we could not limit introspection to cases where this is possible. James' difficulty arises from the requirement that the present description should refer always to the present consciousness. Fortunately, there is nothing to be gained from such a procedure.

As a matter of fact, it seems to me that all of these arguments of the psychologist concerning the difficulties and peculiarities of psychological time are on about the same plane as those which are involved in Zeno's classical paradoxes.[202] The concept of time as a linear series of non-overlapping instants is highly useful for purposes of scientific description, and its justification lies wholly in such practical applications. If we confuse time, as a scientific concept, with the temporally conditioned facts of experience, we destroy it by a process of contradiction. The intelligent procedure is to use the concept in accordance with the usual rules, but not be misled into regarding its properties as universal psychological facts.

108. The Problem of Psychophysical Simultaneity.— If we regard physical and psychical time as two distinct manifolds, but having the same logical structure, we are evidently faced by the problem of the manner of correspondence of these two systems, or of the facts which they contain. Given any instant in the physical schema, we should be able to identify a corresponding instant or group of instants in the psychical sequence. On account of the manner in which we represent time, by means of spatial diagrams, we can formulate this general problem in much the same terms which were used regarding the relation of consciousness to physical space (see Fig. 6). Thus any given con-

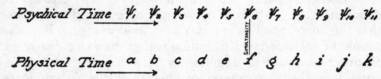

FIG. 6.   DIAGRAM TO SHOW THE TIME RELATIONS OF CONSCIOUSNESS AND RESPONSE STAGES.

The lower line of letters represents a series of corresponding response stages, as in Fig. 4. The upper line symbolizes a succession of consciousnesses in the correlated experience field. The vertical line stands for direct determination, or maximal correlation between the members of the respective series which it joins. See text for explanation.

sciousness may be said to possess *a region of determination in physical time,* within which its direct determinants are temporally located. We may limit ourselves, in the first instance, to the sequence of events which occurs in the *spatial* region of determination, i.e., the cortical-adjustor mechanism; although the question can be extended to deal with the spatially indirect determinants.

The criterion for the identification of the temporally direct determinants must be the same as that which is employed in the spatial case. Those moments of time should be chosen which contain the variables correlating perfectly, or to a maximal degree, with the factors in consciousness. From a purely logical standpoint, it is conceivable that the temporal region of determination should be polyphasic, i.e., that a single consciousness should be correlated directly with events occurring at a number of different times on the physical side. In this case, the relationship between the two temporal series would be of the so-called "one-many" rather than of the "one-one" type. A one-many scheme in this situation might provide us with an intelligible interpretation of the notion of the "specious present." Although it is absurd to think of a single psychical instant as containing many psychical instants, it is by no means inconceivable that a single consciousness should be concurrently determined by a group of temporally separable *physical* events.

However, it seems more likely that a one-one correspondence between the two time orders will actually be demonstrated. In this case, we may be tempted to suppose that the corresponding instants are *simultaneous*. But, this should be regarded as a definition rather than as a discovery. In order to establish simultaneity between two isolated systems, it is always necessary to operate through some interrelation between them. In the psychophysical situation, functionally determined concomitant variation is our nearest approach to interaction or intercommunication. Of course, we are not logically compelled to regard *corresponding* instants as simultaneous. If anything can be gained by retarding or advancing the physical with respect to the psychical, by some definite amount, this would appear to be entirely legitimate.

In any event, if we assume a definite temporal correspondence between physical and psychical time, we have a basis for speaking of a compound manifold to be known as *psychophysical time*. This manifold is not to be regarded as an existent temporal container, in which the physical and psychical systems are carried, but merely as a logical system for dealing with their interrelations. The general relationship between any concrete individual experience and the physical time manifold can be conceived by the same method which applies to the interrelations of separate "local times" in the physical system alone. Each individual experience has its own "local" psychical time, and must be related individually to corresponding portions of the physical world, i.e., its own particular "direct determinants." However, this will not prevent us from generalizing the relationships between *any* such individual experience and the direct or indirect determinants thereof, and discussing these relationships as types, and as typical of the psychophysical time manifold.

109. The Problem of Psychical Simultaneity.—Temporal relationships between separate individual experiences apparently must be established via their individual time linkages with the physical system. If the existence of *telepathy,* as a purely psychical means of intercommunication, without any physical parallel, should ever be established, we might then become able to link separate psychical systems together without physical intermediaries. A profound philosophical analysis of the psychophysical relationship as a whole may also reveal some way of eliminating the physical links in this temporal chain. But, from the present standpoint of psychophysiology, and also of practical life, this does not seem to be feasible. In practice, I say that events in my experience are simultaneous with particular events in yours, if they occur in introspective conjunction with the same reading "on the same clock." However, there are actually two separate experiential clocks, the one in your experience and the one in mine; and the relationship between them is established only along two separate, complex paths of response conduction which radiate from the single physical timepiece.

It will be noted that there is also a problem of the basis of simultaneity *within* a single individual experience or consciousness. In general, we conceive of any single experience instant as being structurally complex, and hence as being capable of embracing a plurality of simultaneous events. Consider, in this connection, the classical question as to the number of things which can be grasped in a single "act of attention." (See Volume III.) Now, the basis of simultaneity within the individual conscious moment is to be sought in the so-called *unity of consciousness,* which refers to the fact that all of its parts are causally interrelated in a very direct and effective manner. A change in any portion of consciousness reacts upon all of the other concurrent portions. This is particularly true of the relationship between components of consciousness, in general, and the reporting process which constitutes introspection. The conditions for the latter are set to make the report respond immediately and flexibly to any present property of the given consciousness; and the confluence of a plurality of such intra-experiential effects upon a single reporting process is the criterion for simultaneity within a single psychical field.

110. Time Relations of Consciousness and Predeterminant Response Stages.—Let us suppose that a one-one relationship can actually be demonstrated between consciousness and its direct determinants in time, as well as in space (or coexistential patterns formations). Suppose, furthermore, that no reason appears for regarding the temporal relationship as being other than a simultaneity. It is clear that, under these conditions, what we have called the predeterminant stages of response will be prior in psychophysical time to the direct determinants, whereas the postdeterminant stages will be subsequent. In general, the lag or lead of any indirect determinant, with respect to the corresponding consciousness, will be the same as the measure of its precedence or succedence of the corresponding direct determinant. Since the velocities of propagation along separate response paths may be different, the physical events which are represented simultaneously in consciousness are not necessarily themselves simultaneous. Sometimes the lag of one line of propagation behind another is due to the stimulus phases, as in the case of thunder which follows distant lightning. At other times, it is referable to some delay in the receptor or conduction processes. The familiar visual illusion of the "fluttering heart" (see Volume II) is an example of a receptor effect, while the phenomenon of "prior entry" (see Volume III) illustrates a conductional or central difference of this sort.

Such apparent failure of simultaneity between physically simultaneous events, or the converse, offers a serious difficulty for realistic theories of consciousness, and forces them into hypotheses of one-many interrelationships between experiential and physical time. However, if we adopt the straightforward assumptions of classical physiological psychology, these phenomena are exactly what we should expect. In general, it seems most reasonable to adhere to the classical assumption of a central monophasic region of determination, the pattern components of which are in one-one correspondence with the parts of the corresponding consciousness, for single instants of time on either side of the psychophysical relationship, these instants being treated as simultaneous. There is apparently no convincing evidence against any of these assumptions, and there is a great deal of evidence in their favor. However, our preference for these principles is based to a large extent upon the relative logical simplicity of their consequences.

Chapter VIII

Aspects of Psychophysiology as a Science

Section 27

ELEMENTARY PSYCHOPHYSICAL RELATIONS AND GENERAL PSYCHOPHYSICS

111. Seeking the Fundamental Psychophysical Functions.—If the general assumptions which we have indicated in the preceding chapter, as characteristic of present-day psychophysiological science, are valid, it would appear that the direct relationships between consciousness and matter are limited to a very small region of the total physical universe. It would seem that only where we find human cerebral cortices which are functionally active, can we allege the existence of consciousness. Of course, there are many millions of such cerebral processes, but if they were all put together they would form a very minute fraction of the entire material system. Now, in our everyday thinking, we do not ordinarily restrict consciousness to human organisms, but assign it also to nearly all forms of animal life. The majority of introspective psychologists are likewise willing to believe that something of the same general nature as the human introspective consciousness exists in association with the more complex nerve processes of the higher animals. The more these processes differ from those of human response, the less similar to the human the accompanying consciousness is supposed to be.

This line of thought inevitably leads to perplexities. The general criterion for the existence of psychical reality, in association with material structures and processes, must evidently be the *similarities* of the latter to the human cerebral cortex and its activities. But such similarities may be observable along many distinct lines or dimensions, some of which are probably important and others quite unimportant. Thus, if a material body happened to have the same *weight* as the human brain, this would not be accepted as a criterion for the existence of consciousness in association with the body in question. Neither is general chemical constitution an adequate test. A great deal of ingenuity has been expended in the attempt to arrive at a satisfactory "criterion of mind" in animals,[203] or in nature in general. Spontaneity of movement, adaptive reaction, associative memory, and various other characteristics of human activity have been advocated by different thinkers. The majority of such criteria have necessarily been applied to animal behavior as viewed from the outside, without reference to the details of the nervous mechanism. None of them has proven to be entirely satisfactory, principally because their technical consequences have not harmonized with our pre-established convictions. We naturally expect a valid test for the existence of mind to reveal a definite discontinuity at some level of material organization, but formal criteria have shown a tendency to shade the mental, to some extent, over the entire scale of physical things. Plants are not totally devoid of intelligence, and even rocks may show spontaneity of movement.

Such difficulties are characteristic of a primitive condition of psychophysiological concepts. In order to progress in our understanding of the universal relationships of mind and matter, we must analyze both the physical and the psychical systems into their elementary constituents. Having done this, we must formulate the psychophysiological or psychophysical relationships which obtain between the simplest significant factors on each side of the equation. These factors may not be ultimate elements but they can be expressed as combinations of such elements. In any event, the fundamental relations must be regarded as being logically elementary, in the sense that they are irreducible to any simpler terms. In the present infancy of psychophysiology, we may be compelled to deal with psychophysical relationships which are very far from being elementary in this sense. It is to be expected that protracted investigation will be required in order that we should be able to separate out the fundamental psychophysical laws. But eventually it may be found possible to determine psychophysical principles which will be analogous to those of Newton, in mechanics, or to the Maxwell-Lorentz equations, which dominate the theory of electrical phenomena.[204] Such "atomic laws" may be few and absolutely rigorous in their applications, even though the concrete situations which they explain may appear to be very complex and variable. It has been shown in other branches of science that a few fundamental laws may be compounded in diverse ways, so as to produce systems which suggest the presence of a vast multiplicity of complex irreducible relationships, or even the absence of any uniformity whatsoever.

This analytical method of dealing with the psychophysiological problem is to be contrasted with that which considers "organic wholes," a conception which is popular in some psychological and philosophical circles. A study of the history of science shows that results which have been based upon incomplete analysis have never proven themselves final or satisfactory. Distinctions which are built up in accordance with the idea of different levels of combination of ultimate units, finally receive complete explanation in terms of the latter. This has happened, to a catastrophic degree in modern physics, in the eradication of all qualitative boundaries between such sciences as optics, electricity, and mechanics. It is characteristic of scientific thinking to formulate the complex in terms of the properties of the simple; and insofar as it succeeds in doing this it simplifies both its terms and their modes of interrelationship. It appears to be impossible to carry this program of analysis as far in introspective psychology as it can be carried in physics; perhaps because physical science has eliminated from its domain, and left to psychology, all of those factors of immediate experience which have resisted the analytic procedure. This being the case, there can be no excuse for not carrying analysis to its final limit in the physical science which we call physiology, wherein we may find the clue to a more profound psychological analysis.

112. Human Psychophysiology May Yield a General Psychophysics.—Now, if it turns out to be possible to arrive at a relatively small number of fundamental laws which, in various permutations, symbolize all of the direct relationships between the human introspective consciousness and its direct determinants, we may find that the limitation of our psychological material to the human form of consciousness no longer holds. It seems almost certain that all of the fundamental constituents and properties of physical reality are exemplified in the region of determination of human consciousness. It is equally probable that all of the "atomic laws" of physics are operative within the region in question. In this case, it is to be expected that the direct psychophysical relationships of the human introspective field will exhibit all possible elementary psychophysical laws. Of course, in different individuals and at different times, these elementary laws will be given in many diverse constellations, but not in all of the forms of combination which are theoretically possible. However, if we become conversant with the exact character of the elementary laws, including the ways in which they combine with each other, we shall probably be able to determine the properties of constellations other than those which have actually been observed. This kind of reasoning is the rule, rather than the exception, in all sciences which have mathematical form.

Under such conditions, a process of pure deduction should enable us to ascertain the structure and functions of the psychical system which accompanies any specified physical configuration. Thus, although we may be unable to persuade a dog to introspect and provide us directly with a description of his consciousness, nevertheless, we may eventually find it possible to arrive at a detailed analysis of his brain structures and processes. Upon inspecting this physical formulation, we may find elementary factors that are identical with those which are present in the analytical account of the human "direct determinants." Although these factors will undoubtedly be in a different constellation in the canine than in the human case, we shall nevertheless be able to apply the elementary psychophysical laws, which we have learned from the latter, so as to ascertain the nature of the canine consciousness. The logical process, here, may be compared with that of translating a passage from one language into another, by means of our knowledge of the relationships between words in the two respective tongues. These relationships may have been exemplified to us within a particular original pattern of ideas, but later on we can employ them in translating quite a different word formation from one language into the other. Thus, by studying the details of the psychophysical relation between the human introspective consciousness and its direct determinants, we may be able to construct a general *lexicon,* which will permit us to interpret the psychical significance of any physical structure or process, whatever.

In this way, we shall be able to develop a general science of *psychophysics,* which is not limited to the special phenomena of human psychophysiology; and which, possibly, may reach beyond all biological limitations. Whether or not the latter possibility is realized, must depend upon the exact physical character of the factors which enter into elementary psychophysiological laws. If these physical factors are relatively complex and special, being found only within living organisms, then the inference to mind will be biologically or physiologically restricted. On the other hand, if it should turn out that the physical terms in the "atomic psychophysical relationships" are of a very simple and general character, we shall be justified in extending the implication of psychical existence, beyond the organic into the inorganic realm. Although the facts do not permit us to choose between these two alternatives, at the present time, it is nevertheless entirely conceivable that the psychical and the physical should finally prove to be coextensive, in the sense that there is a psychical counterpart for every form of physical existence, regardless of its complexity or simplicity. In this case, we could speak of a one-one correspondence between all material things and a parallel psychical system, and such a doctrine would properly receive the name: *panpsychism*. Under these conditions, we might be tempted to discard the notion of the physical system entirely and to regard the psychical one as constituting the sole reality, the physical being only a sort of conceptual shadow of the psychical. Concerning this theory, we shall have more to say in the final volume of this work.

However, it must be admitted that we are now very far distant from any such ideal scheme of psychophysical deduction. We can hardly claim even to be definitely conversant with any direct psychophysical relations whatsoever. Nearly all of our psychophysiological data are of an indirect kind. Such information as we actually have concerning the direct determinants of consciousness is extremely vague or general. We know that certain portions of the brain are necessary to particular mental functions, but we do not know exactly what is going on in these brain areas when the functions in question are operative. Nevertheless, it seems worth while to advance some hypotheses concerning certain elementary or quasi-elementary psychophysical laws, to see whether they will lead us to any simplifying lines of thought. In the present state of brain physiology, it appears that the *method of hypothesis* is the only one which we shall be able to employ. This method has yielded excellent results in general physics, where the subject matter may also be inaccessible to direct observation. Therefore we shall not hesitate to utilize it in our psychophysiological discussions. It is only necessary that we should guard against too affectionate an adherence to any particular speculative view; since all such ideas must be judged on the basis of their combination of simplicity and degree of correspondence with the facts.

Section 28

THE CLASSIFICATION OF PSYCHOPHYSIOLOGICAL FACTS AND PROBLEMS

113. Indirect Psychophysical Relationships and Classical Concepts.—If the technique of psychophysiological investigation were completely adequate, we could restrict the task of the science to the study of the relationships between consciousness (or experience) and its direct determinants. All of the other factors and relationships could be dealt with by non-psychological physiology. If we were perfectly acquainted with the fundamental relationships between consciousness and the brain, on the one hand, and, on the other hand, with all of the details of the series of events in response, we should require no further information. If we wished to know how the object of response is related to the corresponding consciousness, this could be determined by the proper combination of psychophysiological and purely physiological data. However, practically, such indirect relationships are the ones which interest us the most. Moreover, perhaps unfortunately from a scientific standpoint, they are the only ones which are readily amenable to investigation, in the present state of psychophysiological technique.

It follows that any attempt to present the results of present-day psychophysiology must deal not only with direct psychophysical laws but also with a complex array of indirect relationships. We must consider what is known concerning the apparent dependency of consciousness upon the object of response, upon the stimulus, upon the sense-organ process, upon the receptor activity, as well as upon other factors on the afferent side. Furthermore, we must consider the manner in which consciousness associates itself with behavior and with aspects of efferent or motor control. A study of these various relations has occupied the attention of psychologists throughout the modern history of the science, and numerous terms have been employed to designate the corresponding facts and problems. It is necessary that we should arrive at a systematic interpretation of some of these concepts, in the interests of order in our subsequent discussion.

We have noted that the doctrine of psychological faculties purports to subdivide mind, or its functions, into a number of separate departments, which are treated individually in textbooks. Although the modern point of view does not favor the conception of a faculty as a real subdivision of a substantial mind, nevertheless it is necessary, practically, to partition a psychological discussion in some manner, and the lines of cleavage in the majority of such treatments are still similar to those which characterize the more ancient schema. Spearman [205] has analyzed thirty-three recent psychological texts and finds the following "faculties" to be preferred: sensory perception, intellect, memory, imagination, attention, language and movement. In James' *Principles of Psychology,* we find the following outstanding concepts: habit, attention, conception, discrimination and comparison, association, memory, sensation, imagination, various kinds of perception, reasoning, production of movement, instinct, emotion, and will. Titchener divided his well-known *Text-Book of Psychology* under the headings of: sensation, affection, attention, perception, association, memory and imagination, action, emotion and thought. Each psychological text has its own peculiar method of classifying the subject matter of the science.

Now, if we endeavor to partition the problems of psychology into separate categories, using only introspective criteria, we may arrive at results quite different from those which would appear from the standpoint of psychophysiology. Such concepts as sensation, perception, attention, and will can be developed exclusively from the introspective standpoint. But they can also be given a psychophysiological interpretation which is rather more significant than that based upon pure introspection. If we study the ways in which these and allied psychological categories are used, we shall find that their physiological relations have played an important part in their determination. Thus, we might define sensation as an element of consciousness, but in practice it usually stands for such portions of experience as are determined by the action of stimuli upon sense-organs. Volition, on the other hand, might be defined exclusively in terms of internal "conation," but in the majority of cases it implies expression in bodily action.

114. The Classification of Psychophysiological Facts. —It would seem appropriate, even if not strictly necessary, in a presentation of the facts of psychophysiology, to define the outstanding concepts so that they involve both psychical and physical factors. We shall see that this can be done without departing radically from current psychological categories, or even from those which are handed down to us in the doctrine of faculties. Our explicit definitions may be formally different from those of classical discussions, but the actual treatment and classification of the facts will show rather less difference, when compared with actual performance (instead of expressed intentions) in classical or recent treatments of psychological problems. The psychophysiological method of definition permits us to give the fundamental concepts of psychological science a more clear-cut form than is usually possible from an exclusively introspective standpoint. Although we shall endeavor not to deviate any more than is necessary from classical conceptions, the criterion for the acceptability of a definition must involve its utility and clearness as well as its historical consistency.

We have seen that psychophysiology is concerned essentially with the relationships which hold between experience and the physiological process of *response*. Such relationships are divisible into the directly determinant, the pre-determinant, and the post-determinant, respectively. Each of these three fundamental groups, in turn, can be subjected to further subdivision. The immediate determinants of experience present a constellation of factors which is ordinarily complex in both space and time. The pre-determinants comprise a protracted series of afferent response stages, while a similarly intricate series is presented by the post-determinants on the efferent sector of the response arc. These considerations readily suggest that *the fundamental concepts of psychophysiology*—or of psychology from the psychophysiological standpoint—*should be correlated with the several stages or phases of the response process.* Thus, in one chapter of our discussion, we might consider the indirect relationships which obtain between the *object* of response, and experience. In another chapter, we could study the manner of indirect determination of consciousness by the stimulus or sense-organ activities. In still a further chapter, we could deal with the direct relationships of consciousness to the brain process. Later we could treat, as a separate topic, the indirect determination of behavior, or other motor aspects of the response, by consciousness. Such a scheme would lend itself to minute subdivisions, all of which, however, would cohere in a logically consistent and complementary manner. The order of discussion of these various topics would naturally be arranged so as to correspond with that of the several stages in the response process itself. Thus, we could start with the object relation, and work from afferent to efferent, terminating with the adjustment of the organism to its environment. This general scheme could be modified at various points in deference to classical conceptions, which might not fit neatly into its plan. Furthermore, the various subdivisions of psychological facts and principles, thus specified, would need to be cut across by other modes of distinction, such as those of spatial pattern and temporal sequence.

115. The Concept of Perception as an Example.—We may endeavor to make these ideas somewhat clearer by considering an illustrative application. The concept of *perception,* as it is defined by its context in the majority of psychological discussions, appears to be concerned with the relationship between experience and the object of response. The concept of *sensation,* on the other hand, seems to deal with the relations of determination between experience and processes in sense-organs. It is true, of course, that perception has been defined in other ways than the one just indicated. Thus, we may regard a perception as a combination or compound of ultimate psychical elements, which are themselves known as sensations. Moreover, the majority of discussions of perception emphasize its *synthetic* character: the manner in which it combines the deliverances of many separate sense channels, together with records of past experiences. These redintegrative principles are so important in the understanding of the perceptual consciousness that they have sometimes been regarded as definitive of the latter. However, it is still possible to claim that the fundamental characteristic of perception lies in the relationship of the given consciousness or experience to the supposed real object, which must apparently be identified with the physical object of response in the given physiological situation. The reproductive and integrative aspects of perception are instrumental to its representative function.

Suppose, therefore, that for the purposes of psychophysiology, we define perception so that it is significant of the (indirect) relationship between experience and the response object. This indication of the meaning of the term is of course still rather indefinite. The actual facts which we have to consider are *relations,* manners of apparent dependency of experience upon the response object. Shall we say that these relations, themselves, constitute the perception in any given instance? An affirmative answer to this query might provide us with an intelligible interpretation of the old-time notion of perception as a form of awareness. We might say that the experience is aware of the response object, in the sense of being determined by the latter in a definite manner. From another standpoint, which is perhaps the most important one, we might neglect the question as to what perception is as a substantive meaning, and concern ourselves primarily with the definition of a *science of perception,* consisting in the systematic study of the kind of psychophysical relationships which we now have under consideration. From this standpoint, the chapter on perception would discuss these relationships without regarding perception as a special entity or process.

However, even if we consider the determinative relationship to be the essential feature in the situation, we can nevertheless derive from it a substantive definition of perception, in the following manner. Let us say that perception is that aspect of experience which can be related determinatively with the object of response. This formulation makes perception a purely psychological thing in substance but resting upon physiological conditions for its demarcation from other psychological categories. Such a conception can be made very definite by giving it mathematical form. Thus, we may say that perception is a *derivative* of experience with respect to the object of response; it shows how experience changes when and as the object changes. In symbols, if E is the experience, and O is the object, then perception is defined as: $P = \dfrac{dE}{dO}$. (The second and other higher order derivatives may be regarded as included, along with the first derivative.)

This manner of treating the concept of perception may seem to be unduly abstract, but a study of the facts will show that it permits us to handle them in a rather clear-cut manner. Moreover, psychophysical definitions, on this model, are actually interpretative of both popular and scientific psychological ideas concerning the problems which are here under consideration. If we ascertain the meaning of the word, "perceive," in everyday speech, and then reduce this meaning to its scientific equivalent, we find that it stands almost exactly for what we have chosen in our formal definition above. When I say that I perceive a ship on the horizon, I may tacitly identify the physical ship with a certain item in my visual consciousness. But if I follow this proposition through in the light of all established scientific facts, the most that I can make out of my statement concerning perception is that there are certain aspects of my present experience which are determined by the physical ship; and insofar as I regard the perception as an introspective phenomenon, it can only consist of the collection or system of these aspects. Now, the aspects in question cannot be the colors, depth elements, or other subjective features in themselves, but only the way in which these are controlled by the physical ship. This manner of control is indicated in the concept of the derivative of the subjective system with respect to the object.

Having marked off the domain of perception in this manner, we may then proceed to subdivide the realm in question in other ways. It is evident that experience and the object of response are, ordinarily, complex both in space (or coexistence) and time. Hence, we may divide the study of perception into spatial (coexistential) and temporal sections. We must consider, furthermore, the perceptual relationships of the elements or attributes which enter into these two fundamental types of patterns: the problem of *perceptual components*. We are also confronted by the question as to the exact position of the line of demarcation between the response object and the stimulus. For example, in vision, shall we limit the object to the configuration of electrons and protons which emits visible radiant energy, or shall we define the objective realm so that it includes certain aspects of the radiation in question, particularly in the region of space between the object and the corneal surfaces of the eyes? In the case of audition, shall we say that the object is limited to the sound-emitting body, or may we permit it to include the sound waves in their propagation through the air, at least up to the point of being received by the auricles? When we are listening to a radio loud-speaker, shall we say that the response object is the diaphragm of the speaker, or shall we decide to include the musical instruments in the broadcasting studio, with all of the intermediate electro-acoustic devices and media? We shall discuss these questions in greater detail in our subsequent presentation of the facts of perception.

116. Duplicate Relations with Successive Response Stages.—Objections to the above general plan may be

raised on the ground that the characteristics of each stage
of the response are represented to some degree in succeeding
stages.   This might seem to require that there should be a
reduplication of relationships with experience.   However,
such relationships will be *corresponding* rather than identical.
Thus, color relates itself to the rate of vibration of electrons
in the object, and also to the wave-length of the stimulus;
but electronic vibration and electromagnetic waves are two
different things.   In general, the object in consciousness can
be reproduced on the basis of a complete reduplication of
any afferent stage (and its natural successors) in the response, even in the absence of the preceding stages.   However, this fact does not obliterate the problem of the relationship between experience and such prior stages, when they
are actually present and operative.   Moreover, the relations
in question are different for separate stages.   The laws
which associate experience with the distribution of electronic
vibrations over an object surface, will necessarily be expressed in a different manner from those which relate it to
the directionalities of rays at a point in space near the pupil
of the eye.   Yet, under normal conditions of response, the
visual consciousness is fairly determinate with respect to
either one of these physical mosaics, neglecting the other.

However, when it happens that certain characteristics of
one stage of the response are duplicated in subsequent stages,
economy of exposition demands that the relationships between any such common attribute and experience should not
be considered separately for each stage or sub-stage.   The
best plan in this situation appears to be to postpone the
consideration of a given type of psychophysical relationship
to as late a response stage as possible.   In this way, we shall
be approaching as nearly as possible to a direct psychophysical principle of determination, with a minimal number
of intermediate physiological or physical links.

As an example of this kind of situation and its treatment, we may consider the relationship between brilliance
and radiant intensity, for constant wave-length composition.
This has the general form of Fechner's law, $B = k \log I + K,$

which can be demonstrated between consciousness and the intensity factor of any stage in the response from the source to the receptors, provided the conditions are properly chosen. Consequently, following the plan above approved, we should postpone the consideration of the Fechner relationship, as such, until we come to deal with the operation of the visual stimulus within the eye. However, the exact details of the logarithmic equation will vary for different objective stages of the response. For example, the values of the constants, k and K, will not be the same for the source as for the object surface, or for the retina. Hence, we cannot avoid dealing with the relationship between brilliance and intensity for each stage which manifests intensity, but we should endeavor to restrict ourselves at each stage to the aspects of the relationship which are characteristic of the stage in question and cannot be passed on to subsequent stages.

Considerations of this sort suggest that the most logical way in which to discuss the psychophysiological relationships of the various portions of the afferent arc, would be to start at the cerebral cortex, and work outwards. By this method, we could deal, first, with the direct psychophysical laws, and then in succession with determinants which are progressively more and more indirect, but explanatory of the given values of the direct determinants. Proceeding in this manner, we might first discover the logarithmic relationship at the receptor stage, and could then modify it progressively to fit the bearing of prior stages upon the latter. The difficulty with this method lies in our lack of knowledge concerning the constitution of the intra-neural stages of the response and the exact relationships which obtain between their constituent factors and experience. Our present day psychophysiology is necessarily a tentative system, based upon the exigencies of the given scientific situation. Under these actual conditions, it seems best to treat the response stages in their propagational order, starting with those which we know the best—the object and the sense-organ—but utilizing our knowledge of the relations of subsequent stages whenever helpful.

A slightly different way of viewing this situation might be formulated as follows. Where we have a definite knowledge of the mode of dependency of one response stage upon its predecessors, we may use this knowledge to simplify our discussion. We know that if we have a series of stages, a, b, c, d . . ., all of which are indirect determinants of experience, with the possible exception of the last, the psychophysical relationships of the last member of the series will be superimposed upon those of preceding members. Hence, if we choose, we can separate out the component relationships and not reduplicate their treatment in each stage unless something is to be gained thereby.

We shall work out the details of the general scheme which has been outlined above, in the body of the present book. It will hardly be possible, at the present point in our discussion, to list and define all of the fundamental concepts which are to be employed. However, we shall divide the presentation of psychophysiological facts and principles under four general headings, as follows: perception, sensation, cerebration, and action. The definitions of perception and sensation have already been indicated above. In general, perception involves the relationship between experience and the objective stage of the response; sensation is concerned with the afferent arc, starting at the sense-organ surface, and ending somewhere on the "sensory side" of the cerebral cortex. Cerebration involves the relationships between experience and the cerebral processes, primarily those of the cortex; while action is concerned with the interrelations of experience and processes in the efferent arc, including overt behavior and adjustment to the environment. The four general categories will be subdivided further, not only in parallel with subordinate stage divisions, but also with cross-sectional patterns in space and the succession of events in time.

Section 29

PSYCHOPHYSIOLOGY AS A COMPLETE PRACTICAL PSYCHOLOGY

117. Psychophysiology Must Deal with All the Facts.
—In our formal development of the definition of psychology, we have regarded psychophysiology as a subdivision of general mental science. We found that introspective psychology deals with experience *per se*. Physiology is concerned with the organic processes by themselves. Psychophysiology considers the relationships between factors on the two sides. However, in order to discuss these relationships intelligibly, a textbook of psychophysiology must present both the psychological and the physiological facts which are thus related. It will not do to assume that the reader is already entirely familiar with either of these sets of facts. Since not all of the data of physiology are significant, or equally significant, in their psychophysical bearing, it will not be necessary to recapitulate the whole of physiology. But this sort of statement is much less applicable to the data of introspective psychology, because of the fact that psychophysiology *starts* with these latter data and seeks the physiological and physical factors which are related with them. It is thus compelled to deal with the entire system of introspective psychological facts.

These conditions make it appear that a thorough and intelligible treatment of psychophysiology must present *all* of the facts of psychological science, both introspective and psychophysiological. It may be that, in the present state of our knowledge, there are numerous introspectively identifiable phenomena which have no known physiological correlatives. But we cannot abandon the problem of looking for the latter, and in almost all cases we can consider interesting and reasonable hypotheses concerning their nature. Consequently, it would appear that, although psychophysiology is formally only a portion of general psychology, in practice it embraces the entire system of psychological knowledge. In fact, it must constitute a *complete practical psychology*. Our presentation of psychophysiology as a scientific system, in the present book, will recognize and exemplify the validity of this proposition.

118. Progressive Psychology Necessarily Psychophysiological.—Now the proposition in question is not merely a logical or pedagogical expedient; it is significant of the actual development of psychology as a science. It stands for what is permanent and distinctive in the progress of this science, as opposed to the whims of individual thinkers, or the schools which they have founded. In the quest for novelty and personal preëminence, such thinkers may advocate radical ideas which seem to upset the historical continuity of a science; but when time has carried these individual figures into the dim and belittling distance, we see that the continuity still exists and that something of value has accumulated steadily, in spite of the inevitable fluctuations of opinion. This thing which is distinctive in psychology, and different from the data of any physical science, is comprised as a unit in psychophysiological knowledge.

These statements are not intended as denials that a strictly introspective psychology is theoretically possible. Indeed, the logical conceivability of such a system is essential to a clear formulation of psychophysiological problems and principles. However, in practice, the strictly introspective technique is seldom used, and is lacking in the practical value of the psychophysiological method. If we are to control mind, we must know its *conditions*. Since relatively few of the conditions of experience are contained within itself, we must look beyond experience as well as within it for the data upon which to base a psychological technology.

Our much vaunted laboratory or experimental psychology is almost necessarily psychophysiological in method. The typical psychological experiment consists in placing a human organism under determinate conditions, applying certain stimuli, and recording the resulting reactions. Probably the most important among the latter take the form of introspective reports, and in general it is legitimate to regard such reports as descriptive of the consciousness of the given subject. We cannot agree with the behavioristic refusal to treat the vocal reactions as other than physiological in their significance. However, the described consciousness or experience is evidently surrounded and conditioned by physiological or physical factors. In the absence of such factors, it would be impossible to characterize the experimental situation at all adequately.

Of course, from one standpoint, these experimental conditions can be regarded as psychological phenomena in the consciousness of the so-called *experimenter,* who may sometimes be identical with the subject of the experiment. However, in formulating the results of such psychological experiments, we almost inevitably interpret the conditions in terms of the ideas of physics or of physiology, which are not supposed to refer to the individual experimenter's experience. It would appear, in the light of historical and current tendencies in psychophysiology, that the more thoroughgoing such a physiological interpretation is made, the more scientific value there will be in the resulting formulations.

PART THREE

PERCEPTION: CONSCIOUSNESS AND THE WORLD

Chapter IX

The Concept of Perception

Section 30

THE GENERAL NATURE OF PERCEPTION

119. Current Definitions of Perception.—The definitions of perception which we find in extant textbooks of psychology show considerable variation, and involve a mixture of characteristics. A perception is ordinarily supposed to represent a "real" object or external condition, but at the same time to be a synthetic product, which involves subjective factors and processes in a very essential way. Perceptions are supposed to be based upon sensation but to incorporate the associated consequences of memory. Percepts are contrasted with sensation, as being complex while the latter are simple. Percepts combine the simultaneous deliverances of many different sensory channels. Commonly, perception seems to imply the actual existence and operation of the object which it represents; if the object is "really" absent, even though perfectly depicted in consciousness, we have a case of hallucination, and not of perception.

To quote from Pillsbury: [206] "Perception may be defined as the process of becoming aware of an object. A perception is different from sensation in that it is the appreciation of an object as an object, while a sensation is not known for itself or at least by itself, but is always a part of something else from which it is abstracted. The perception is initiated by some sensation. It begins with the stimulation of some one of the senses. But as a result of that stimulation we add to the sensation a mental construction or series of mental processes which result in giving us the impression of a whole object." Hollingworth [207] defines perception in a more strictly subjective manner, saying: "Perception . . . is a typical mental or redintegrative sequence, in which an act or verdict or other event is dictated by a partial feature (clue, sign, symbol) of a previous complexity." According to Titchener: [208] "The simplest kind of perception . . . implies the grouping of sensations under the laws of attention but it is clear that perceptions are, as a rule, not made up solely of sensations; we see and hear and feel more than is presented to eye and ear and skin; the given sensations are supplemented by images. Most of our perceptions are mixed perceptions, complexes of sensory elements; and the life of perception is, far more than one is apt to suppose, a life of imagination."

Now, from the standpoint of psychophysiology, it appears that these indications of the nature or meaning of perception involve an undue complexity of criteria. Assuming that perception is a mental representation of actual objects or environmental conditions, the usual psychological treatment deals with all of the processes which are concerned in the supposed synthesis of this representation. Consequently, it is compelled to consider the relation of the experience not only to the object stage of the response, but to the associative activities of the cerebral cortex. Thus, we find James [209] saying: "From the physiological point of view, both sensations and perceptions differ from 'thoughts' in the fact that nerve-currents coming in from the periphery are involved in their production. In perception these nerve-currents arouse voluminous associative or reproductive processes in the cortex; but when sensation occurs alone, or with a minimum of perception, the accompanying reproductive processes are at a minimum too."

Now, there can be little doubt that the original and primary meaning of the word, "perception," lies in the relation of consciousness to the physical or "real" object, rather than in its determination by the associative processes of the cortex. In popular thought, perception is an "awareness of the object" or of certain objective conditions. The notion of perception as being essentially a redintegrative process has been developed in an attempt to formulate the psychophysiological mechanism of this "awareness." Although, as in the quotation from Titchener, it purports to be an essentially introspective principle, the redintegrative interpretation is actually more physiological than introspective in its foundations, as suggested by the quotation from James. Treatments of the problem of perception, such as that of Titchener, are based upon the presupposition that perceptions can only be explained as consequences of the combination of sensory elements. They must be treated as "psychical compounds," in Wundt's sense: [210] "any composite component of our immediate experience which is marked off from other contents of such experience by characteristics peculiarly its own, in such a way that it is recognized as a relatively independent unit and is, when practical necessity demands it, designated by a special name." According to Hunter: [211] "The term *perception* is better used, if used at all, to refer to *any object present to sense which is composed or two or more sensory qualities*. If one sees a bit of blue (quality) of a certain intensity, clearness, duration, location, and meaning, he experiences the state of consciousness termed sensation. On the other hand, if what one sees is two or more qualities—red, white, and blue, e.g.—plus the other characteristics mentioned, he experiences a perception."

120. Perception as the Psychophysics of the Object.— Now, when we study the interrelations of objects and experience, by the psychophysiological method, we are not obliged to presuppose the existence of any sensory elements of this character. We shall, of course, find separate points of contact between the object and the surface of the organism, and learn that in the majority of instances, many different afferent channels are involved. But the given experience stands for what it may happen to be, as given: complex, simple, static, dynamic, or what not. Its structure can be described introspectively in terms of qualitative constituents and their interrelationships, but it is questionable whether we should be tempted to call these constituents "sensations" if we did not suppose them to be dependent upon the activities of sense-organs and afferent nerves. We have no reason, *a priori,* for supposing that the introspective analysis will correspond with the analysis in accordance with the natural lines of separation between different sense-channels, or between the characteristic processes in any single sense-channel. An actual study of the situation shows that this correspondence is quite imperfect; there are many aspects of experience which have no physiological sensory counterparts. The subjective phenomena which are usually designated as "perceptual," exemplify this proposition in a striking manner.

Now, as we have already suggested in the preceding chapter, we shall define the problem of sensation as that of the indirect determinative relationship between experience and the "afferent arc," which begins at the surface of the sense-organ and ends on the afferent side of the cerebral cortex. The sensory relationship is such as to demand a highly analytical treatment of experience, as well as of the corresponding physiological mechanism. This fact furnishes the historical and only reasonable foundation for the ordinary psychological notion of perception as a synthesis of sensory components. There is apparently no actual synthesis within consciousness or experience; the experiential facts are given as already synthesized. But on the physiological side, the brain processes must almost certainly involve actively synthetic operations, since they are compelled to put together nerve currents which are received along many physiologically insulated paths. *It is this afferent insulation which causes the treatment of the problems of sensation to assume the character of an atomic analysis.*

In view of the above consideration, and in the interests of a clear-cut classification of psychophysiological problems, we shall limit the notion of perception to the relationship between experience and what we may call the *objective stage or phase* of the corresponding response process. This relationship is not, however, of the type considered by the "awareness psychology," but is rather one of indirect psychophysical determination, as previously defined. It will be recalled that our definition of response has been such as to make it include things, conditions and activities in the environment, as well as inside of the organism. We have felt justified in treating the concept of response in this manner, on account of the physical continuity of the chain of events which is involved. Thus, under ordinary circumstances, visual response may be considered as starting at a reflecting surface, or even at a luminous source, rather than at the cornea of the eye or in the retina. Now, *the objective stage of the response can be defined in broad terms as consisting of all factors, external to the surface of the organism, or possibly to the nervous system and its sense-organs, which enter into or condition the sequence of events comprising the response.* As a rule, the primary factor in the objective stage of the response is actually a definite physical object, but it will nevertheless be recognized that the total stage, as we have defined it, will have a constitution more complex than that of the object alone. We shall consider the problem of the general analysis of the objective stage in the next Section.

121. The Domain of the Objective Stage.—The domain of the perceptual relationship is to be considered as ending where that of the sensory relationship begins. It will be advantageous, at the present point in our discussion, not to define this boundary too exactly. The division between perception and sensation is more or less arbitrary and for purposes of convenience in discussion. In some cases, it may be best to draw the line at the bodily surface; in others, at the entrant surface of the sense-organ; and in still others, strictly at the receptors. However, perceptual relationships should never be extended so as to include any aspect of the nerve processes, in the ordinary psychophysiological situation. The problem of perception is essentially limited to the consideration of such factors as can be demonstrated, or at least represented, in the *environment* of the active organism.

Nevertheless, it is important to recognize that the environmental factors which are thus chosen are picked only because of their participation in the response process. They cannot be selected on the basis of any purely environmental criterion. Thus, in the visual example, we are concerned only with such rays of light as actually succeed in entering the pupils of the eyes. Other rays are equally real and interesting from a purely physical standpoint, but have no bearing upon the response. Again, not all of the rays which enter the pupils are actually relevant. Those which fail to fall upon retinal receptors are ruled out of the response system. A similar process of elimination can be applied to some extent along the entire series of pre-determinant stages of the response. The exact domain of the objective stage can be ascertained by retracing the lines of propagation of influence which converge upon the central nervous system, and determining what environmental factors are actually effective in this way.

Nevertheless, after we have fixed the relevant lines of demarcation in the environment, by this method, we can proceed to study the relationship of experience to these environmental factors without any explicit reference to the part which is played by other response stages. Some of the reasons for discussing seemingly artificial relationships of this sort have already been indicated. Many of our experimental findings in psychophysiology are immediately of this perceptual nature. We are usually more interested, from a practical standpoint, in the relation of our experiences to the environment than to the intra-organic phases of the response. Furthermore, we are assisted in systematically subdividing the study of an intricate set of problems and facts.

122. Further Developments of the Concept of Perception.—Now, these problems and facts are essentially all of a *relational* character, in the sense of being psychophysical functions in which we may treat certain features of experience as *dependent,* and corresponding features of the objective stage of the response as *independent* variables. Thus, the shape of a visual presentation in consciousness is normally a *function* of the shape of the corresponding physical response object, of the angle of the latter with the line of sight, etc. The essence of our psychophysiological science consists in the formulation of such functional relationships. There is no strict necessity for stating the facts in any other form than that of a mathematical or logical function, containing psychical variables on one side of the equation and physiological or physical variables on the other side. However, owing to the peculiarities of language or grammar, it is frequently very convenient to use somewhat different modes of expression. Thus, instead of saying that the perceptual relationship between experience and the object is thus and so, we may wish to state (1) that the object is *perceived,* or (2) that there is a perception *of* the object in experience.

Now, according to our view, for "me" or "my experience" *to perceive* an object or objective condition can only mean that "my experience" is *correlated* with the object or condition in question. In other words, the two vary concomitantly in a reliable manner. Experience has one form when the object is there and a different form when it is absent; and the first form is predictable by means of a psychophysical law from the nature or specification of the object. These are merely other ways of saying that experiences, or certain of their constituents, are mathematical functions of certain objective factors. To perceive an object, in this sense, does not mean to have this object given in experience. By definition, the *physical* object is outside of experience entirely. The visual object or presentation, within experience, is a totally separate and very different thing, made up in large part of the facts which we have to correlate with the physical object.

Now, the ordinary meaning of "a perception," as a substantive term, is identified with the so-called presentation or thing-in-consciousness. However, as we have noted, this presentation is not usually regarded as being a perception unless it possesses a basis in the objective stage of the response. When such a basis is absent, exactly the same experiential formation is called an *hallucination*. Thus, it seems difficult to avoid the psychophysiological condition, even from an essentially introspective standpoint. A technical way of incorporating this seemingly inevitable requirement of the physical or "real" object in our definition of perception, has already been indicated in the preceding chapter. This consists in saying that the perception is that aspect of experience which is related in a determinative manner to the object. Technically, we can define "a perception" as the *mathematical derivative* of experience or consciousness *with respect to* pertinent features of the objective response stage. Such a concept can be regarded as deducible by a purely logical process from the psychophysiological functions which are involved in the given perceptual situation. Thus, starting with the equation $\psi = f(\phi)$, we may differentiate, yielding: $d\psi = d f(\phi)$, from which we can presumably find the value of $d\psi/d\phi$. In qualitative terms, this derivative interpretation of "a percept" stands simply for the manner in which experience changes, or would change, for a unit or predetermined change in the response object. In the case of an hallucination we may have the same form of experience as in true perception, but there will be no predictable modification of this experience when factors in the environment are altered. Hence there is no perception.

By way of further illustration, suppose that we are "looking" at a book, by which we mean that there is a physical book before the eyes, producing the normal sequence of afferent processes, with a corresponding visual presentation in consciousness. Now, suppose that the physical book is opened and closed. There will be a corresponding, but certainly not identical, alteration in the visual book or presentation. However, *the kind of change* which occurs in the visual pattern, for any particular modification of the physical one, will comprise the perception. Now, it is clear that there are many different ways in which the physical book, or other object, may change; some of these actually occurring under ordinary conditions, whereas others are merely conceptual. Thus, the book can be conceived as changing in color. This does not ordinarily occur in the case of a single book, but the covers of separate books show variations of this sort which are followed by corresponding variations in consciousness. Hence perception, defined in this derivative manner, will involve a group of such derivatives, applying to all pertinent dimensions of the object or objective stage of the response. Experimentally, we modify any desired objective dimension or observe its natural varieties, and may then note the corresponding alterations or species of experience. All of this is obviously just a special way of viewing the determinative relationship of experience to the specified objective factors.

123. Redintegrative Factors in "Perception."—Such a notion of perception, although harmonizing with the most important aspects of the idea as it is usually considered, evidently neglects other classical aspects. The redintegrative feature is not explicitly involved. This does not mean that we deny the existence of physiological mechanisms and processes of associative reproduction, or the importance of these mechanisms for the complete psychophysiological understanding of "presentations" as features of experience. We are merely transferring this problem from the category of perception to that of cerebration. However, there is nothing in this act to prevent a redintegrated product from entering into the perceptual relationship. Even abstract redintegrative aspects of experience may well play such a rôle, in some instances. In general, however, our perceptual analysis will proceed in technical ignorance of the relationships of experience to the later stages of the response process. If we do not utilize sensory and cerebral data, neither are we limited by concepts which are derived from them. Many different channels of sense are actually operative in establishing perceptual relationships, but it is not necessary for us to deal with their specific mechanisms, nor to consider how their deliverances are combined in the cortex.

Now, perception is ordinarily regarded as involving not only the synthesis of separate concurrent sensory factors, but also the arousal and incorporation of *memory records*. This is an essential aspect of the redintegrative process. Thus, according to Breese,[212] perception is not only a "consciousness of the qualities of an object synthesized into an object," but it is "the consciousness of sense impressions interpreted in terms of past experiences." "In sensation, what we experience is determined by the stimulus. On the other hand, in perception we supplement and interpret the presented stimuli by past experiences." Breese is not content merely to say that "in perception, what we experience is determined by the object," obviously because what he means by perception seems not to be adequately accounted for in this manner. However, insofar as this perception is representative of the object, even the revived experiential components must be psychophysiologically dependent upon the latter. Consequently, it may be possible for us to include such mnemonic factors within our perceptual functions. In fact, certain aspects of these historically operative determinants cannot be eliminated.

When we are considering a case of perception in an experienced adult, we shall usually find that the exact psychophysiological relationships, which obtain between such an adult experience and the corresponding response objects, will have a functional form dependent in large measure upon the records of past responses of a similar nature. A less mature, and possibly infantile, mind might show quite a different perceptual function under the same external and general neurological conditions. The crucial question in this situation may be as to whether the mnemonic contributions are excrescences upon the immediate sensory factors, or whether they mold the latter into the given form. The second alternative seems to be the most plausible one. The

criterion for choosing between these two interpretations is
to be found in the following test: When we modify the
response object, do the mnemonic factors stand out as invariable constituents of consciousness, or do they combine
with the alterations which result from the objective changes?

However, the problem of perception does not *include*
that of the relationship of experience to the memory records
or impressions in the central nervous system. It is only by
virtue of the bearing which these records have upon the
perceptual functions that they enter into the situation at all.
Nevertheless, these records are themselves to a large extent
functions of *past* objective response stages, so that the
aspects of experience which depend upon them have a certain perceptual history. Moreover, a study of the evolution
of perceptual functions of any given kind, during the life
of a particular individual, should provide us with evidence
from which we may deduce the nature of certain of his
memory records.

Section 31

THE ANALYSIS OF THE OBJECTIVE RESPONSE STAGE AND THE CLASSIFICATION OF PERCEPTUAL FUNC-TIONS

124. Choosing Variables in Perceptual Analysis.—
Numerous schemes have been adopted for the subdivision
of the problems of perception. James, in his *Principles of
Psychology,* deals separately with "the perception of time,
of 'things,' of space, and of reality." Titchener, in his *Textbook of Psychology,* treats of "spatial, temporal, qualitative,
and composite perceptions." Perceptions are also frequently
classified in accordance with the departments of sensation
or reception which are involved, as visual, auditory, tactual,
kinaesthetic, etc. Now, although the point of view of the
present book is somewhat different from that of James,

Titchener or the majority of other writers on the topic of perception, the methods of subdividing the problem may be generally similar.

In the first place, it seems entirely legitimate, and indeed necessary, to classify perceptual relationships in correspondence with the sensory channels which are concerned. In spite of the fact that the sense-organs and the other factors on the afferent nerve sector of the response arc are not explicitly concerned in the perceptual functions, they are nevertheless involved in the selection of the objective variables which must be considered. Visual objects can only be objects which send rays to the eyes, and the locations of the pupillary areas in space must therefore be included in a complete presentation of the facts of visual perception. Similarly, in the study of the facts of auditory localization, we cannot avoid reference to the spatial positions of the two ears. Since the spatial characteristics of the various receptive systems are thus involved, the established classification of these systems provides us with a natural scheme for dealing with the corresponding perceptual problems.

When we consider the perceptual relationship, either in general or from the standpoint of individual sense departments, we note certain lines or dimensions of cleavage of the subject matter. In the first place, we may deal with the perceptual connections of *simple components or aspects* either (1) of the objective stage of the response or (2) of experience. As examples of such constituents, we may mention terms like electrons, frequencies, speeds, densities, wave quanta, etc., on the objective side; or, within experience: points of color, pure musical tones, sweet, hot, and the like. Sometimes, such constituents will be *elements,* in the sense that they are separable parts of the whole, and at other times they may be more abstract *attributes* or "aspects." The essential point is that they should constitute the *fundamental* concepts or variables in the particular field of relationships under consideration. They are not necessarily ultimate from every point of view, but only sufficiently simple so that their further analysis throws no light upon the relationships into which they enter. For example, the concept of intensity of radiant energy is elementary in certain visual relationships, although the physicist can break it up into a complex system of factors which are more fundamental from his point of view. However, the attribute of brilliance, on the psychological side, is quite ultimate, since it cannot be expressed in any terms other than its own.

In the study of such *component perceptual relationships,* we can proceed in two different ways. We can single out certain simple aspects of experience, such as hue or visual depth, and determine what functions these are of factors in the objective stage of the response. Or, on the other hand, we may pick out a particular element in the objective stage, and ascertain what changes occur in experience when the nature or value of the element in question is varied. Our choice between these two methods will be determined in favor of the one which yields the simplest formulations, but as a rule the first method will be preferred for the final expression of the facts, since it yields an equation of the form, $\psi = f(\phi_1, \phi_2, \phi_3, \ldots)$. Actual experimental procedure is apt to employ the second method, since we can usually isolate the individual components of the objective situation and vary them experimentally, whereas the corresponding thing cannot ordinarily be done in experience.

However, when we alter the values of an objective variable, experimentally, we usually find that a considerable number of experiential factors are modified simultaneously. We might represent this result by writing:

$$\phi = f(\psi_1, \psi_2, \psi_3, \ldots),$$

but if our primary interest lies in ascertaining the physiological conditions for the psychical factors, rather than *vice versa,* we shall be inclined to formulate the observations by writing separate functions:

$$\psi_1 = f_1(\phi) \, ; \, \psi_2 = f_2(\phi) \, ; \, \psi_3 = f_3(\phi), \text{ etc.}$$

We can then neglect all of the changes except the one which

bears upon the particular problem which we have in hand.

It is naturally a general condition, in any such experimentation, that all physiological factors, other than the one which is under special examination, are held *constant*. Thus, if we vary the wave-length of a luminous stimulus, its intensity, area, surroundings, etc., must remain invariable. It is only on the assumption of such constancy of other conditions that we can determine the individual law of correlation which characterizes the physiological variable under consideration. However, the fixed conditions are necessarily specific in character, and may be quite arbitrary; and we might repeat the experiment under quite different constant conditions, and find a different result. Consequently, we must be careful not to generalize unduly from single determinations. If variation in the values of the so-called conditions is accompanied by changes in the psychical factor, the latter must be regarded as a function of these conditions as well as of the variable first considered. Hence in the end, we shall be compelled to express the psychical factor as a function of many physiological determinants, simultaneously. Sometimes, the exact values of certain alleged conditions may have no bearing upon the result, and in this case they can be ruled out of the psychophysiological situation. The majority of indirect psychophysiological relationships are highly intricate in their complete functional form.

125. Analysis by Response Stages, Patterns, and Changes.—The constituent factors of the objective stage are compounded in a number of different ways. In the first place, we must consider their combination along the *line of propagation of the response*. We have seen that response, as a whole, shows a very considerable complexity in this dimension, the objective stage being only one general section. However, as a rule, this latter stage is itself capable of being analyzed along the direction of propagation. Let us consider a case of visual response as an example. The process of physical propagation may be regarded as starting at a luminous source, such as the sun, an electric lamp, or a candle flame. However, in the particular instance of the electric lamp, we might carry the propagational series back through the power lines to the generator, the steam turbine, the boilers, and ultimately to the chemical processes of oxidation of the coal or other fuel. The *termination* of the objective phase of the process would ordinarily be considered to be located at the cornea of the eye. The analysis of the perceptual relationship on the basis of different sub-stages of the general objective phase of the response, may be characterized as *propagational* or *longitudinal*. The corresponding departments of perception can be named after the several sub-stages which are involved. Thus, in the case of vision, we might consider perceptions of the luminous source, of the angle of illumination, of the reflecting surface, of the direction of the latter with respect to the line of sight and so on.

A second way in which the constituents are compounded is found in the cross-sectional or coexistential pattern of any single stage of the response, or of consciousness. In the typical case of visual response there is a multitude of simultaneously operative lines of optical propagation, the coöperation of these being responsible for the formation of definite images upon the retinas of the eyes. However, these lines can be represented in space, outside of the eyes, by means of appropriate diagrams. In the study of the perceptual relationships, we abstract from the intraocular factors and deal only with such conditions and processes as can be demonstrated, or at least represented, in the environmental domain. Such cross-sectional patterns are commonly, although not inevitably, spatial. In visual response and experience the spatial feature seems to predominate, but in the case of audition, the intermingling admixture of numerous acoustical frequencies must be regarded as furnishing a definite cross-sectional pattern which cannot be described in spatial terms. The adjective, *compositional,* may be suggested for the designation of this general aspect of response stages and the corresponding department of perceptual analysis.

Still another way in which the components of the perceptual system are combined is along the dimension of *time*. *Temporal analysis* involves elementary, longitudinal, and compositional aspects as essential terms in its descriptions. In general, such analysis rests upon the study of concomitant *changes* in experience and in the objective stage. Thus, in investigating motion perception, we are concerned with changes in spatial pattern as a function of time: a concomitant spatial and temporal comparison. One sort of change on the objective side, perhaps a stroboscopic substitution, is accompanied by a different event in experience, say, the "phi phenomenon." The relationship between them constitutes a law of temporal perception. (It may be noted, in this connection, that although we speak of "changes" and "modifications" as means for ascertaining the psychophysiological relationships, in general, we do not ordinarily conceive such experimental variations in a temporal sense. In practice, they are of course successive in time, but they should be free of all effects which have a strictly temporal foundation, or are transitional in character.)

126. Other Methodological Problems.—In sketching the broad outlines of the perceptual system, it seems advisable to choose the notions of component, compositional, and temporal as the bases for the most general lines of demarcation. This method will not only yield a minimal number of general categories, but will favor the intercomparison of principles between various sensory divisions. Under each of these general captions, we may subdivide the discussion, first, in correspondence with the specific sensory or receptive mechanisms which are concerned. Then, under each of these sensory headings, we may consider the various significant sub-stage relationships. It is to be noted that the notions of component, compositional, and temporal apply equally to response and to experience. The sensory analysis can also be followed in experience, but the longitudinal scheme is essentially peculiar to response.

Certain difficulties are encountered in the attempt to carry out, in practice, the plan which we have outlined above. These difficulties are especially marked in dealing with the relationships of experience to its indirect determinants. In these relationships, component factors of experience are not representable, in general, exclusively as functions of single component factors in the response stages which are singled out for consideration, but are complicated functions of many such factors. A simple psychical phenomenon, such as color, or even a selected attribute such as hue, is determined not only by primary response variables, such as wave-length and intensity, but by the particular spatial and temporal configurations of the whole concurrent visual process. Hence, it appears that true components, on the experience side, may be determined by composition and even by temporal sequence, on the physiological side. This seems to place us in a dilemma regarding the classification of such relationships. The difficulty will be met, in practice, by allowing the experiential or introspective aspect to govern our classificatory policy. We shall regard the given problem as one in "component perception" if it has to do with the manner of determination of a component of experience, regardless of the possible complexity of its conditions; or as a problem in "composition" if it relates to the simultaneous aggregation of experiential components, even if the aggregation has a simple physiological basis; or as a "temporal" problem, if a succession of different conscious states is concerned, without reference to the classification of the corresponding physiological conditions.

We shall find that the general categories which have been established above apply not only to the problems of perception but to all other classes of psychophysiological relationships.

There are many different ways in which the total response process can be analyzed in its *cross-sectional* dimension, but the one which yields the most illuminating results, at least in the study of perception, is based upon lines' of demarcation between different classes of *receptors*. This is because the forces which are involved in the objective stage of the response must converge upon the receptive surfaces of the body in order to become effective. Although there is still a great deal to be learned with regard to the different species of such receptive mechanisms, available physiological data provide us with a fairly adequate basis for a sensory treatment. Having selected a particular receptive mechanism, our next problem is to identify the environmental influences which are operative upon this device, in the arousal of intraorganic response effects, and the evocation of an accompanying experience.

For the purposes of perceptual analysis, the best order of treatment of the various receptive or sensory departments would appear to be from the outside, inwards. In other words, we shall preferably begin with those forms of response which are determined by objects or conditions that are in general farthest removed from the central nervous system; and then follow an order of treatment which leads us finally to the least external conditions. In terms of the Sherringtonian classification of receptive systems,[213] the general sequence in accordance with this plan would be: distance receptors, other exteroceptors, proprioceptors, and interoceptors. Among the distance receptors, the order would be: vision, audition, and olfaction. Other exteroceptors might fall into an order such as: temperature, touch, pain, and taste. The proprioceptors might be placed in the series: equilibrative (inner ear), articular, tendinous, and muscular. The exact order of the interoceptive systems in accordance with our criterion is rather difficult to establish, and hence may be regarded as immaterial.

The outstanding problems of perception appear mainly in connection with distance and other exteroceptors, the majority of such problems being concerned with distance receptive processes. However, it is not difficult to defend the thesis that even the interoceptive responses possess "objects." Thus, the object of the hunger response is a certain chemical condition and state of muscular contraction of the stomach wall; or of the micturitional response: a full bladder.

The use of the word, "object," to designate either the physical object in the response sequence or the corresponding phenomenon in experience is liable to cause confusion. We can distinguish between these two meanings by using appropriate adjectives, speaking of the *response* object, on the one hand, and the *empirical* (phenomenal, visual, tactual, etc.) object, on the other hand. However, in the interests of a more succinct terminology, we shall consider the term, object, when used without a qualifying adjective, to be restricted to the physical response meaning; whereas the phenomenal object may be designated in a similarly simplified manner by the word, *thing*. The latter involves a common-sense concept which finds its most frequent meaning in direct experiential facts, rather than in recondite physical hypotheses.

Chapter X

Component Perceptions

Section 32 (A)

COMPONENT VISUAL PERCEPTIONS; COLOR AND ITS ATTRIBUTES

127. Identifying the Visual Factors in Consciousness.
—Physiology tells us that the visual receptors consist in the
rods and cones of the retina, but it seems advisable to limit
the domain of visual perception to those features of the
response propagation which are external to the eye, or eyes,
as a whole.   However, in order to ascertain what *environmental* factors are to be considered, we may retrace some
of the optical paths, starting at the retina and traveling
backwards to the luminous sources.   This method does not
establish any logical dependency of the objective factors
upon the sense-organ, and is not the only method which can
be employed successfully.   We could identify the relevant
objective factors solely on the basis of their *correlation*
with later variables in the visual response.   But, from the
general theory of the response propagation, we know that
only those features of the environment which can act upon
the retina will really show a correlation of this sort.

The next problem is to identify the visual components
of *consciousness* or experience.   Although we may feel that
we can determine, by mere introspection, what portion of
experience is visual and what is non-visual, it will be found
that our ability to mark out the visual facts depends upon
psychophysiological observations, although of a familiar and

common sort. There seems to be no inherent reason why we should attribute the existence of objects in the so-called visual field (in experience) to processes occurring in the eyes, or with reference to them, unless we have tried the experiment of intercepting the forces which act between objects and the eyes. Of course, this experiment is performed every time the eyelids are closed, or, in fact, whenever one object appears in front of another. We may roughly demarcate the visual field as a section of consciousness, by identifying it with that portion of the latter which undergoes a radical reduction in its internal differentiation, whenever radiant energy of visible wave-length is prevented from acting upon either eye.

The elimination of the objective stimulus, in this manner, does not by any means remove the visual field from consciousness, nor does it cut off all sensory influences upon this field. The retinas are still intact and probably more or less self-active. In order totally to eliminate the sensory phases of vision, it would be necessary to sever the optic tracts, close to the cerebral cortex. Even under these conditions, there would still remain a division of consciousness which we should call visual because of its dependence upon brain mechanisms that are normally attached to the eyes. Now, in order that we should be able to discuss intelligibly the perceptual relationships of the visual consciousness or experience, we must first consider the constitution of the latter from the purely introspective standpoint. In particular, we must pick out the *essential components* of this experience, with a view to ascertaining their correlations with analogous constituent factors in the objective stage of the response.

If we define the *visual field* as that portion of consciousness which is delimited by the simple act of opening and closing the eyes, we find that this field is a three-dimensional spatial structure, capable of exhibiting a practically infinite variety of patterns, which are nevertheless made up of a restricted array of possible psychical elements. These elements are of two introspectively different species, the one consisting of *colors,* which are nearly always in the form of two-dimensional surfaces, forming the boundaries of the visual space at the farthest point from the eye; and the other consisting of *depth elements,* which intervene between such color surfaces and the eye, forming the *volume* of the spatial structure. We shall consider further structural characteristics of the visual consciousness in a later Section, in which also we shall deal with the depth elements. For the present, however, our concern is with the elements which we have called colors.

THE INTROSPECTIVE PSYCHOLOGY OF COLOR

128. The Definition of Color.—The word color has numerous more or less discrepant meanings in scientific, as well as common-sense, discussions.[214] Ordinarily, when used in the affirmative mood, it includes those visual qualities which exhibit hue and saturation—that is, which are to some extent reddish, yellowish, greenish or bluish—and excludes black, white and intermediate grays. In the interrogative mood, however, color frequently becomes sufficiently comprehensive to include black, white and the grays, so that it becomes the universal name for elementary visual qualities of the species which we wish to consider. It is in this comprehensive sense that we shall employ the word.

Physicists frequently use the term, color, as a synonym for wave-length,[215] or wave-length composition, when speaking of radiant energy. This usage, however, is at the present time coming under a ban, since physicists are recognizing that color is wholly a psychological or introspective phenomenon, having no place in the world of energy and atoms. Since, in this way, we regard color as wholly psychical in its nature, we shall find it unnecessary to speak of "color sensations" or of "sensations of color." The problem of color sensation is concerned with the determinative relationships which hold between color and various characteristics of the stimulus, sense-organ and receptor stages of visual response. We might, perhaps, assert that color is a *sensa-*

tion or perception of radiant energy, but this would add nothing to our exposition of the facts.

129. The Classification of Colors.—Introspection shows that, although a very large number of qualitatively different colors are given in visual consciousness, this number is nevertheless definitely restricted, so that it is readily possible to form *a catalogue of all possible colors.* Upon comparing such colors amongst themselves, it becomes evident that they exhibit resemblances and differences which invite classification and the formation of a system. A preliminary study of these relationships leads us to divide colors into two general classes, which we may call the *achromatic* and the *chromatic,* respectively. The former consists of black and white, with a long series of intermediate grays. The latter consists of all colors which we can describe as reddish, yellowish, greenish or bluish. It may seem a contradiction in terms to speak of "an achromatic color" and a redundancy to refer to "a chromatic color," but it will be seen that this is not the case if color is defined in the broad way above indicated and if, on the other hand, we employ the term, *chroma,* as a synonym of the common affirmative use of the word, color, in the restricted sense.

130. The Achromatic Series.—If we contemplate the achromatic colors, it becomes evident that they can be arranged into a quantitative series, in accordance with our general criterion for the production of a psychological system. If we dispose all of these colors, or grays, as we may call them (including black and white), so that the sum of all of the differences between neighboring members of the arrangement is a minimum, we arrive at a linear, or one-dimensional, system. The limiting members of this system are black and white, the intermediate ones being various grays, ranging from dark grays near black to light grays near white. The natural reference point of this linear system is the gray which is midway between black and white, and which is called the mid- or *median gray.* If this scheme of achromatic colors includes all possibly discriminable grays, and no duplicates, each member will be just noticeably different from its neighbors. Since this is by definition a unit difference, it becomes possible to specify any gray numerically in terms of its position in the series, with respect to some arbitrarily determined reference member, such as the mid-gray. According to Külpe,[216] the number of members in such a series is 810, while König[217] puts the number at 660. Referred to the mid-gray, other achromatic colors would be measured by positive and negative numbers, the former finding a maximum in white and the latter a maximum in black. Although, actually, it is difficult to identify the ideal black and the ideal white, it seems best to specify the position of any gray in the series by reference to black as member No. 0, so that all of the numbers are positive, white having the highest position. This scheme enables us to define a concept of *brilliance,* which is a color attribute determined by the scale of grays and corresponding to our general notion of apparent "brightness." In practice we shall be obliged to identify black with the darkest gray which we can find, while white will consist of the lightest of all realizable grays.

131. The System of Chromatic Colors.—The peculiar nature of the chromatic colors, as contrasted with the achromatic ones, seems to be evidenced by our sharp distinction in common discussion between "colored" and "colorless" objects, the former possessing the attribute which we here call *chroma.* However, a study of a representative collection of chromatic colors shows at once that they also possess the characteristic attribute defined by the achromatic system, namely brilliance. Hence we may proceed at once to consider the properties of a group of chromatic colors which are all possessed of the same or *equal brilliance.* If we arrange all possible *chromas* of this sort into a system, such that the sum of the differences between all neighboring members is reduced to a minimum, we find that they form a two-dimensional manifold, or a surface. (See Fig. 7.) We discover, however, that there is a single point in this surface which is naturally reserved, on account of the similarities and differences of adjoining colors, for the unique achromatic color which possesses the brilliance value com-

mon to all of the chromas in the arrangement.   This unique
achromatic color, or gray, furnishes a natural reference point
for the chromatic attributes in general.

Since the dimensions of the chromatic system, above
established, are two in number—corresponding to the surface or plane character of the system—there must be *two
independently variable* chromatic attributes.   These attributes, as ordinarily defined, consist of hue and saturation.
Saturation is measured radially in the chromatic plane, with

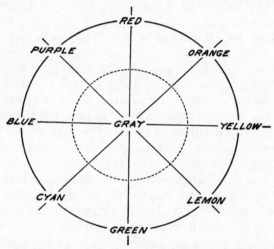

FIG. 7.   COLOR CIRCLE, SHOWING THE RELATIONSHIPS OF COLORS OF A SINGLE
BRILLIANCE VALUE.

The four psychologically primary hues are represented on the periphery
of the circle, together with four intermediates.   The gray of the same
brilliance lies at the center of the circle.   Saturation is measured outwardly
along any radius, while hue follows the circumferential dimension.

respect to the single gray component as a reference point.
In other words, as expressed for any chroma in terms of
number of just noticeable difference steps from the gray,
it is a measure of the degree of difference of the chroma
in question from an achromatic color of the same brilliance.
However, it is evident, from the fact that there are a large
number of radial systems in the plane, that there must be

a second dimension which is always perpendicular to any given radius, or which, in other words, has a tangential or cyclic direction. This second chromatic dimension or attribute is of course that of *hue*. Hue, thus defined, will naturally be measured in terms of the number of just noticeable differences from some standard point or radius, along a circle having the gray point as a centre. Such a circle will be defined as a series of colors, varying in hue, but having equal saturations as well as brilliances. This means that they are separated by equal numbers of liminal steps from black and also from the gray of the same brilliance.

132. The Psychological Color Solid.—When we consider chromatic surfaces or planes of different brilliances, it becomes evident that these must be arranged, so to speak, into a pile, so as to form a solid figure, the axis of this figure consisting of the entire system of *achromatic* colors. In this way, we inevitably arrive at a construction which includes all possible colors, whether chromatic or achromatic, and the total system must possess three dimensions, corresponding respectively to the three attributes known as brilliance, hue and saturation. The simplest external form to assign to this system is that of a cylinder, the axis of which comprises the grays, while various radial planes contain individual hues, having saturations that vary with the distance of any point or line in such a plane from a perpendicular to the axis. (See Fig. 8.)

However, it should be noted at once that the question as to whether the psychological color solid is a cylinder, or some other figure, is one which rests upon psychophysiological evidence and has nothing to do with the definition of the color system in itself. Indeed, the latter consists simply in a kind of conceptual space, having no definite boundaries, although possessing an arbitrarily established reference system, or set of axes. This space of the color system does not necessarily have the same mathematical properties as does geometrical or physical space. In other words, it may not be Euclidean. As an illustration of this possibility, it may be noted that there is no particular reason why the ratio between the saturation of a cycle of equally saturated chromas and the number of just noticeable hue steps in such a cycle should be equal to 2π, the corresponding ratio of the radius of a geometrical circle to its circumference. The conceptual color space may perhaps be compared to some of the non-Euclidean spaces of modern physical theory.

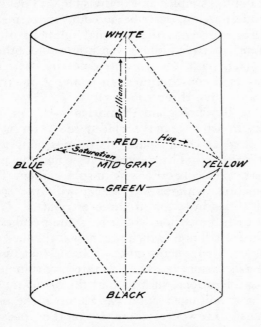

FIG. 8.   THE PSYCHOLOGICAL COLOR SOLID.

The essential purpose of this diagram is to reveal the three-dimensions of psychological color space. For this purpose, the color solid is represented as a cylinder, although the alternative form of a double cone (indicated by the dotted lines) may perhaps be preferable. See the text for complete explanation.

It is evident that the identity of any color can be specified completely in terms of its position in the color space. This position is represented, in fact, by the measures of the three color-attributes for the individual color in question. These measures correspond to the three coördinates, X, Y and Z, of a point in three-dimensional physical space, as the latter is treated in analytical geometry. It is very doubtful whether, ultimately, the three attributes of color can be given any other meaning than that which is embodied in the structure of the color space. It is wholly evident that no color possesses in itself a triplex constitution, each color being absolutely simple and indivisible. The complexity which compels us to describe a color in terms of three variables lies entirely in the external relations of similarity and difference between the given color and other similar qualities. (*Cf.* page 121.) Any color by itself is thus no more complex in constitution than is any geometrical point, although both have three coördinates.

133. The Psychological Primaries.—It is an interesting question as to why we have placed the reference axes of our psychological color space in the positions which they ordinarily occupy. Theoretically it would be possible to rotate these axes, or otherwise displace them from their present position, without interfering with the specification of color qualities in terms of three attributes. Under such conditions each dimension would be some peculiar resultant of the three attributes which we now call hue, saturation and brilliance.[218] It seems quite probable that our positioning of the axis system has been dictated by common psychophysical considerations, such as that the *brilliance* of a color is especially conditioned upon variations in the *intensity* of the stimulus. However, there is another possible view, which is that certain points in the color space possess unique relationships of similarity or difference with respect to their neighbors, so that they can be singled out, by a purely introspective test, as natural reference points.

A demonstration of the possibility of such a psychological origin for reference points in the color system is found in the almost universal admission that red, yellow, green and blue are *unique hues,* in terms of which all other hues can be described, but which are themselves indescribable in terms of other hues. Black and white also seem to possess this same sort of uniqueness. Any gray can be described as a blackish white, while orange is specified quite intelligibly as a reddish yellow, but no one would know what was meant by a "reddish green" or a "yellowish blue," unless he had studied the psychophysiological relationships of colors and stimuli.   There has been a great deal of debate concerning the validity [219] of these so-called psychological primaries, black, white, yellow, red, green and blue, but very little has been accomplished by way of elucidating their significance. To the present writer, it seems that a wholly introspective justification of their selection can be established if we admit the possibility of comparing and discriminating, not only the colors themselves, but also *differences* between separate pairs of colors.   Thinking in this way, we can recognize that the difference between red and orange is the same, qualitatively, as that between orange and yellow, while the latter difference is itself different from the difference between yellow and yellow-green.   Thus, the psychological primaries would be defined as colors which lie at points of *sudden transition in the mode of variation* from one point of the color space to another.   These ideas involve us in a sort of calculus of qualitative differentials or derivatives, analogous to the quantitative concepts with which mathematicians are already familiar.

134. Boundaries of the Color Solid.—As above indicated, we can only ascertain the boundaries of the psychological color solid by experimental studies, directed towards determining what is the widest variety of colors that can actually exist.   A consideration of such experiments forms a natural part of the psychophysiological portion of our discussion, but a few words are required in anticipation in order to set aside some extant misconceptions.   In the first place, it should be noted that the representation of the color solid as a double pyramid or other *four-sided figure,* on the basis of the uniqueness attached to the psychologically primary hues, is incorrect both logically and experimentally. Such a representation, as given by Titchener [220] and others, implies a necessary relationship between psychological primacy and saturation, whereas in fact no such relationship can exist, because the concepts of hue and saturation are so defined as to be independent of each other. Psychological primacy can be represented in the color solid only by means of lines or points laid down within it in certain positions. It has nothing to do with the boundaries of the solid. Another important misconception identifies the equator of the figure with the spectral colors, and regards the latter as being of equal saturation. As a matter of fact, it is easy to produce colors which are much more saturated than the normal spectral colors, and the latter are very far from being of equal saturation, although the *purity* of the physical stimuli is perfect. But the most important point in the present discussion lies in the fact that the spectral colors must depend, for their location within the color space, upon detailed psychophysiological measurements.

135. Other Color Attributes.—Hue, saturation and brilliance do not exhaust all possible attributes of colors, since it is possible for them to vary in dimensions distinct from any of these three. Any psychical element is said by Titchener [221] to possess the attributes of intensity and duration, and possibly extensity. It is possible that we should not identify intensity with brilliance, in the case of color, but rather with the difference between vision, of any kind, and complete blindness. Black differs as much as does white from the absence of all visual consciousness. In normal visual experience, difference in intensity is perhaps observable between the center and the periphery of the visual field, while "vision behind the head" is of zero intensity.

Other color attributes which are of importance in perceptual studies include the so-called "modes of appearance," or *Erscheinungsweisen.*[222] Thus, colors may appear as "body," "surface," or "film." They may also be lustrous or non-lustrous. We shall consider these "modes," with their psychophysical relations, in the next Section.

Section 32 (B)

COMPONENT VISUAL PERCEPTIONS; PSYCHO-
PHYSICAL RELATIONSHIPS

136. Statement of the Problem.—We may now consider the objective stage of the visual response process. In endeavoring to pick out the significant components of this stage, we should begin with the subdivison of the latter which is most remote from the eye. We have already seen that the domain of the objective phase can be pushed backwards in varying degrees, according to the particular case, but it may be considered as beginning ordinarily, in vision, at the so-called luminous source. Now the non-patterned characteristics of such sources which are relevant to visual response should be reduced to: (1) physical "candle power," and (2) physical "color," or the distribution of radiant intensity with respect to frequency (or wave-length).

Unfortunately, the terms which are commonly employed in describing such sources are not strictly physical in their significance. Even the words, "light" and "luminous," have psychophysical meanings, so that all *photometric conceptions,* such as that of "candle power," fail to express the facts in purely physical terms.[223] Strictly speaking, the source consists simply in a vast number of electrons, protons, and aggregates thereof, which are vibrating at various rates and amplitudes, thus sending off a complex mixture of electro-magnetic waves. The common notion of "color" also needs to be modified to give it a strictly physical significance.

Now, in dealing with such concepts as those of photometry, the psychophysiologist may substitute their purely physical analogues; but this is not absolutely necessary to a clear analysis. Since photometric conceptions involve the degree of response of the psychophysiological system (see Volume II), they may be regarded as containing both ϕ and ψ. Consequently, if we correlate experiential factors, represented in terms of pure ψ, with them, we shall have a function of the form: $\psi = f(\phi, \psi)$. But this is just as much a psychophysical function, as if we had segregated all of the ψ terms on one side of the equation. Moreover, if we know the form of the function, $f(\phi, \psi)$, we shall be able to reduce it to an equation of the definitely separated type. It happens that the form of the photometric function is quite clearly defined.

Now, the problem which is before us is that of ascertaining the functions which link the logically simple properties of the light source with aspects of experience. In order to do this, we must vary these properties, preferably in a continuous manner, and note the corresponding variations in experience. All other factors in the response process must be kept constant, except insofar as they naturally vary as functions of the given attributes of the source. Of course, instead of introducing actual changes into a single source, we may replace one source by another one which differs from it in a known manner, since the actual physical identity of the source is of no importance. Such a program of experimentation could be started in complete ignorance of what portions of experience should be classed as *visual,* or as related to the eyes. By observing the concomitant changes in experience we should be able to identify some of the visual features.

137. The Psychophysics of the Light Source.—Now, in considering the relations of the source to experience, we may profitably combine the properties of the former with those of the stage of the response propagation which is intermediate between the source and the object. This consists in the passage of the radiant energy from the source to the object surfaces. The properties of the source, in combination with those of the intermediate space, determine the concept of the *illumination* of the object, although, strictly speaking, the illumination can be defined wholly in terms of conditions in space just prior to the object surface. In accordance with the well-known law, the illumination is proportional to the candle power of the source and inversely proportional to the square of its distance from the object surface. It also depends upon the angle of incidence of the rays upon the surface in question.

Now the most fundamental characteristic of the source, as such, is probably to be found in the vibration rates, or frequencies, of its constituent electrons or other radiation-emitting particles. In the commonest cases, there will be a multitude of such frequencies, interminging with each other. The emitted radiant energy will have a corresponding complexity of wave-length composition. "White light," which constitutes the normal condition of illumination, involves a very thoroughgoing mixture of different frequencies. The most interesting variations in the characteristics of the illuminant consist in (1) changes in candle power or "foot-candles" of "white light," from zero to some high value, and (2) deviations in frequency composition from white to various representative pure frequencies (or "monochromatic" radiations, *cf*. Volume II) as limits. The corresponding forms of consciousness are to be noted.

It is clear that these experiential concomitants will depend upon the values of constant conditions in other portions of the response arc. Thus, the state of adaptation of the retina and certain adjustments in the cerebral cortex will have an important bearing. In studying the perceptual relationships of the light source, we may wish either to specify these further response conditions in particular, arbitrary, ways or to permit them to reach values which are in normal equilibrium with the given values of the illumination. Again, we may accept the conditions of everyday perception or we may consider the more artificial circumstances of scientific observation in the laboratory.

138. The Psychophysics of Illumination.—Now, under ordinary conditions, the approximate intensity and frequency composition of the illumination have a representation in experience which is introspectively separable, as to brilliance and chroma, from the color characteristics of the illuminated surface. Thus, as was pointed out by Hering,[224] we commonly distinguish between bright and dark (*Dunkel-Hell*), as characteristics of the illumination, and white and black

(*Weiss-Schwarz*), as corresponding features of phenomenal things. In the ordinary perceptual consciousness, there is supposed to be an "abstraction of the illumination" factor from the related properties of the represented object surfaces. This hypothetical process of abstraction, with its corollaries, has been designated as "transformation," by E. R. Jaensch [225] and his co-workers, because they feel that experience should primarily represent the intensities of the retinal image areas, rather than those of component features of the environmental situation.

K. Buehler [226] has endeavored to establish an objective basis for this perception of the illumination, in the scattering of light by particles suspended in the air. He believes that this atmospheric haze furnishes a reliable cue to the intensity and frequency composition of the illumination, thus providing a basis for an experience of visual space, not merely as a volume, but as possessing a definite brilliance and chroma. However, the experiments of Katz [227] appear to disprove this doctrine, by showing that the impression of illumination intensity and chroma is not affected by changes in this haze factor. The actually operative condition for the separation of the illumination in consciousness seems to lie in the presence of a complete field of objects, showing spatial continuity and differentiation of the sort which characterizes common mundane environments.

The separate representation of illumination in experience is particularly manifest in the case of *shadows,* or other local variations in illumination. From the phenomenological standpoint, a shadow differs radically from the representation of a reflection surface which gives off an objectively equal intensity of light. It appears as *a local variation in the illumination.* However, when the pattern of the visual field is obscured in artificial ways, as by the use of diaphragms, shadows and corresponding reflection values may yield identical results in consciousness. The recognition of shadows, as such, depends upon their relationships to object surfaces which they intersect, their ordinarily blurred or graduated edges, the known position of the light source, etc.

At a later point we shall consider the principle of *illumination perspective* [228] and other aspects of shadows which involve compositional features.

It is to be noted, however, that, over a wide range of intensity and deviation in frequency composition from "white," there is relatively little correlation between the illumination and the experiential quality of object surfaces. This is Hering's principle [229] of the "approximate color constancy of visual things." However, at very high and very low intensities, the gradations of achromatic and chromatic contrast among things are reduced in range. At extremely low illuminations, such as moonlight, chromatic differences disappear entirely, especially when the response is allowed to get into equilibrium with these conditions. When the illumination is zero, the entire structure of visual space is radically affected. The dimension of depth shows severe shrinkage, and, although patterns may appear in the visual field, they have no correlation with the structure of the object field before the eye. [230] Variations in frequency composition which depart so far from "white" as to approach the "monochromatic" condition also seriously reduce chromatic contrast between phenomenal things, and alter their chromatic values in correspondence with the given illumination change. It therefore appears that, under everyday conditions, the general as well as the specific structure of presentations in visual space must rest upon a finite intensity of illumination; but that, over a wide range of medium intensities, and of frequency constitutions not departing radically from "white," these phenomena are nearly independent of the illumination and its representation.

139. Seven "Modes" of Color "Appearance."—Now, conditions can readily be found under which this separate representation of the illumination, in experience, disappears. They are realized, for example, in the laboratory when we look into the slit of a spectrometer, or when we look through a hole in a dark wall at a uniformly illuminated surface of any kind. Under such conditions, the color area in consciousness takes on the aspect which is known as *film,* appearing not as the surface or volume of a visual thing, but as an isolated phenomenon. Under these circumstances, the intensity and frequency characteristics of the illumination combine with those of the remainder of the optical system, so that a variation in the illumination has the same effect as a corresponding change in the reflection characteristics of object surfaces, or other factors which may influence the nature of the rays that enter the eye. These are the conditions under which we usually study the functional relationships between color and the attributes of radiant energy, in the psychological laboratory, and are involved in the establishment of so-called *sensory* functions.

In some cases, as when we gaze at a luminous source, the rays proceed directly to the eyes, without reflection and possibly without refraction, so that no object other than the source is concerned in the response propagation. Under everyday conditions, the visual presentations of light sources manifest the peculiar "modes of appearance" known as *luminosity* and *glow.* The former is associated with opaque sources, such as ordinary gas flames or electric filaments; the latter with transparent sources, like that of the blue-flame gas burner. Glowing solid metal, particularly at red heat, also evokes the impression of a source of light having visual volume. Luminosity is characteristic of the visual representation of a surface source, while glow characterizes a source which visibly emits light throughout a volume or three-dimensional region.

Sometimes the rays pass to the eyes through a transparent medium, such as glass, which absorbs a certain proportion of them and introduces changes in direction by the process of refraction. A certain amount of regular reflection may also be involved. Under these circumstances, a number of peculiar phenomenal aspects are noted in consciousness. If the transparent medium shows practically no selective absorption, as in the case of white glass, there is a representation in consciousness of transparently filled volume, which Schumann [231] calls the "glass sensation." According

to Schumann, this "sensation" shows gradations in an attribute or dimension designated as "compactness." It can
be generated in very compact form by favorable stereoscopic
stimuli, and in its least compact form it is said to constitute
our perception of ordinary unfilled visual space. When the
transparent body shows selective absorption chromatic colors
appear, which fill its volume. This mode of appearance of
color is characterized by Martin [232] as *bulky,* corresponding
to the *Raumfarben* of Katz' [233] classification. A third condition is found in the case of thin colored transparent sheets,
such as gelatine filters, which yield a further "mode" in
consciousness: the *plane transparent color,* which hangs in
visual space in front of other color surfaces, but without
obscuring them.

A phenomenon which is closely related to that of the
plane transparent color appears in the case of *mirrored
colors.* The objective condition for these lies in regular
reflection from the polished surface of a body which has
some selective absorption of its own, for example, gold or
copper. Here, our experience ordinarily represents the
color of the body, with that of the reflected objects superimposed upon it. The famous Ragona Scina experiment,
as described by Helmholtz,[234] provides an objective condition, involving reflection with superimposed transmission,
in which the experience is ordinarily that of one color surface
seen through another. Regular reflection also yields the
appearance of the surfaces of things known as *luster,* which
has numerous forms: metallic, graphitic, etc. This is attributable to the presence on, or in line with, the object surface, of optical images of other objects. The most intense
luster is dependent upon binocular relations of the reflected
rays, which we shall consider in greater detail below.

The seven different modes of appearance of colors which
we have considered above, are strictly phenomenal or experiential attributes, not reducible to physical terms, and
demonstrable only by introspection. However, as we have
seen, the conditions for their presence in consciousness can
be specified objectively, if we assume the response system

to be normal in its other stages. The detailed psycho-physiology of these *Erscheinungsweisen der Farben* can be found in the books by Katz and by Buehler, under this title, and in the article by Martin.

140. Properties of Opaque Surface Colors.—However, the commonest "mode" still remains to be considered. This is the *opaque surface* character, which is a feature of the vast majority of visual things, and is determined, psycho-physically, by reflecting objects having matt, or highly dif-fusing surfaces. Such opaque visual surfaces carry most of the typical color phenomena of everyday experience, and hence are worthy of particular attention. From the most analytical physical standpoint, the so-called reflecting surface really re-radiates the electromagnetic waves, but for prac-tical purposes we consider it as merely changing their direc-tions with a certain amount of accompanying absorption. Each element of the surface thus has (1) a reflection co-efficient, and (2) a diffusion characteristic. These may be different for each separate electromagnetic frequency. The reflection coefficient shows what fraction of the incident energy of the given frequency is reflected, while the diffusion characteristic determines the distribution of the energy through various angles with the surface and the incident beam.

Now, we find that if the reflection coefficients are prac-tically the same for all frequencies, the color of the cor-responding thing or phenomenal surface is achromatic, under ordinary conditions of illumination. Between reflec-tion coefficient values of approximately 0.005 (black velvet) and 0.90 (magnesium carbonate), the color of the phe-nomenal surface will exhibit potentially continuous gradations between black and white, passing through a series of grays of ascending brilliance. If we arrange a series of reflection grays such that each member is just noticeably different in brilliance from its neighbor, we find that the number of pos-sible gradations, and their interrelationships, are nearly independent of the intensity of the illumination, over a wide range of medium values. As was recognized by Fechner,[235] this fact implies a logarithmic relationship between the subjective gray scale and the corresponding radiant intensities, since the fixed reflection coefficients merely establish a constant proportionality among themselves. Accordingly, Fechner's law in vision, insofar as it is valid at all, may be regarded as an arrangement for the identification of reflection relationships, independently of the absolute illumination level. The subjectively determined scale of reflection coefficients is also practically independent of the frequency composition of the illumination over a wide range of variation. Under extreme conditions of illumination, the just noticeable difference between reflection coefficients is subject to increase, for reasons which will be considered in our discussion of the laws of visual sensation. Ordinarily, a one per cent decrease is just appreciable, yielding a logarithmic series in correlation with the subjective scale of grays.

141. Pigment Colors, and Systems Thereof.—If the reflection coefficients are not the same for different frequencies, the phenomenal surfaces will take on a chromatic aspect. Assuming the illustration to be effectively achromatic, the hue will depend upon the exact selection of frequencies which is involved in the unbalancing of the coefficients. The greater the unbalancing, in general, the more saturated the chroma will be. The hue will be approximately complementary to that corresponding to the frequency which is maximally absorbed. A more accurate statement is that the hue will be that for the frequency which corresponds to the position of the centroid (center of gravity) of the curve showing the photometric brightness of the surface as a function of frequency.[236] Substances which possess selective absorption may be designated technically as *pigments,* although this term is also frequently used for non-selective absorbers. Assuming conditions of normal vision, with recognized illumination, opaque surface colors can be specified satisfactorily in terms of particular pigments or their mixtures. As previously noted, when the character of the illumination is independently represented in experience, the empirical color quality will be substantially constant in its relationship to the given pigment or pigment combination.

A number of very systematic attempts have been made to construct actual pigment schemes which shall be representative of all possible "subtractive colors." The best known of these are by Munsell,[237] Ridgway,[238] and Ostwald,[239] respectively. Each of these systems is three-dimensional, exhibiting variations in brilliance, as well as in hue and saturation. The Munsell system is based upon ten hues and five degrees of "value," or light reflecting power, each of the hues being shown at every level of reflectivity in a considerable number of saturation steps. The Ridgway scheme employs thirty-six hues, which are spaced about equally in terms of just noticeable hue difference. Each of these hues is diluted with "white" in three degrees, and also with "black" in three degrees, making a total of 1115 colors. The Ostwald system, as presented in a Color Atlas, comprises 2500 colors, which are arranged in accordance with their "color tone" (hue) and content of "black" or "white," respectively.[240]

It should be noted that, although the majority of psychophysical discussions of color are expressed in terms of the properties of the electromagnetic waves, the writers are usually concerned also with opaque surface colors in relation to pigments. The laws which govern relationships of the latter type are really separable from those for the *film colors* which are determined in the usual type of spectrometric experiment. It is questionable whether we should use the terms, briliance, hue, and saturation, indiscriminately to apply to these two situations, unless the context makes it quite clear which one is involved in the given instance.

142. The "Subtractive" Mixture of Pigment Colors.— The laws of color-mixture in terms of *primary pigments* are different, in their most useful manner of formulation, from those for primary "lights," or radiation frequencies. In practice, pigment mixture is probably more important than that of lights. Experiment shows that all possible hues can be matched by properly proportioned mixtures of three

primary pigments.   These may be chosen in a variety of
different ways.   The commonest choice among artists is red,
yellow and blue, green being produced by the mixture of
the last two; but the best selection seems to be: a yellow
(minus blue), a purple (minus green) and a blue-green
(minus red).   If these pigments are mixed in equivalent
proportions—which depend upon their exact spectral absorption curves—they yield black or various grays, and their
complete absence would correspond to white.   However, in
practice, it is necessary to employ a "white" background,
upon which the elementary pigments can be superposed in
various absolute amounts and proportions.   In ordinary
painting, where the background (e.g., the canvas) is wholly
obscured, a "white" pigment must be admixed with the
colors to produce the same results.   The chromatic pigments may also be mixed with "black" to yield various
reductions of brilliance in the given hue.

Such mixtures with "black" and "white" "pigments" involve a decrease in saturation, as well as changes in brilliance.
Maximally saturated pigment colors have a fixed brilliance
or gray value, and lighter ones are necessarily less saturated.
The reason for this is found in the so-called *subtractive
principle* which governs the action of all pigment chromas.
The chromatic effect is due to the subtraction of particular
components from the radiation which characterizes the given
illuminant.   Thus, in dealing with the action and mixture
of pigments, we take uniform spectral reflection or transmission as a standard reference condition, and increase the
absorption for particular frequencies.   In the special case of
mixtures of primary pigments, these frequencies are determined by the nature and proportions of the pigments in
question.   Since white corresponds to maximal uniform
reflection, all pigment chromas are necessarily darker than
white, the darkness increasing with saturation up to a definite
limiting value, which depends upon the particular hue which
is involved.   When two or more pigments are mixed, the
resulting color is determined by the *residue* of spectral rays
which are not absorbed by any of the pigment components.

Ostwald's system is especially interesting in this connection, because it attempts to formulate the properties of colors in terms of pigment conditions.

These same subtractive principles also apply to chromas which depend upon selective *transmission* rather than selective reflection, provided that the illumination is constant, and that the transmissive pigments (such as dyes) are placed one behind the other, or are intermingled. However, quite frequently, the illumination conditions for such transmissively produced colors are different from those for adjacent reflection, or opaque surface, colors. This is usually true, for example, in the case of a stained-glass window, viewed from the interior of a building. Under such conditions, the transmissively produced chroma may show extraordinary brilliancy and saturation.

Reflection chromas have certain qualitative characteristics which cannot be duplicated outside of a perceptual situation that involves a defined illumination and opaque surface colors (either naturally or artificially produced). Blacks and very dark grays, together with browns, olives, dark blues and purples, fall in this category. They all seem to be capable of description in terms of various degrees of blackness, combined either with median gray or with specific chromatic components. Film colors, as they are ordinarily studied in the psychological laboratory, against a visual field which is otherwise completely dark, are never brownish or very "dark." A brown can be synthesized by the use of spectroscopic apparatus, in place of reflecting pigments, but only by presenting the spectral light in a contrast environment similar to that which is normal for reflection browns, in other words, so that it yields an illusory opaque surface color.

143. Visual Projection and Binocular Effects.—We may now leave the object stage of the objective phase of the response, and pass on to consider stages which intervene between the object surface, or mass, and the eyes. Here, we have to deal with the nature of radiant energy and the laws which govern its propagation through space, or the atmosphere. Although the visual consciousness presents things at a distance in empirical space, without any representation of the connecting means, we know that the perceptual relationship of the visual things to the physical objects is made possible only by the radiation link between the object surfaces and the eyes. The most direct manifestation of this fact in immediate experience is given in the principle of visual obscuration or *eclipse*. An opaque surface color along any empirical line of view excludes all other colors along this line. When one color can be seen "through another," it can be shown that the second color corresponds to an object which transmits rays without appreciable diffusion or diffraction. We are so accustomed to this phenomenon of eclipse that we take it as a matter of course, but the principle which it involves is a special characteristic of visual space, not shared by the physical space within which the response process occurs. However, this property of visual space is strikingly similar to those of the process of *optical projection,* within physical space, and is evidently explained psychophysiologically by the application of the principles of such projection to the visual response propagation.

Now, when we consider this application of the principles in question, we immediately encounter the fact that there are two separate points, or areas, upon which the projection has to be made, in the ordinary case. These are the entrance pupils of the two eyes, respectively. A consideration of the separate relationships between objects—or, more particularly, rays—and the two eyes introduces us to the problems of *binocular vision.* The majority of these problems have to do with the *composition* of visual experience, rather than with its elemental components, and hence their treatment must be postponed to a subsequent chapter. It might be possible to regard the *position* of any single point in visual space as an elemental fact, or to treat the three independent dimensions of this position in this manner. However, on account of the relativity of the dimensions in question, it seems best to consider them in relation to the complex patterns which they help to determine.

Nevertheless, there are a few aspects of binocular vision which can properly be treated as elemental from the standpoint of experience. The phenomenon of *binocular luster* may be considered as an example. This is determined by a process of projection of a given object pattern upon the two eye-points, such as to yield substantially the same contour for each eye, but discrepant distributions of intensity. The commonest cause of this condition, of course, lies in the regularly reflecting properties of polished or semi-polished surfaces. In general, these will not send the same quantities of radiation in any two different directions, since the intensity of the reflected ray is a function of the angle with the surface. Consequently, the two eye-points will usually receive different intensities. It is obvious that similar stimulus conditions can be produced by means of a stereoscopic set-up which shows patterns to the respective eyes that are geometrically similar, but discrepant as to reflection coefficients at corresponding points. The luster phenomenon is apparently an elementary attribute of visual experience, in spite of the complexity of its physiological or physical conditions.

144. Atmospheric Fog.—Another perceptual aspect of the particular phase of the objective stage which we are now considering, is that of the perception of fog, haze, or atmosphere. This is, of course, attributable to rays which are scattered by reflecting or diffracting particles in the air between the object surface and the eyes.[241] The effect is to interpose a luminous, and possibly a chromatic, screen between the visual things and the empirical viewpoint. When the amount of light is abnormally great, it is represented as a fog or a smoke but, in normal intensity, merely provides a partial foundation for impressions of distance. It has the effect of reducing the number of just-perceptible gradations of reflection coefficients, especially in the region of the lower or darker values. This effect can be explained (from the standpoint of sensation), in terms of Fechner's logarithmic law, since the haze makes an arithmetically constant addition of light to all of the reflection values. Haze belongs in the category of "transparent bulky colors," although varying in transparency and sometimes taking on the aspect of glow.

Now, the outstanding aspects of the rays which pass from the object surfaces to the eyes are *intensity* and *frequency* (*or wave-length*) *composition;* and it would be legitimate to study the relationships of these factors to visual experience under the category of component perception. As a matter of fact, practically all experimental studies of these relationships fall naturally, on account of their objective methods, under this heading. However, we are convinced that substantially the same kind of relationships can be established with the properties of the radiant energies *after they have entered the visual sense-organ,* and even up to the point where they penetrate the receptor cells. Consequently, following the principle which we have previously adopted, we shall postpone the discussion of such psychophysiological functions to the chapter dealing with visual sensation (Volume II). This plan is supported by the fact that in everyday perceptual situations the relationships between color attributes and those of radiant energy, considered by itself, are seldom independently involved. These relationships are ordinarily isolated only in the laboratory, with experimental arrangements such as to evoke the *film* mode of color in consciousness.

Section 33 (A)

COMPONENT AUDITORY PERCEPTION; AUDITORY
QUALITIES AND THEIR ATTRIBUTES

145. The Classification of Auditory Elements.—
Auditory experience may be defined or identified, by psychophysiological means, as consisting of those experiential as-

pects which exhibit a reliable correlation with the action of sound waves upon the ears. If both ears are entirely shielded from acoustic influence, auditory experience will normally be at a minimum, and when sound waves are aurally operative, the variations in such experience are closely determined by the character of the waves in question. Similar forms of experience, based upon *spontaneous* sense-organ activities or brain excitations may, of course, be observed, as in the case of vision.

If we study the aspects of experience which are thus delimited, a purely introspective analysis yields the following general results. Auditory experiences are normally complex, both coexistentially and in time; although the temporal aspect of auditory forms of combination is the more important, just as the spatial aspect predominates in vision. The proximate constituents of such experiences show a wide variety of qualities, which are rather difficult to classify, although some of them exhibit definite systematic similarities. The most outstanding subdivision is apparently that between *tones* and *noises*. The former furnish the fundamental materials for musical composition, whereas the latter are primarily non-musical. Intermediate between the purest tones and the purest noises, we find a great many qualitatively different auditory constituents, most prominent among which are so-called *vocables*. The latter are characteristic of the auditory representation of language. Among the vocables, the *vowels* are predominantly tonal, whereas the *consonants* are predominantly noisy. The majority of concrete musical tones, also, are *somewhat* noisy, and practically all noises have some tonal quality. The distinctions between these several classes of auditory qualities can only be appreciated by concrete exhibition in experience, although we may identify them by means of their psychophysical correlations, thus providing the information needed for staging an actual demonstration.

The components of auditory experience characteristically show varying degrees of *fusion,* so that a thoroughgoing description in terms of elements is seldom possible. Insofar as fusion actually exists, it is evidently illegitimate to report upon the experience in terms which are one hundred per cent analytical. (*Cf.* pages 132–137.) However, as a rule, the "fusions" are not complete, the elements still being salient to some degree. Recognizing these facts, we may say that tones and noises are fundamental auditory elements, while vocables, clangs and other intermediates correspond to highly fused combinations of such elements, according to a wide variety of formulae. Observers differ greatly in their ability to analyze auditory experiences which have complex stimulus conditions.

146. The Attributes of Tones.—Tones [242] may be considered first, because they lend themselves to the construction of a continuous system much more readily than do vocables and noises. However, the tonal system appears to reveal properties which are characteristic, also, to some degree, of the other classes of auditory constituents. Musical scales involve the arrangement of tones in order of their attribute of *pitch*. This arrangement permits of a continuous series of tones, each just noticeably different from its neighbor, ranging from the lowest bass to the highest treble. In an independent dimension, perpendicularly to the pitch line, each tone can show many gradations of *loudness,* or of subjective intensity.

Under ordinary conditions, tones manifest two other introspectively discriminable attributes, which, however, are rather more difficult to identify and to define. These are known as *brightness* and *volume,* respectively, and they both show a very close correlation with pitch. Brightness (or shrillness) is contrasted with dullness or mellowness, and stands for a certain saliency of the tones, against the general auditory background. In the tonal system, it increases constantly as the pitch is raised, so that it can conveniently be combined with the latter to form a single dimension, known as pitch-brightness.[243] In other relationships, as in the comparison of tones with vowels, brightness varies independently of pitch. The attribute of volume should not be confused with that of loudness. It stands for an auditory extensity or expansiveness of the tone, which is large for low pitches and decreases progressively as the pitch increases. Although this extensity can hardly be translated into terms of visual space properties, it seems satisfactory to regard it as signifying the amount of *purely auditory space* which the tone occupies. The separation of volume from pitch in the tonal manifold is justified by the fact that, in terms of just-noticeable differences, it varies more slowly than the latter. It

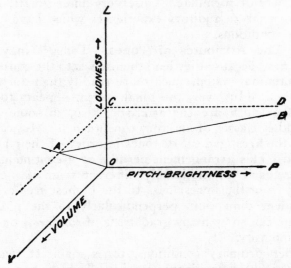

FIG. 9. COÖRDINATES OF THE TONAL MANIFOLD.

The diagram shows a set of three-dimensional Cartesian axes, for pitch-brightness, loudness and volume, respectively. Owing to the fact that volume varies as a function of pitch-brightness and of loudness, only a restricted number of points in this three-dimensional system represent possible tones. They are clustered around some such plane as *POAB*.

also varies independently of pitch in systems involving other auditory qualities.

Thus, it appears that we can represent the manifold of all pure tones by means of a three-dimensional figure, a solid, having the dimensions of pitch-brightness, loudness, and volume, respectively. (See Fig. 9.)

If we compare pitches amongst themselves, we find that

they manifest periodic similarities and differences, along the pitch line. Pitches which are separated by the musical interval known as an octave, or by multiples of this interval, are said to be similar in octave quality. *Octave quality* may be compared with the psychological primacy of the hues, red, yellow, green, and blue in the color solid. Like the psychological primaries, it cannot be represented conveniently by a special dimension in the tonal manifold, but can be designated by means of a scale marked off on the pitch line. Another method is to consider the pitch line as describing a helix in a fourth dimension, so that the coils return to the same value of this dimension, measured in angular units, once every octave. Certain physiological considerations, to be presented later, suggest that the phenomenon of octave similarity is due to a latent complexity of constitution in the tones which exhibit it. Tones are also sometimes said to possess *vocalic quality,* which is defined by their degree of resemblance to particular vowels. However, it would appear that a more fitting way of formulating this resemblance would be to say that the vowels possess tonal or pitch quality, and to reserve the term, *vocality,* for the over-all quality of vowels, as such.

147. The Properties of Noises.—*Noises* are difficult to arrange into a continuous or quantitative system, except in the dimension of loudness. According to Titchener,[244] noises can be divided into two temporally distinguished classes, the explosive and the continuative. The former are exemplified by "crack," "pop," and "snap," and the latter by "hiss," "sputter," and "rumble." However, when carefully studied, noises show a possibility of arrangement in pitch order, as well as in terms of loudness. They also manifest variations in brightness and volume. Their own peculiar qualitative features have, thus far, eluded quantitative systematization from the purely introspective standpoint.

Pure tones are practically never realized even under conditions of laboratory experiments, and the combinations of tones and of noises which actually occur have characteristic qualities of their own. One of the most outstanding of these is *timbre* or "tone-color," which may be viewed as representing the combination of a number of systematically related tones; a given tone with its so-called over-tones. Differences in timbre are demonstrated in the divergences in quality between two different musical instruments, such as the cornet and piano, at the same fundamental pitch. In practice, the majority of musical instruments also involve characteristic noise components, such as that accompanying the scrape of the bow in the case of the violin. Vocality, or vowel quality, is another example of this sort of over-all qualitative distinctiveness of auditory combinations.

Other qualitative aspects of auditory experience will be discussed in connection with the psychophysiological treatment. In general, writers upon auditory psychology have found it necessary to refer to the physiological or physical conditions for the various aspects of auditory experience, in order to make themselves clear. This is not due to any real implication of these conditions in the definition of the subjective aspects, but it indicates the unsettled state of the psychological analysis and terminology. It also suggests that the established facts concerning audition are mainly psychophysiological rather than purely introspective in their foundations.

Section 33 (B)

COMPONENT AUDITORY PERCEPTION; PSYCHO-PHYSIOLOGICAL RELATIONS

148. The Physical Nature of Sound.—The objective phase of auditory response can be considered as beginning, ordinarily, with the sonorous body: the human vocal organs, a piano string, a tuning fork, or, perhaps, a radio loud-speaker. However, in the case of the latter, as we have previously suggested, it would be fitting to regard the stage as being extended back from the loud-speaker along the very complex line of propagation to the originally resounding bodies in the broadcasting studio. Similar considerations also apply to ordinary telephonic intercommunication. The disturbances which are noticed in the majority of telephonic circuits introduce some very interesting problems in auditory perception, particularly from the standpoint of the users of misbehaving equipment of this sort. However, if we start with a simple vibrating body, such as a piano string, we find that its acoustic properties can be specified in terms of *intensity* and *frequency*.

The vibrations, in this case, are, of course, mechanical rather than electromagnetic (as in vision), but the mathematical properties of the two forms of oscillation are very

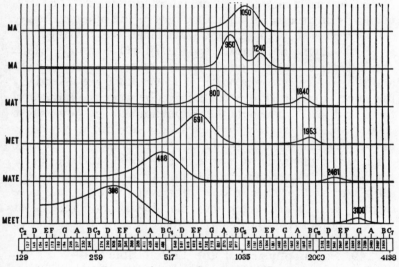

FIG. 10. ACOUSTIC DISTRIBUTION CURVES.

These curves, taken from *The Science of Musical Sounds* by Dayton C. Miller (Macmillan, 1916), show the manner in which acoustic energy varies as a function of frequency for various vowel sounds.

similar. Ordinarily, the sonorous body vibrates in a complex manner, which is, nevertheless, periodic and can be resolved into a series of pure harmonic forms. Such an analysis [245] enables us to plot a *distribution curve* showing the intensities of the various component frequencies, just as in the case of a complex form of radiant energy. (See

Fig. 10.) These vibrations, say in the case of a tuning fork, set up corresponding vibrations in the air, or other medium, and generate waves which are propagated to the external ears. Such a propagated disturbance is called *sound,* a term which, in scientific usage, has a purely physical meaning. The lengths of the sound waves depend, of course, upon the velocity of propagation as well as upon the frequency. The velocity is about eleven hundred feet per second in air and about four thousand feet per second in water. The value of the wave-length is of direct importance in connection with certain binaural relationships, but can be replaced by frequency for all monaural problems. The frequency is invariable through all stages of the objective phase of the response, although the wave-length may change.

Now, there are certain aspects of relationships which obtain between the various attributes of auditory experience and the frequency composition of sound, that are essentially the same in general form at all points between the latter and the ear-drum. It would be redundant to consider these relationships separately for each subdivision of the objective, as well as the sensory, stage of the response. Hence we shall follow our usual principle of postponing the consideration of the relationships in question until we deal with the subject of auditory sensation. However, we may note here certain facts which enter into the special modification of these relations for particular subdivisions of the objective stage of the response.

149. Psychophysics of the Sound Source.—With regard to the sonorous body, the *pitch* is determined primarily by the frequency of vibration, when the latter follows the simple harmonic law, which is approximately the case with a tuning fork or with a thermophone driven by an appropriate vacuum-tube oscillator.[246] However, the majority of ordinary vibrating objects, or systems, are subject to complex forces, which produce complicated movements, although these are quite commonly periodic in character. In the case of bodies which can be employed in the construction of musical instruments, these complex vibrations are ordinarily resolvable into a "fundamental" and its "overtones," or into a series of harmonics, of which the fundamental is the first. The frequencies of the second, third, fourth, etc., harmonics are commonly double, triple, quadruple, etc., that of the first, or are represented by integral factors. In the case of a piano string or the air column of an organ-pipe, the harmonics are attributable to the vibration of the body, not only as a whole, but in various proper fractional parts. Hence the term: "partials." The attribute of complex musical tone experiences which we call timbre represents the identity and intensive proportions of these partial vibrations. The trained "musical ear" is able to separate the representation of these partials from one another in experience.

Loudness [247] may be taken to correspond with the amplitude of vibration of the sonorous object, although it does so very imperfectly when comparison is being made between sources which have different frequency characteristics. The attribute of *volume* is perhaps associated with the relatively large physical sizes of vibrating bodies which emit low as compared with high frequencies. Volume may also be related to the fact that low-frequency sounds possess a vastly greater energy, in general, even with equal loudness, than do any high-frequency sounds which we ordinarily encounter. The attribute of *brightness* appears to lack a specific correlate in the objective realm, although it must be associated with the same features which determine pitch, because of its combination with the latter to form the pitch-brightness dimension.

Noises are determined by vibrating bodies, whose movements are either really aperiodic or have a complex inharmonic constitution. In general, noises, as representative of objective vibrations of this sort, determine experience in ways which are more specific than those which are characteristic of tones. At any rate, this is true of the effects which are associatively aroused within consciousness. Very few people have a reliable perception of "absolute pitch," but nobody mistakes the crash of falling china, the bang of a closing door, the hiss of escaping steam, the rumble of an approaching motor-truck, or the roar of thunder. Noises, as factors in consciousness, are thus very specifically determined by special objective conditions. They tend to form a set of discrete experiential items which are difficult to arrange into a quantitative series, perhaps because the corresponding objective events do not fall into such an order.

150. The Objective Psychophysics of the Vocables.— The *vocables* are, of course, associated with the various components of spoken language. The "object" in their case may perhaps be regarded as the vocal organs of the speaker, or the movements thereof. In modern times, it may be a radio loud-speaker or a phonograph. Possibly, in the case of the directly spoken word, we should extend the propagational series backwards, not only to the person's vocal organs, but along the motor nerves which control the latter, to the motor speech centers of the cerebral cortex. Then we could say that the true source of the disturbance lies in the speaker's cortex, and we could consider a perceptual relationship to be established between one experience and the determinants of another. Telephone engineers [248] have made very extensive studies of the perceptual relations between vocables and their objective conditions, since their business consists primarily in the transmission of such conditions over distances. They have found that different vocables require different intensities in order to render them equally intelligible. In general, consonants require a higher level than do vowels, although the vowel, *e,* is the most difficult sound of all to identify. The auditory experiences corresponding to *l, r,* and *ng* are among the easiest speech sounds to recognize at average intensities, *th, f,* and *v* have the highest thresholds of all, accounting for fifty per cent of all of the errors ordinarily occurring in telephonic communication. *Z, h,* and *s* are also relatively unintelligible at low intensities.

Telephone engineers distinguish between *intelligibility* and *faithfulness of reproduction.* In human speech, the greater part of the energy is contained in the vowels, at relatively low acoustic frequencies, but *articulation,* which determines intelligibility, depends much more upon the higher frequencies. Experiments show that the elimination of all frequencies lower than fifty cycles per second reduces the average energy by sixty per cent, but the articulation by only two per cent. Eradicating all frequencies higher than 1500 cycles cuts the energy by only ten per cent, but reduces the articulation thirty-five per cent. Intelligibility can also be reduced by excessive intensity. Telephone engineers regard seven or eight hundred cycles as the best representative single frequency for the perception of the vocables (or for speech) when they are replaced by a test tone.

151. Psychophysics of Acoustic Space Effects.—The frequency composition of the sound which impinges upon the eardrums may differ from that for the vibrating source, for a number of reasons. First, the radiation of energy in the form of sound is ordinarily more efficient in the case of high than in that of low frequencies, so that the low-frequency components of the vibration of the sonorous body will usually receive less adequate representation in the sound waves than will the higher frequency components. Secondly, the sound waves are reflected and absorbed by bodies which they strike, just as in the case of electromagnetic waves, although regular reflection is limited to very high frequencies. These effects are usually selective with respect to frequency, thus altering the composition as well as the total intensity of the sound. Within a closed space, foci and null points (loops and nodes) may be produced which are in separate positions for different frequencies. Distance, in the open, tends to attenuate all of the frequencies physically in about the same proportion, but subjectively increases the ratio of high to low pitch loudness, owing to reduction of the "masking" action of the low on the high constituents. (See Volume II.) Finally, the head and the outer ear introduce certain distortions, some of which depend upon the direction of the source.[249]

Now, ordinarily, the auditory consciousness seems to represent the *acoustic source,* rather than the properties of bodies which reflect, transmit or absorb the sound waves. Under such circumstances, the auditory perception may be compared with that of the light source in vision. However, in other cases, the quality of the auditory experience carries with it a definite impression of the size and wall material of the enclosing space, attributable largely to specific "reverberations." [250] Telephone experts learn to recognize the character of the enclosure which houses a microphone, from the quality of the incoming telephonic signal. The behavior of a blind person is guided in a similar manner by sound reflections and qualitative modifications, which are indicative of the nature and positions of nearby objects. The relationship between these two aspects of the auditory experience seems ordinarily to be the converse of that for the usual visual case, where the illumination conditions the perception of the object. In the auditory instance, the surroundings condition the perception of the source. This difference is attributable to the failure of ordinary acoustic frequencies to be propagated in straight lines; they do not cast clearly defined shadows, and the sound-waves usually reach the ears in a form which is largely independent of the orientation of the head or the presence of intercepting bodies.

In general, the auditory psychophysiological system is not very sensitive to changes of the above indicated nature, unless they take some significant form. Physical instruments may show wide variations in the frequency composition of musical sounds when the average ear fails entirely to appreciate them. Radical deviations from physical faithfulness of reproduction in the action of electro-acoustical devices may not be recognized even by an attentive and technically informed listener, if the sounds which are being reproduced are complex. Auditory experience, in the ordinary perceptual situation, also abstracts from variations in intensity which are due to moderate changes in the distance of the source. The loudness of the source is represented as fixed, and the intensity change is translated into an auditory representation of the distance. This effect is analogous to "the color constancy of visual things" under varying illumination, but applies to the acoustic source rather than to the intervening phases of the response. A similar compensation apparently occurs in the case of moderate alterations in the frequency composition due to recognized surroundings.

Experience embraces an auditory space which, in the case of the totally blind, may be quite independent of visual space. In the normal individual, however, the two spaces are interpenetrative. Sounds have a fairly definite localization within the auditory space, and this is determined by certain definable relationships of the sound to the two ears. However, as in the visual case, we shall reserve the discussion of these problems of spatial position for the chapter on auditory compositional perception.

Section 34 (A)

COMPONENT OLFACTORY PERCEPTION; OLFACTORY QUALITIES AND THEIR CLASSIFICATION

152. Classifications of Odors.—Following our previously established order of treatment, the experiences which we must next consider are those which are associated with olfaction, or "the sense of smell." From the introspective standpoint, these comprise a group of unpatterned qualities which exhibit an astonishing variety. They are closely associated with, and similar to, the gustatory or "taste" qualities, being confused constantly with the latter in everyday life. It is only by means of a psychophysiological criterion that we can separate these two classes of experiences with any degree of certainty. However, on a physiological basis, we can identify the olfactory qualities by excluding vaporous substances from the higher cavities of the nose or, more accurately, by noting what forms of consciousness are lost when the first cranial nerve is destroyed or anaesthetized.

Numerous attempts have been made to arrive at a satisfactory classification of the olfactory qualities from the introspective standpoint. Although some progress has been made, we are still unable to outline a system which is as definite and well-authenticated as are those which we have considered for visual and auditory experience. The most primitive division is that made by von Haller, into sweet, indifferent and foul odors, a classification which is evidently based upon the affective rather than upon the purely sensory aspects of the experiences. Although these affective aspects are highly characteristic of the system of odors, they are far from being invariable. A more sensory classification is that of Linné, who distinguished between the following species: aromatic, fragrant, ambrosial, alliaceous, hircine, repulsive, and nauseating. This system, as expanded by Zwaardemaker,[251] may be tabulated, with examples, as follows:

TABLE I

ZWAARDEMAKER'S CLASSIFICATION OF ODORS.

1. Ethereal — Odors of fruits, ethers, aldehydes, ketones, beeswax.
2. Aromatic — Odors of camphor, turpentine, ginger and other spices, lemon, nitrobenzol.
3. Balsamic — Odors of flowers, vanilla, and the like.
4. Ambrosial — Odors of amber and musk.
5. Alliaceous — Odors of hydrogen sulphide, rubber, chlorine, bromine.
6. Empyreumatic — Odors of roast coffee, tobacco smoke, benzol, and phenol.
7. Caprillac — Odors of cheese, rancid fat, cat's urine.
8. Repugnant — Odors of henbane, certain bugs.
9. Nauseating — Odors of faeces, decayed flesh, and the like.

153. Henning's Olfactory Prism.—Classifications such as these are based upon the relationships of similarity and difference between the multitude of distinct odors which can be realized in experience. The Zwaardemaker scheme suggests that the olfactory qualities fall into discrete classes, with no transitional members. However, common experience provides plenty of evidence that this is not the case, and it would seem that a careful study of all kinds of olfactory experience should reveal a qualitative continuum. Such a continuum has been proposed by Henning [252] in the form of a so-called *smell prism*. Henning bases his system upon the statements of individuals who have had a particularly wide experience in discriminating odors. He concludes that six primary reference points are sufficient to establish the system of olfactory qualities. These correspond to the following odors:

    F = Fragrant (= flowery, *blumig,* or *duftend*)
    E = Ethereal (= fruity, *früchtig*)
    P = Putrid (= foul, *faulig*)
    S = Spicy (= aromatic, *würzig, gewürzhaft*)
    R = Resinous (= piny, balsamic, *harzig, balsamisch*)
    B = Burned (= burning, scorched, empyreumatic, *brenzlich*)

These primary, or simplex, odors are placed upon the six respective corners of a triangular prism, in the manner

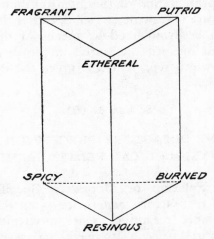

FIG. 11.   THE OLFACTORY PRISM, ACCORDING TO HENNING.

The figure represents a prism, of triangular cross-section, with the six, supposedly primary, odors at the respective corners. Henning regards the prism as hollow, distinctive qualities being represented on the edges and faces only. However, variations in subjective intensity can be taken into account by viewing it as a solid.

shown in Fig. 11. The prism is regarded as being hollow, i.e., qualities are supposed to be represented by points on its surface only, not within its volume. **Points** on the five faces of the prism must obviously stand for qualities which are intermediate between those placed upon the corners. Macdonald [253] designates the primary odors as simplex, those lying along an edge as duplex, those on the top and bottom faces as triplex, and those on vertical faces as quadruplex, or multiplex. Macdonald's experimental studies of the system indicate that it is an advance over previous schemes, but has serious logical difficulties in relation to characteristic stimuli. No odors were found for the triplex surfaces, and only one odor which could be interpreted as belonging to the EPBR face. Odors which are judged to be either duplex or triplex may occur in relations such that they must be placed upon quadrilateral faces.

As described by Henning, the olfactory prism provides no explicit representation of the intensity dimension. However, if the figure is regarded as solid, rather than as hollow. intensities can be symbolized by means of distances from a central point or locus measured in the direction of the surface point which represents the given quality.

Section 34 (B)

COMPONENT OLFACTORY PERCEPTION; PSYCHO-PHYSIOLOGICAL RELATIONSHIPS

154. The Relation of Odors to Specific Chemical Objects.—Since olfactory experience is correlated with a so-called "distance receptive" sense mechanism, it should have a perceptual aspect. Its perceptual psychophysiology is much less intricate, structurally, than is that of vision or audition, but as regards the number of qualitatively different components, it perhaps constitutes the most complicated system which we can find. It will be noted, from the contents of the preceding section, that the identification of a specific odor almost universally demands reference to some particular kind of object or substance. Sometimes objects are classified on the basis of their olfactory similarities, but usually the quality is named after the object. At any rate, the psychophysiological relationships which have been established in this domain are essentially of a perceptual character, since they relate specific qualities of experience to particular kinds of matter in the environment. The progress of psychological research in this field is leading to the specification of the stimuli in definite chemical rather than common-sense terms. Olfaction is *par excellence* a system of specific chemical perception.

Now, there can be no question that if we relate specific olfactory qualities, in this way, with particular kinds of bodies or conditions, in the environment, we are dealing definitely with a perceptual correspondence. However, if we consider the vapors which are given off by these bodies, and which are convected or diffused so that they finally reach the olfactory epithelium, we may consider that we are dealing with the stimulus rather than with an objective phase of the response. In the former case, we should classify the relationship as sensory, rather than as perceptual. It will be noted that in the following list of conditions, given by Macdonald (from Henning's data) for various olfactory qualities, there are twenty chemical substances and fifteen objects.

TABLE II

QUALITY	OBJECT OR SUBSTANCE
Simplex	
Fragrant	Ionone
	Oil of jasmine
Ethereal	Acetic ether
	Citral
Putrid	Carbon disulphide
	Asparagine
	Thiophenol

TABLE II—*Continued*

QUALITY	OBJECT OR SUBSTANCE
Spicy	Anisol
	Nutmeg
	Anethol
Resinous	Frankincense
	Balsam of Peru
	Eucalyptol
	Pinene
Burned	Tar
	Pyridine
	Nicotine

Duplex

Fragrant—ethereal	Citronellol
	Geraniol
Ethereal—putrid	Rotten fruit
Fragrant—putrid	Rotten flowers
Spicy—resinous	Allspice
	Myrtenol
Resinous—burned	Burned mastic
Spicy—burned	Burned coffee
Fragrant—spicy	Vanillin
	Vanilla
Ethereal—resinous	Xylene
Putrid—burned	Amyl alcohol

Multiplex

Fragrant—ethereal—spicy—resinous	Menthol
	Wormwood
Ethereal—putrid—resinous—burned	Grapefruit rind
Fragrant—putrid—spicy—burned	Celery
	Onion
	Apiol

The names which are italicized were adopted by Macdonald as representative conditions or stimuli for the six simplex odors.

Where the chemical substances which are included in the above table represent pure molecular individuals, we may assume that these identical molecules can reach the olfactory epithelium of the nose. Hence it would appear that they can function both as object and as stimulus, although in the present state of our knowledge, we cannot be absolutely sure that the substances, as such, constitute the stimuli. On the assumption that they do, we may confine the discussion of perceptual relationships to bodies or processes in the environment, reserving chemical substances —technically defined—for the Section on olfactory sensation. It is clear that *conditions or processes,* as well as objects, in the environment may be especially associated with the generation of odoriferous vapors. Thus, fire and putrefaction are important objective conditions for olfaction, and experience relates to these, as processes, and not merely to the burning or putrefying objects.

The presentation of a complete list of such perceptual relationships would amount to little more than a recital of many commonplace propositions. Thus, we say that "a rose smells sweet," we judge a cigar or liquor as good or bad by its aroma, we "smell fire," or perhaps a "dead rat." In the majority of instances, we have no name for the olfactory quality which is distinct from that for the object; we say that the quality is the odor *of* the object, because it is consistently correlated with the latter. A detailed study of the chemical constitution of such objects, and especially of the vapors which they emit, will provide us with a much more sophisticated set of propositions.

155. Biological Relations of Olfaction.—One very important aspect of olfaction is to be found in its relation to the process of deglutition or swallowing. The food-substances which have a so-called "taste" differing from "sweet, sour, salt and bitter," or their combinations, differentially affect the olfactory rather than the gustatory sense. When we say that they "taste" thus and so, we are actually dealing with a perceptual relationship through the channels of smell. In this case, the perceived objects are contained within the mouth, and the passageway for the olfactory effluvia is through the posterior rather than through the anterior nares. Unfortunately, in the human being, this action occurs subsequently to swallowing, rather than in advance, so that the guardianship of the sense of smell over the alimentary canal is not as effective as it might be. Nevertheless, the relationship between the character of the food-objects in the mouth, and the corresponding olfactory experiences may be treated as a perceptual one. It is clearly a relation which is of the utmost importance for the welfare of the organism.

In this connection, we may note the following rather obvious biological associations of the several classes of olfactory qualities. In Henning's system, the fragrant and the ethereal are correlated with flowers and fruit, and are generally indicative of beneficial food substances. Although flowers furnish food directly only to insects, they are apt to be a sign of fruit- or nut-bearing plants, and are associated with the presence of sugar-containing bodies. The spicy and the resinous are also indicative of vegetal matter which is liable to belong to a beneficial species, including nuts, tubers, and the like. The putrid is obviously specific to decayed nitrogenous or fecal substances, which might prove to have a toxic effect, if ingested. The burned also indicates materials which are unfit for ingestion, and is a warning of the presence of fire, in certain cases. It is interesting that the qualities which are correlated with beneficial food-substances are normally pleasant, in consciousness, whereas those which are particularly associated with deleterious materials are commonly unpleasant.

We cannot doubt that in the case of many of the lower vertebrates, and the lower animals in general, olfactory perceptions are of far greater importance than they are in the human being. It is probable that, for these animals, they are more complex and specific than are the visual and auditory perceptions. Olfaction is usually regarded as being in a decadent or vestigial state, in man.

Section 35 (A)

COMPONENT CONTACT PERCEPTION; THE CLASSIFICATION OF CONTACT QUALITIES

156. Psychological Basis of Analysis in this Field.— We come now to deal with a group of perceptual relationships for which the object must ordinarily be in intimate proximity to the body surface, in order that it should participate in the determination of consciousness. The sense channels which are involved in this case may be characterized as contact-receptive in contrast with distance-receptive. The subdivision of contact perception along sensory lines has offered many difficulties in the past and, even at the present day, cannot be regarded as complete. For example, we are unable to select, upon an objective basis, certain specific receptors in the skin and say that temperature experience consists in those psychical factors which are correlated with the functions of these particular end-organs. Instead, we are compelled to utilize the qualitative differences which we find directly within experience as the principal clues to our analysis. However, the introspective distinctions are substantiated by a few specific correlations which we can discover between the psychical differences and physiologically separable sense channels.

After having established some of these analytical relationships, we usually feel impelled to say that the deliverances of the separate sensory systems *fuse* with one another. Thus, the taste of lemonade is said to be a combination of gustatory, olfactory, touch, and temperature sensations— although, to the naïve observer, it seems to be a simple qualitative experience. However, there is no actual *process* of fusion, within experience, but only a determination of the experiential resultant, simultaneously, by the operations of a plurality of sensory receptive mechanisms and nerve channels. The psychophysiologist is, of course, compelled to consider the nature and relationships of such resultant experiences, but in order that he should understand them,

he must first become acquainted with the correlations between experience and the separate functioning of the individual afferent systems.

From the purely introspective standpoint, it is easy to
divide contact experiences into those of taste, touch, temperature and pain. Each of these has a number of discriminable kinds. Thus, taste may be sweet, salt, sour or
bitter; touch presents either neutral touch or tickle; temperature consists of warm or cool; while pain has various qualities, including itch. Intermediate or "fusion" qualities of
all possible sorts are found between these primary contact
experiences. They also shade into the distance-significant
olfactory experiences, on the one hand, and bodily experiences, such as lust and kinaesthesis, on the other hand.

The olfactory perceptions seem to stand on the boundary
line between distance and contact systems. Although the
olfactory processes are definitely correlated with objects and
processes at a distance, they also coöperate in a very intimate manner with the gustatory system, and the body surface sense in general, in registering the nature of objects
within the mouth or pharynx. Taste, however, must be
classed definitely as a contact receptive or perceptive system,
although the contact may be less direct than in the case of
touch. Certain constituents of the objects which are placed
in the mouth must go into solution before taste experiences
can be evoked, the solution phase being analogous to the
vapor phase in olfaction. Although taste is confined to the
head-end (buccal portion) of the alimentary and respiratory
tracts, in man, it has a much wider distribution over the
body surface in the case of animals which live in water. It
seems more logical to class it with touch, temperature perception, and pain than with the exteroperceptive systems of
vision, audition and olfaction. Neurologically, it is closely
affiliated with the visceral or interoceptive systems. However, it should be recognized that there are no sharp lines
of demarcation in this classificatory scheme. For a fish,
taste may be definitely distance-receptive; and temperature
is frequently distance perceptive for man.

157. Systems of Gustatory and Tactile Qualities.—
The separation of the gustatory perceptions from those
which involve tactual, thermal, or algesic channels has been
made possible only on the basis of psychophysiological
studies, which show that the experiences—localized within
the mouth and called sweet, salt, sour and bitter—are correlated with the stimulation of characteristic sense-organs,
known as taste-buds. The four primary taste qualities vary
separately in intensity, along a continuous scale. They
readily show intermediates at low intensities, but at high

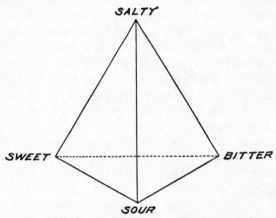

FIG. 12. THE GUSTATORY TETRAHEDRON, ACCORDING TO HENNING.

The figure represents a concatenation of four triangular surfaces, with the
four elementary taste qualities at the respective corners. According to Henning, the structure is hollow, but it is best regarded as a solid.

intensities they tend to be mutually exclusive. Henning [254]
has advocated the use of a tetrahedron to represent the
system of gustatory qualities, the four primaries being placed
at the four corners, respectively, as shown in Fig. 12. Intermediate qualities, or gustatory "mixtures," find positions on
the edges and faces. According to Henning, the tetrahedron
is to be regarded as hollow, but we can represent the intensity dimension by treating the figure as a solid and measuring

intensities from a central point, in the direction of the surface point which symbolizes the given quality.

The remaining distinctive experiential qualities which are correlated with contact action upon the body surface have already been indicated, above. In addition to temperature, touch, and pain, we might include certain aspects of sexual feeling, which is on the border line between the contact and interoceptive classifications. These qualities may be localized at almost any point on the experiential body surface, including zones extending some distance within either end of the alimentary canal. They are all qualitatively distinctive and are capable of independent variation in intensity. With certain exceptions, they may show all conceivable qualitative intermediaries, having either simple or complex relations with the primaries. Warm and cool are ordinarily mutually exclusive, but may be regarded as possessing an intermediate in the experience which is known as "hot." "Burning heat" also involves a similarity to pain.

The non-gustatory experiences may be represented by means of a three-dimensional diagram, such as that shown in Fig. 13, in which the thermal qualities are treated as algebraically related. This latter treatment evidently finds an exception in the case of "hot," which is excluded by the geometry of the diagram. In general, with this exception, any non-gustatory contact experience can be represented by a particular point in the given three-dimensional manifold.

Section 35 (B)

COMPONENT CONTACT PERCEPTION; PSYCHO-PHYSIOLOGICAL RELATIONSHIPS

158. General Aspects of Contact Perception.—The perceptual relationships of the contact experiences are in general much simpler than are those of the distance-significant experiences. This is particularly the case for their analytical components. Of course, we can formulate a

wealth of perceptual interrelationships between intermediate
or "fusion" qualities and the corresponding objects, or
properties of objects, in contact with the skin.   Thus, the
"taste of lemonade," as an experience, is perceptually related to lemonade, as a physical substance.   The "feeling of
wetness" stands in a similar relationship to liquids in general,

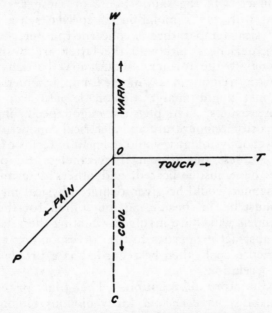

FIG. 13.   THE MANIFOLD OF CUTANEOUS SENSIBILITY.

The diagram shows a set of three-dimensional Cartesian axes, for warm-
cool, touch and pain, respectively.   Warmth is measured positively from the
point, O, and cool negatively from the same point.

especially as applied outside of the mouth cavity.   "Roughness" indicates a certain texture of object surfaces, and so
on.   However, such a list of correlations would hardly
prove to be illuminating from the scientific standpoint, since
it would merely reiterate common-sense propositions in a
manner quite tautological from the common-sense point of
view.   What we ordinarily mean by a "rough object" is
one which "feels rough."   Consequently, it is advisable to

treat these contact perceptual relationships in an analytical manner, and the most significant lines of cleavage for such analysis are those which are indicated by the neurological separations between different sensory channels.

Another method of analysis would involve a consideration of logically separable properties of the objects which make contact with the skin. Some of these are definitely associated with the stimulation of specific sense channels. Thus, physical temperature is concerned in determining the thermal experiences, although the latter are by no means proportional to the former. Touch may be definitely correlated with weight, mass, momentum, or kinetic energy. The chemist might analyze lemonade into water, sugar, and citrus extracts. The physicist might specify its volume, mass, viscosity, temperature and electrical conductivity. But only a psychophysiologist would define it in terms of sapidity, coolness, wetness and aroma. Nevertheless, the properties which we have just indicated, and others determined in a similar manner, could be given definite physical meanings— as they must be, in considering the stimuli for the various sense channels which are involved. Stating the relationships of these abstract properties to the corresponding aspects of the experience could then be regarded as a problem in perceptual correlation.

159. Gustatory Perception.—The four primary gustatory qualities have certain fairly obvious biological connections. In the first place, they correspond to rather well-defined classes of soluble, crystalloidal substances. Sweet is evidently determined ordinarily by substances known as sugars, which furnish the fuel for the muscles of the body. It may also be taken to represent the carbohydrates in general, since starches and similar food-substances are converted into sugars by the salivary ferments, and hence will yield a sweet-taste, if sufficiently masticated. Salt is correlated with essential mineral constituents of food, primarily sodium chloride, which are required by the body in moderation. Sour is obviously associated with acids, which may be characteristics of unripe fruit, and other substances which are relatively unfit for ingestion. The preservation of the proper balance of acidity in the tissues of the organism is a matter of the utmost physiological importance. Bitter is related, in general, to the class of alkaloid substances, which occur naturally in certain plants and which have a highly toxic effect, particularly upon the nervous system. Examples are: quinine, cocaine, morphine, nicotine and curare.

It would therefore appear that the primary gustatory qualities can be regarded as perceptions of certain classes of chemical substances which are of peculiar physiological significance. It may be noted in this connection that the characteristic affective qualities of the gustatory experiences are quantitatively indicative of these biological values. Thus, the normal pleasantness of sweet represents the high food value of the carbohydrates, whereas the normal unpleasantness of salt, sour and bitter stands for the necessity of protecting the organism from excessive quantities of the corresponding substances. Salt and sour, however, are pleasant at low concentrations of the corresponding substances, a fact which is related to their beneficial action, in moderation. It is not at all surprising that a thorough study of the conditions which evoke the various gustatory qualities should reveal some which are not of this biologically significant character. The taste responses necessarily involve a specific physiological mechanism, resting upon certain general forms of physical or chemical action, and these may accidentaly be exerted by substances which were not primarily concerned in the evolution of these sense mechanisms.

The relationships between gustatory experience and the objective stage of the corresponding responses are primarily to the objects—solids, liquids or gases—which are taken into the mouth. However, we might also consider, independently, the nature of the *buccal solutions,* which may depend in part upon such objects, but also in part upon the natural chemical constitution of the saliva. From one standpoint, we might regard gustatory experience as presenting perceptions of the departure of salivary constitution from the normal standard. Thus, a person having acid saliva will not experience sour until a higher concentration is reached than that which will evoke this experience for a normal individual. When the mouth is washed with a liquid, such as distilled water, which reduces the normal acidity or saltiness of the saliva, there is a corresponding experience of *insipidity*.

160. Thermal Perception.—Thermal experience is characterized by a considerable degree of distance-receptive significance, although it is primarily determined by the temperature of the skin, itself. It should be noted, in the beginning, that the distinct bimodality of the thermal sense finds no correlate in the physical conception of temperature or heat. Temperature, for modern physics, consists in the average kinetic energy of vibration of the molecules which constitute all material substances; and this is zero only at the excessively low thermometer reading of — 273 degrees, Centigrade. At — 272 degrees, there is still a definite amount of heat, and there is no such entity or condition as "cold," from the physical standpoint. Early physical ideas concerning heat, such as the notion of "phlogiston," were largely determined by psychophysiological preconceptions, which have now been entirely abandoned. However, our thermal experiences are *controlled,* in a fairly definite way, by real physical temperatures, or their variations. But in order to formulate these relationships, we are obliged to introduce the concept of a *physiological zero,* which approximates the normal temperature of the body surface, or the skin. This is in the vicinity of 28 degrees, Centigrade, or 82 degrees, Fahrenheit, for the exposed portions of the body. We say on this basis that, in general, the warmth experience is determined by an increase in the temperature of the skin above this value, while the cool experience is attendant upon a decrease below the physiological zero point.

Now, the temperature of the skin itself is a function of a complex group of variables. At all times, it represents a balance between thermal gains and losses. The body surface is ordinarily losing heat to outside space by conduction, convection, and radiation. It is also subject to thermal depletion in consequence of the latent heat of vaporization of the moisture evaporating from the skin. It gains heat, firstly, from the blood-stream, which circulates through the capilliaries and the larger vessels of the skin, and, secondly, through conduction, convection or radiation from external media. All of these processes are occurring, to some extent, at all times, although sometimes one or the other may be dominant. When the balance is "normal," there is no thermal perception; both warmth and coolness are absent, although there is still a resultant loss of heat from the body, an outward thermal flux.

If we follow our usual scheme of tracing the relationships of experience, first, to the most remote factors in the response chain, we must consider that, under some circumstances, we have to deal with thermal "sources," which are analogous to light sources in vision. Thus, when we are "basking" in the sun, our thermal experience is a function of the source, some ninety-two million miles away, although its action is conditioned by the atmospheric absorption for infra-red and other rays, as well as by the angle between these rays and the particular portion of the earth's surface upon which we may happen to be lying. Again, we may be sitting in the beam of an electric glow-heater. In both of these cases, the thermal experience is localized on the experiential body surface, rather than in external space, but this does not prevent us from considering the perceptual relationships which obtain between the source, the intermediate radiant energy, the atmospheric conditions, the angle of incidence, etc., on the one hand, and the experience on the other.

Under other circumstances, we may have to consider directly the temperature of the surrounding atmosphere, which may be imparting heat to the body, interfering with the normal flux of heat away from the latter, or perhaps abstracting it at an undue rate. We say: "It is hot," or

"It is cold," referring in a general manner to the properties of the space which surrounds us.

A particularly interesting case of thermal perception appears in connection with contact between the skin and bodies, such as metals, which have a high degree of thermal conductivity. When these are at a somewhat lower temperature than the skin, they are perceived as being cold, although their physical temperatures may be identical with those of other poorly conducting bodies which evoke no thermal experience. Substances, such as water, which have a high specific heat, may act in a similar manner. Volatile liquids, spread out in thin layers upon the skin surface, yield cold because of their evaporation, and a "draught," or agitation of the surrounding air, enhances this effect. Highly conducting substances also feel hotter than do poorly conducting ones because of their ability to transmit heat into the skin at a high rate, when they are at a superior temperature. When the body is surrounded by non-conducting wrappings, such as clothes or bed-clothes, the normal flux of heat from the skin is reduced, so that the skin temperature rises, and we feel warm, or comfortably protected from cold, as the case may be. In such cases, we may be said to be dealing with the *perception of thermal conductivity* as well as with absolute or relative temperatures. "Flushing," "blushing" and bodily exercise increase the supply of heat to the skin, from internal bodily sources—and hence yield corresponding alterations in thermal experience.

It is well known that our thermal impressions also depend upon "the humidity," or the relative saturation of the surrounding air with water-vapor. When the air with which the skin is in contact is completely saturated, there can, of course, be no evaporation from the cutaneous surface and hence no cooling through this agency. However, if the temperature of the air is raised, its capacity to hold moisture is increased, so that evaporation can now occur. Hence an actual increase in air temperature may yield the experience of greater coolness, rather than of greater warmth. Living beings are able to endure very high temperatures if the air is very dry, because under these conditions the evaporation is rapid and the cooling effect is correspondingly large. This effect will naturally be dependent upon an adequate supply of perspiration, and if sweating should cease, there would be an experience of increased temperature. Agitation of the air, as by a fan, also helps by removing the saturated layers of air close to the skin surface.

Cold is evoked when the blood temperature is depressed or the speed of circulation through the skin is reduced, although external conditions may remain unchanged. This action accounts for some of the thermal experiences which accompany pathological conditions. We apparently have no representation in consciousness of the temperature of the body mass, as a whole, but only of that of its superficies. The subjective intensity of the warmth experience may be taken to represent, perceptually, the degree of increase of the skin temperature above the physiological zero; while that of cold stands for a corresponding decrease. These intensities also represent, to some extent, the rates at which such departures from the normal temperature are established, or inversely the times over which they have endured. But such considerations lead us to relationships which are more appropriately considered in the chapters on sensation.

161. Tactual or Pressure Gradient Perception.—The experiential quality which we call "touch" or "pressure sensation" is correlated with certain forms of mechanical contact between the skin and external objects. In order to obtain this experience in pure form, the contact should involve no appreciable alteration in the process of heat exchange between the body and its environment, and should also be free from injurious action upon the skin. However, it occurs, possibly in conjunction with thermal and pain experiences, even when these conditions are not fulfilled. The "object" in tactile response may not always be in direct contact with the skin surface. Thus, it is a familiar fact that mechanical forces may be transmitted from a body, A, through another body, B, and thence to the skin; and in this

case, the experience frequently represents the contact action
of A, separately from that of B. This occurs, for example,
when we hold a pencil or a cane in the hand, and touch some
other object with either of these implements. A skilled
workman appreciates by touch exactly what is going on at
the end of a tool which he may be using, and under such
circumstances there is a definite correlation between his
experience and mechanical forces existing at a distance from
the skin. A similar relationship may be conceived to hold
for those cases of tactile stimulation which depend upon
contact with the hairs of the skin. In this case, the stimulating force is transmitted along the hair, just as along a
pencil, but the experience represents the contact at the
hair-tip.

Tactual experiences show some variations in elementary
quality, but they are relatively slight compared with those
which are found in other experiential domains. The distinction between tickle and touch is quite definite, the former
being correlated with a light and unsteady pressure, whereas
the latter accompanies firmer contacts. Some qualitative
differences can be distinguished between tactual experience
localized at different points on the experiential body surface,
but these differences are small and certainly not sufficient to
constitute so-called "local signs," by means of which it has
been supposed that one region can be discriminated qualitatively from other regions. However, both tickle and touch
show a continuous gradation of intensites, which can be
represented as functions of the degree and kind of contact
which exists between the object and the skin.

Not all contacts with the skin yield tactual experience,
even when they are physically quite intense. Thus, the
atmosphere presses upon all portions of the body, to the
amount of about fourteen pounds per square inch, and yet
this fact receives no representation in consciousness. Similarly, if the hand is immersed in mercury, the resulting
tactile experience corresponds to the locus of contact of the
surface of the liquid, only. There is a ring of pressure
(say) around the wrist, but no feeling on the experiential

areas which correspond to the immersed region. Such observations indicate that touch is elicited only by forces which *distort* the skin, mere uniform compression being ineffective. Other things equal, the intensity of the experiential touch is greater the greater such distortion. For this reason, touch intensity will not necessarily increase with an augmentation of the total amount of force which is acting upon the skin. If this augmentation depends upon an increase in the total effective area, due to the application of further units of force to regions previously unacted upon, there may even be a reduction in the touch intensity. Such a reduction will inevitably occur if the given amount of force is spread over an increased area, so that the pressure is lowered. This seems to mean that the general physical condition for the arousal of tactile feeling is not force, nor pressure, but *pressure gradient* or the rate of change of pressure with respect to distance, or position.

If we maintain constant the area and pattern of application of the force, the pressure gradient will vary with the force. Under such conditions, we can determine the relationship between the intensity of the subjective touch and the magnitude of the applied force. Such measurements are best carried out with very small areas of stimulation, like those obtainable by using the tips of hairs or fibres of glasswool. Employing stimuli of this sort, Hensen [255] found that a force of less than 0.001 grams is readily perceivable on the skin of the face. The classical studies of Weber showed that the subjective scale of touch intensities stands in a logarithmic relationship to the forces which are applied to the skin. Each just noticeable increase in the tactile experience intensity corresponds to a from $\frac{1}{10}$th to $\frac{1}{20}$th increment in the acting force.

Touch presents many important perceptual aspects which depend upon the spatial distribution or shape of the stimulating objects. These relationships will be discussed in the chapter on composite perception, below.

162. Pain and Tissue Injury Perception.—The word, pain, applies to a wide variety of qualitatively different forms of experience, of which cutaneous pain is only one. Even in the domain of the bodily surface, many qualitative varieties of pain are observable. These differences seem to be correlated in part with the location, and in part with the intensity and temporal course of the stimuli. In general, cutaneous pain stands, in experience, for actual or incipient injury to the skin. Such injury may be due to various influences: mechanical, thermal, chemical, or electrical. If the skin is distorted by contact with a sharp object, to a degree which places it in danger of laceration, pain will be felt. Excessive heat, capable of bringing about chemical decomposition, at temperatures in excess of about 48° C., yields a similar result. Low temperatures, below about 12° C., approaching the freezing point and interfering with normal metabolic processes, also bring pain. Acids, such a glacial acetic or sulphuric, in contact with the skin, elicit pain with great facility. Electrical voltages or currents evoke pain rather than touch.

Although pain appears to correlate primarily with conditions of the body itself rather than with external objects, nevertheless, in some cases it is clearly indicative of the character of the latter. Thus, the perception of sharpness in a contacting object is nearly always referable to the pain feature of the experience. The qualities which we called "burning hot" and "freezing cold" owe their peculiar qualities to the algesic component. Pain is also associated with mechanical contacts which are excessively forceful, as when we find ourselves "in the grip of an enemy," or caught by accident in some mechanical trap.

As applied to the body surface itself, pain may be indicative of states of infection, inflammation, or of damage which has already been done by outside forces. The normally unpleasant quality of pain is associated with the desirability of avoiding these conditions. We should be careful, of course, not to confuse the affective tone of the experience with the pain quality. The experience which is called *itch* is closely related to pain, usually being indicative of a mild inflammatory process in the skin. It appears to be dependent upon a weak, and possibly an unsteady, condition of the same sort which yields pain at higher intensities. Quite frequently, it is pleasant, rather than unpleasant, although it gives rise to movements directed towards its abolition. In general, the intensity of the pain experience increases with the degree of injury, or threatened injury, of the skin, although there are many exceptions to this rule.

Section 36 (A and B)

COMPONENT ORIENTATIVE PERCEPTION

163. Classification of Kinaesthetic Experiences.—We must now consider a group of experiences which are very difficult to analyze introspectively. They have to do with the position and movement of one's own body in space, and with postures and relative displacements of the parts of the body itself. The term, *kinaesthetic,* was suggested by Bastian [256] to designate all of these experiences, whether they represent static or dynamic conditions. It is convenient to divide them into two classes: the *absolute* and the *relative*. The first class is concerned with the geometrical and kinematical relations between the body and its environment, while the second stands for the postures and relative movements of the bodily members. Each of these sets of facts can also be represented visually and, to some extent, tactually. It is very easy to eliminate the visual factors, apart from images, by closing the eyes; and the tactual ones can be avoided by the proper application of anaesthetics to the skin. The remaining representations are predominantly kinaesthetic.

Since the kinaesthetic impressions are concerned principally with forms and movements, rather than with differences of kind or degree, it is natural that they should be closely structured and difficult to break up into component qualities. Indeed, these experiences exemplify the principles of fusion and configured wholeness more radically than do

any other conscious phenomena. Consequently, their
most significant aspects must be considered under the captions of composite and temporal perception. Nevertheless,
it would certainly be incorrect to imply that they are wholly
unanalyzable, or that they cannot be regarded at all as subjective mosaics of characteristic qualitative elements.

We can distinguish at least five component aspects of
experience which belong in the kinaesthetic class. In the
group of absolute kinaesthetic experiences, we have: (1)
the kinaesthetic vertical and (2) dizziness or vertigo. In
the group of relative kinaesthetic experiences, we can recognize: (3) attitudinal qualities (having to do with posture
and bodily movement), (4) tensive (or weight-resistance)
qualities, and (5) exertive (or muscular pressure) components. The first three of these modes of kinaesthetic
experience are rather difficult to conceive apart from specific
configurations. Thus, the concept of the vertical, even as
defined introspectively, seems to imply a relationship between a number of spatial components. Dizziness, again,
seems introspectively to be a movement, and hence to be
characterized by directionality and change. It is not easy,
moreover, to get a concrete impression of what is meant by
an element of kinaesthetic attitude.

However, a more careful consideration of the actual
subjective facts, as well as of the scientific system into which
they must enter, will probably justify us in believing that
these five factors correspond to qualitatively distinct experiential elements. We must have a combination of such
elements, in the form of a fused spatial mosaic, in order
to yield the kinaesthetic patterns which appear in concrete,
everyday experience. Combinations of this sort may involve kinaesthetic components of the same species, or simultaneously of different species, or even definite concatenations
of kinaesthetic with non-kinaesthetic factors. Concepts,
such as those of the vertical and of rotation, which are relative from the standpoint of physics, are actually absolute
subjectively. The introspective vertical can be regarded as
a fixed qualitative constituent of consciousness, which is

normally related in a certain way to other concomitant experiential factors. When these relations are disturbed, we designate the experience as that of a departure of the body from a vertical position. The vertical itself is thus not the product of a relationship, but is a reference axis with respect to which such relationships can be established. Although motion may necessarily be relative for physics, it is usually absolute for psychology, because certain portions of consciousness are accepted as being definitely "at rest."

164. The Perceptual Psychophysiology of the Kinaesthetic Vertical.—In the present state of our knowledge, we do not know whether the kinaesthetic vertical should be regarded as introspectively simple, or whether it has an inherent structure. We may also feel some doubt as to whether it can possess intrinsic directionality. However, there is no difficulty in picking out the objective variable of which it is primarily a function. This is the resultant of the gravitational and linear accelerative forces which are acting upon the body and, especially, the head, at the given moment. According to the general theory of relativity,[257] these two kinds of forces cannot be distinguished from each other, by any tests which depend solely upon the inherent character of the forces in question. By accelerative forces, we mean those which are generated within a moving system when its mode of motion is altered, either in linear speed or in direction. The most familiar example is centrifugal force, which results from a directional change. Einstein supposes that the gravitational field is actually due to acceleration.

We do not know what would happen introspectively if the gravitational field were obliterated, but it seems quite certain that the kinaesthetic vertical would disappear. At any rate, its direction would cease to be a function of the objective vertical. Effective obliteration of gravitation could be secured temporarily by permitting a man to fall freely in space at the normal acceleration, *g,* due to gravity. An experience closely approximating this is given to parachute performers prior to the opening of their parachutes, but we apparently have no reports regarding their kinaesthetic impressions under such circumstances. Introspection would undoubtedly be difficult even for a practiced performer, owing to the appearance of intense organic feelings, accompanying the release of various bodily parts from the gravitational action.

However, the experiences of aviators flying in the clouds or in the absence of significant visual field patterns, confirm the view that the kinaesthetic vertical is determined by the gravitational-accelerative force field. Although they may have a definite impression of the vertical, it fails to correlate with the geologic vertical, in proportion as the gravitational field is modified by components due to accelerative changes in the motion of the aeroplane. The impression of a correct vertical under water is also dependent upon the head being at rest or in uniform motion. If we adopt Einstein's theory, we can forget about gravitation as a special force, and say that the kinaesthetic vertical is a function of the resultant linear accelerative vector which is acting upon the body or the head at any moment.

165. The Perceptual Psychophysiology of Vertigo.— The experience which is called "dizziness" or *vertigo* arises when the body or the head is subjected to rotatory motions. It is ordinarily regarded by the common-sense individual as an index of rotation, as such, because it depicts a movement of this sort in consciousness. However, a careful study of its conditions shows at once that they cannot be specified in terms of motions having constant angular velocity. A *change* in the mode of rotatory movement or orientation of the organism is required. When rotation has been constant for sometime, the vertigo disappears, only to arise again temporarily when the objective motion is stopped. The experience seems to have an inherent directionality, or polarity, representing rotation of the body either to the right or to the left. Whether this is really an intrinsic attribute or whether it depends upon relations to other components of experience, we cannot decide at the present time. At any rate, the intensity of the vertigo increases with increase in the rate of *angular acceleration,* of the head or body, and its direction is determined by that of the accelerative vector, being in the same direction as the angular velocity when the latter is increasing and in the opposite direction when it is decreasing.

It must be noted, however, that the correlations between the vertigo experience and the angular acceleration are by no means perfect. If the body is accelerated very quickly, to a constant angular velocity, the vertigo may not appear until after this velocity has been attained, and it will then persist for some time, gradually fading. The same effects are noted when the rotation is suddenly stopped, after the vertigo has disappeared. Experiments with very low angular accelerations, such as those which have been reported by Dodge,[258] show even further complications. Using a constant angular acceleration, he found that the initial positive vertigo was followed by a phase of kinaesthetic quiescence, after which there was a reversal of the apparent movement. These phenomena can be explained, at least in part, in terms of inertia and adaptation in the sensory mechanisms which underlie the vertigo experiences.

Simple experiments show that the rotatory accelerations must be applied to the *head* in order that they should yield vertigo. Insofar as the head and the body can move independently, the movements of the latter can be neglected. We shall discuss the factors determining the plane of the vertigo in the total kinaesthetic field, in the section dealing with composite perception. (See pages 363 *ff.*) This plane is a function of the relation of the plane of the objective rotation to the axis of the head.

166. Perceptual Psychophysiology of Attitudinal and Exertive Components.—There is very little to be said, from the perceptual standpoint, concerning the *components* of attitudinal and exertive experience. The relevancy of attitudinal experiences lies almost wholly in their patterns or configurations. Their general condition seems to be that of more or less normal contact between the various components of the skeleton and associated tissues, at the joints.

It seems that unit attitudinal impressions must vary in *intensity* with changes in the degree of tension or compression along the axis of a limb or other motile member of the body. If this were not the case, it would be difficult to establish specific patterns, which probably consist in differences of intensity among the components of the total bodily configuration. Differences in *quality,* corresponding with separate portions of the skeletal or articular system, may also exist; but in spite of the doctrine of local signs, they do not seem to have been clearly demonstrated.

The *exertive* experiences are conditional upon compression or shortening of the essential tissues of the voluntary muscles. They are, of course, subject to intensity increase with increase in muscular work, either as to the force exerted or the length of time over which the process has continued. When they are aroused by externally applied forces, such as pressure through the skin, they naturally increase in intensity with the degree of such pressure, but show a much higher threshold than that which characterizes cutaneous touch. The arousal of the exertive qualities in this manner probably corresponds to the so-called "deep sensibility" of Head and Rivers' [259] doctrine of surface sensations. Extreme pressure or muscular exertion yields pain, which should not be confused with the exertive experiences nor with the cutaneous pain response, since these have different conditions and qualities.

167. Perceptual Psychophysiology of Tensive Components.—The tensive experiences, "sense of resistance" or *"Kraftsinn,"* can be treated quite satisfactorily in terms of an experiential component having quantitative perceptual relationships. They are, of course, concerned in the estimation of weights, resistances and other forces which the muscular system is set to overcome. Although the tensive experiences show pattern characteristics, these are subordinate to the intensive modes of variation, and the latter can be treated substantially independently of the spatial configurations which may be involved. The general condition for this type of experience appears to be tensions, or stresses in the muscles or tendons, especially the latter. Such tensions are required to maintain almost any bodily posture against gravity, or to bring about changes in posture. The arrangement of many muscular systems into antagonistic groups also involves continuous tensions. When a weight is being lifted, or other external forces are added to those natural to the body by itself, the tensions will, of course, be increased more or less in proportion to the magnitudes of the external agencies. We usually attribute the corresponding increase in the tensive experience to the lifted object, although on close introspection we actually find it to be localizable within the limbs or other bodily parts.

Experiments show that such perceptions of weight, force or resistance follow laws that are different, at least quantitatively, from those which apply to tactual pressure; although the two forms of experience are ordinarily closely associated. The load which is required to produce a just noticeable tensive experience varies with the point of application and the particular portion of the musculoskeltal system which is involved. Goldscheider and Blecher [260] found that when the weight is hung at the tip of the forefinger and lifting movements occur at the shoulder, the threshold is 7.5 grams, but with movement at the elbow alone, the value must be increased to 9.0 grams. Using a finger movement, he found 24.0 grams. Von Frey [261] has shown that a given weight feels heavier when supported at the wrist than at the elbow, if the muscles of the shoulder are concerned. The more rapidly a weight is lifted, the more intense is the corresponding tensive experience. Allowing for such leverage factors, or the "arm" of the force, we find that the absolute threshold is less for proximal than for peripheral portions of a limb.

The conditions for a just noticeable difference between lifted weights were studied at any early date by Weber,[262] and were found by him to comply approximately with the law which bears his name. When weights were compared by cutaneous touch, alone, a relative threshold of 1/30th was found, whereas when the muscular system of the fingers was used the fraction was reduced to ¼₀th. Merkel [263] reported that the threshold was lower when the muscles were actively innervated than when the forces were more passively received. Jacobi[264] found a value of ½₀th, which was constant over a wide range of lifted weights, but Hering [265] showed that the relative threshold is not absolutely constant, being ½₁st at 250 grams, ⅟₁₁₄th at 2500 grams and ⅟₉₈th at 2750 grams, indicating departures from Weber's law similar to those which characterize other sensory departments. This means that the tensive experience increases in intensity at first slowly, then more rapidly, and again slowly with increasing values of the logarithm of the applied force. At very high values of the latter it presumably reaches an asymptotic limit.

Section 37 (A and B)

COMPONENT INTERNAL PERCEPTION

168. The Classification of Internal Perceptions.—In addition to the qualitative experiential components which we have considered above, consciousness frequently contains characteristic qualities which can be correlated with specific metabolic conditions or processes of a non-motor sort, within the organism. These qualites may be treated as "internal sensations," from the standpoint of their stimulus-receptor conditions, or as "perceptions" in their relationships to the gross bodily states which are involved. It seems just as legitimate to regard hunger as perceptually related to a lack of appropriate food substances in the stomach, as to view sweetness, similarly, as being correlated with the presence of such materials in the mouth. The perceptual treatment is particularly indicated by our ignorance of the stimulus and receptor processes for the majority of these experiences.

One of the most satisfactory classifications which has been proposed for the experiences in question is that of Luciani and Magendi.[266] These authorities, however, include the kinaesthetic qualities which, on account of their distinctive relationship to motor conditions, seem worthy of a special category. The non-kinaesthetic internal qualities may accordingly be said to include: (1) desires, (2) gratifications, (3) fatigues, (4) illnesses, and (5) coenaesthesia. Although it is generally stated that these experiences are vague and difficult to analyze, they are nevertheless of the utmost psychological importance. They represent specific organic conditions which must exercise a regulative action over behavior if the organism or the species is to survive. Consequently, the internal experiences and their associated physiological processes are of paramount interest in connection with problems of *motivation,* which we shall consider at a later point in this work (see Volume III), and it is desirable that their psychophysiological relationships should be established as definitely as possible.

169. Desires.—Desires are forms of experience characterized subjectively by an attribute which may be given the name of *urgency.* This attribute is associated with volitional unrest. Although desires may sometimes occur at low intensities, they are capable of becoming very powerful, and may dominate consciousness completely if they are not satisfied. The principal experiences in this class are: (1) hunger, (2) thirst, (3) lust, (4) the desire to micturate, (5) the desire to defecate, (6) the desire for air, and (7) in the case of the female, under appropriate conditions, the desire to lactate. There is also a special kinaesthetic state, popularly known as "nervousness," which may be interpreted as a desire for activity or "a change." These names may be understood as designating subjective qualities, although it is necessary to include the objective conditions in the meanings of some of them. The desiderative experiences have configurational aspects, but the latter are apparently subordinate in significance to the qualitative nature of the experiences, apart from their localizations or patterns. Consequently, we can discuss them quite adequately under the present caption of "component perception." Unfortunately, there will be little that we can add to this perceptual treatment when we come to the chapters on sensation.

Hunger. It is a familiar idea, of course, that the *hunger experience* is correlated with a need for food on the part of the organism. However, this conception is by no means an accurate one. Hunger usually appears far in advance of any serious metabolic deficit and, on the other hand, it may disappear entirely in the presence of a fatal nutritive failure. The investigations of Cannon[267] and of Carlson have made it clear that the characteristic hunger feeling is determined by the contractions of the stomach, which begin, as a rule, four or five hours after this organ has emptied itself. A "hunger pang" goes with each single gastric contraction. However, it is necessary for the walls of the stomach to be in a special physical or chemical condition in order that this relationship should obtain. Gastric movements which occur during the digestion of food have an entirely different representation in consciousness. Under starvation, hunger disappears in about two days, although, according to Carlson,[268] the stomach movements may continue. Hence, we may regard hunger as the perception of gastric contractions in the presence of a condition of the stomach walls which is transitional between that of the normal digestive process and the state of starvation.

The function of hunger is obviously to prevent the incidence of the latter state. Nothing is known concerning the quantitative relationships of the hunger experience and its organic conditions; presumably the mechanism which is involved is similar to that of muscular pain.

Thirst.—The thirst experience introspectively resembles a complex of tactual qualities, being a feeling of dryness and heat in the throat. It can evidently be attributed to a reduction in the amount of water in the body tissues, particular in those of the pharynx. Thirst is more persistent than is hunger, in fasting, but is said finally to disappear. It is common knowledge that thirst can be aroused by eating substances, such as spices and salt, which have a tendency to abstract water from the tissue cells.

Lust.—Sexual desire, or lust, includes a group of experience components which have the common attribute of voluptuousness. We may distinguish, however, between a low intensity feeling of erotic irritation—which may be unpleasant—and higher intensities which are characterized by extreme pleasantness. The orgasmic experience, which constitutes erotic gratification, seems to differ from the preliminary feeling of desire only in its localization and intensity. Experiments have shown that in lower animals, such as the frog, sexual response depends upon pressure between the contents of the seminal vesicles and their walls. However, in the human instance, this seems to be a relatively unimportant feature, since erotic desire is practically independent of periodicity in the reproductive processes and may persist after repeated gratification.

It is apparent that, in man, the sexual process has been given a powerful support in the central nervous system, which liberates it to a large degree from organic stimulus conditions, and connects it more with environmental factors. Thus, sexual desire in man should perhaps be regarded as part of the perception of a sexual object. Nevertheless, from our present standpoint, lust can be viewed as being perceptually determined, to a very important degree, by the state of tumescence of the external genitalia. It is true, of course, that the intensity of the desire is not reliably proportional to the degree of such tumescence, but the intensity is related to the approximation of the physiological condition to that required for ejaculation. However, it would probably be found impossible to specify this condition in non-neurological terms.

Excretory and Secretory Desires.—The *desire to micturate* is ordinarily said to be due to fullness of the bladder. However, it appears that this experience must actually be referred to the magnitude of the pressure between the bladder walls and the contents; and such pressure may arise either from passive distention of the organ or from its active contraction. The latter condition may accompany emotional states such as those of fear or "nervousness." Hence we may view the micturitional experience as a perception of intravesicular pressure.

The *desire to defecate* is to be attributed to the presence of fecal or other matter in the large intestine. It seems impossible to account for the differences in quality between the micturitional and defecatory experiences by means of composition in terms of simpler components. The *desire to lactate* is evidently determined by an excessive pressure of milk within the mammary glands.

The Desire for Air.—The experiences which accompany suffocation are of a very characteristic sort, although uncommon in everyday life. They are probably to be attributed to interference with the normal operation of the respiratory apparatus, rather than to a lack of oxygen or to an excess of carbon dioxide in the blood. The breathing of air which is low in oxygen may result in syncope without respiratory distress; but noxious vapors may bring about an inhibition of the reflexes and produce an effect similar to that due to physical obstruction of the movements.

General unrest or the so-called feeling of "nervousness" will probably require explanation primarily in terms of central factors. It may be due to enforced inactivity or to the associative arousal of desiderative forces, related to those which we have already discussed above.

170. Gratifications and Fatigues.—*Gratifications.*—The release of the organism from the conditions which give rise to desires, yields characteristics experiences. In some cases, the gratifications are similar in quality to the corresponding desires, involving a marked increase in intensity which is followed by a lapse of the given kind of experience altogether. This is the case with lust, micturitional and defecatory desires. The relation of these gratifications to organic processes is very familiar. The sexual orgasm, considered as an experience, is, perhaps, to be attributed perceptually to the muscular contractions which occur in both the male and female organs, although central conditions are undoubtedly involved in a very important way. It is probable that in the cases of micturition and defecation the movements of the excreted materials through the urethra and colon, respectively, furnish the primary condition.

The gratification of hunger involves not only the disappearance of the original experience but its replacement by a sense of gastric fullness, corresponding to the distention of the stomach by food and the beginning of digestive activity. Thirst is gratified by the contact of liquids with the dry membranes of the back of the mouth, with an accompanying coolness and wetness.

Fatigues.—Fatigue experiences exist in numerous qualitative varieties. Muscular fatigue is rather definitely localized and passes over into a pain quality at high intensities. It may be attributed to an excessive breakdown of muscular tissue through work or, possibly, to an accumulation of end-products of the chemical activity in the muscular tissue. General fatigue is a more diffuse experience which does not resemble pain, although it is commonly unpleasant. It is probably due to an abnormal concentration of metabolic end-products in the blood stream. Drowsiness or sleepiness has a similar basis in the direct action of these substances upon the cells of the cortex. We can scarcely classify this latter relationship as perceptual.

The feelings of satisfaction or of satiety which follow erotic gratification or the ingestion of a full meal are grouped by Luciani with fatigue. These feelings are distinct in quality from those which characterize desire and gratification in the respective fields. However, they are rather closely similar for the erotic, micturitional and defecatory cases. These experiences are perhaps to be assigned to the reduction of tension or activity in the given fields below that which is normal or average. The similarity of these feelings to those which go with convalescence from illness suggests the use of the term, *analepsis,*[269] to stand for them.

171. Specific Illness Perceptions, and Coenaesthesia.— In addition to the types of experience which go with the healthy life of the organism, we must also deal with those which accompany pathological conditions. There is a great variety of qualitatively distinct illness qualities. The majority of these must be classed, introspectively, as pains, although differing in quality from cutaneous pain, and among themselves. However, a distinctive feeling such as nausea can scarcely be regarded as a pain, in spite of its great unpleasantness.

Practically every internal organ seems to be capable of yielding a characteristic pain under appropriate conditions, although many of these organs are insensitive to mechanical or thermal stimulation, so that in surgical operations they can be cut or burned without any corresponding modifications of consciousness. However, the external peritoneum, the lining of the abdominal and pelvic walls, yields pain upon mechanical stimulation, while the tissues of the diaphragm may be stimulated mechanically to give pressure experiences, as well as those of pain. Other internal parts can yield pressure feelings under appropriate conditions. These conditions probably involve changes in the physical or chemical states of the tissues, just as in the case of the stomach walls or a rheumatic muscle. Pain or pressure may then arise either in consequence of these changes *per se,* or under the added influence of mechanical forces.

The differences which exist between internal pains will readily be appreciated from a few examples, such as headache, toothache, colic pains, pain due to cramp in the muscles of the rectum, bruising the testicles, etc. Each one of these algesic experiences has a specific organic condition, so that the experience may be said to be a perception of the condition in question. However, our knowledge of the physiological or physical nature of such conditions is very meager. Presumably, headache is to be referred to pressure between the brain and the cranium, which compresses the meninges, the volume of the brain varying with the pulse pressure to give the characteristic throbbing. Toothache stands for decay, or chemical or thermal abnormalities in the tooth substance. Muscular pain may represent cramp, or excessive contraction of the muscular tissue; extreme concentration of metabolic end-products; or damage to the cells due to overwork. Colic pressures or pains are said to be due to pressure of the distended small intestine upon the peritoneum.[270]

Nausea is undoubtedly a complex experience, but has a characteristic quality which furnishes its central nucleus. Its foundation may lie either in the presence, in the stomach, of materials which are unsuitable for food, or to the reflexly induced reactions which tend to expell these substances. Owing to the commonness of nausea in connection with illnesses or emotional disturbances which do not have a digestive basis, the latter assumption seems to be most plausible. In this case, the essential experience must be regarded as a perception of the activity of those muscles which are primarily concerned in vomiting.

Coenaesthesia.—The term, coenaesthesia, is ordinarily used to stand for a general mass of experience which constantly represents the organism in its healthy state. As defined by Henle,[271] this presumably includes kinaesthetic factors. Under ordinary conditions, the experience lies in the margin of the conscious field, furnishing a constant background, against which other impressions are projected. However, in a state of especial organic vigor or "pep," the coenaesthetic factor may assume a high degree of clearness and intensity, constituting a perception of well-being or euphoria. This experience also appears, as an hallucination, in certain diseased states, such as paresis. The disappearance of the normal coenaesthesia under other pathological conditions, sometimes causes the patient to judge that his ego or personality has been obliterated.

Chapter XI

Composite Perception

172. Statement of the Problem.—Although consciousness should be conceived as being constituted by its parts, and not as being a sort of receptacle for the latter, it is nevertheless useful to deal with some of its structural characteristics in an abstract way. From this standpoint, we can speak of the *field* of consciousness as the *place* in which experience occurs. This "place" is not to be conceived as localized in space, although it contains space. The only meaning which we can assign to the word "location" in this context lies in the specific determinative relationship which obtains between any given conscious field and a certain physical organism. However, within the field in question, there are many separable locations, and the arrangement of these determines its nature and form. In spite of the fact that the elementary phenomena which appear within consciousness vary, from time to time, its general structure remains substantially constant. This is entirely conceivable, even if we suppose that the conscious field would cease to exist if it should become entirely without "contents."

Now, the field of consciousness as a whole can be subdivided into subsidiary fields, which are in a real sense *parts* of the larger one. Some of these correspond with different departments of sensation. Thus, we can distinguish between the visual field, the cutaneous field, the auditory field, etc. Each of these fields has its own characteristic general structure, which is more or less independent of the concrete phenomena entering into it at any given time. The problems of composite perception are largely concerned with relations which obtain between such experiential fields and corresponding structures in objective space. However, if it should turn out that there are forms of composition within experience which are non-spatial, these must also be considered in the present chapter. Although most of the component fields of consciousness are spatial in nature, it does not follow that they must all be of this character.

Section 38 (A)

COMPOSITE VISUAL PERCEPTION; INTROSPECTIVE ANALYSIS

173. The Total Visual Field and its Analysis.—The visual field is perhaps the most definitely spatial of all experiential schemata. As given directly to introspection, it is three-dimensional or geometrically "solid." It is in contact with the cutaneous-kinaesthetic, or general corporeal, field in the region of the eyes, as the latter are represented in experience. It can be compared with a hemisphere, or perhaps a very wide cone, which is hung on to the corporeal field at a Cyclopean eye-point. The individual self, who may be identified introspectively with the mass of corporeal experience, seems to stand behind the visual field and to look out into the latter. However, the total visual system must be regarded as being no less definitely a portion of consciousness than is the corporeal constellation.

Now, an introspective examination of the visual scheme shows that its three dimensions are by no means homogeneous. Considered as a spatial manifold, it is anisotropic, or different in different directions. In this respect, it differs from the space of Euclidean geometry and that of classical physics. In order to characterize the introspective, as well as the psychophysiological, relationships of visual space, we must provide it with axes of reference. The primary axis may be taken as the empirical *line of sight,* which is the line connecting the empirical eye-point with the subjective point of fixation, that point in the visual field at which we say we are "looking." The fixation lies in a constant direction in the field, since when we "look from one thing to another" the entire field moves over the system of things which are successively presented. We must next define two other axes, which are mutually perpendicular and also perpendicular to the empirical line of sight. These may be known as the *empirical visual vertical* and *horizontal,* respectively. Under normal conditions, the visual vertical may be specified in terms of its parallelism with the kinaesthetic vertical, a relationship which is made possible by the conjunction of the visual and kinaesthetic spaces through the eye-point. The exact point at which we consider the visual axes to intersect is a matter of convenience. Usually, it will be best to adopt an origin at the empirical fixation point, where the line of sight intersects a color surface.

We next note that the dimension of *depth,* along the line of sight or along other *lines of view* which radiate from the eye-points, differs qualitatively from those of the vertical or the horizontal, or any dimensions within planes which they determine. The inherent nature of this qualitative difference can only be appreciated introspectively, but it is associated with certain differences between the phenomena which appear in the two species of dimensions. These phenomenal differences can readily be described. Let us designate the plane which is determined by the horizontal and vertical axes as the *subjective visual projection plane.* Then, along any line in this plane we may be presented simultaneously with a *very large number* of separable, and possibly different, color elements. However, along any line of view there is ordinarily *only one* color, namely that which lies at that point in the projection plane at which the given line of view terminates. This last proposition has some minor exceptions in connection with transparent and "bulky" colors, the nature of which we have discussed in a previous chapter, but nevertheless the indicated difference remains a gross one. The characteristics of the depth dimension are expressed in everyday thought in terms of the impossibility of "seeing through" opaque things, the size relations between near things and the distant ones which they obscure, and so on.

However, in spite of these peculiarities of the depth dimension, it is not a valid description of the latter to formulate it solely in terms of the eye-point and the color areas which lie at the termini of various lines of view. Something intervenes between these areas and the eye. We may call this something "empty visual space," if we wish, but it is not empty in the sense of being qualitatively blank. It resembles in nature the so-called "glass sensation," described by Schumann,[272] and constitutes a distinctive type of visual experience element, different from color. The amount of this visual depth space which lies between the eye and the subjective fixation point constitutes the distance of the latter.

If we wish to specify positions quantitatively, within the visual field, we can do so in terms of just noticeable differences in position, or *space thresholds*. These can be marked off along the depth dimension, or along any line on the projection plane. Such liminal positions can be designated numerically, starting from the fixation point as an origin. Using units of this sort, we may note the following facts concerning the visual field. First, the magnitude of the field along any dimension is finite; it comes to an end vertically and horizontally and also forwards, along any line of view. The farthest possible point along any such line coincides with the sky surface in out-of-door vision. In the projection plane, the field fades off gradually, vignetting into non-existence at its edges, with no space at all beyond, for it to be set into. Second, the general form of the visual field is similar on the average to that of a flattened hemisphere, although the exact contour of the far boundary depends upon the particular things which are presented within the field. Under the usual conditions of vision, we find that at the end of each line of view there is an opaque surface color which terminates the visual field in the given direction. Such color surfaces may be located at many different distances from the empirical eye-point, along separate lines of view. Between each point on the contoured surface, which is thus determined, and the eye-point, there is a certain number of depth elements or a certain amount of depth distance.

There are some homely features of the visual field which are more or less constantly present, but which are not without importance in an understanding of its relationships to other sections of consciousness. One of these is the *nose,* which is given in the binocular field as a transparent projection both on the right and on the left. Other portions of the body are also ordinarily visible, their exact positions depending upon bodily posture, but they are never at a great distance from the eye-point. The movements of the body, particularly of the hands, establish important correlations between points in kinaesthetic and in visual space.

The purely introspective study of the movements of things in the visual field reveals some interesting relationships. The size of a given thing, such as a book, varies with its distance from the eye-point, or with the amount of intervening depth space. Things which are very close seem to be unduly large, whereas at remote distances they become very small and may vanish entirely. In an intermediate range of distance, however, they maintain their sizes almost independently of distance. The majority of things suffer some change in form when they are rotated with respect to a line of view.

174. The Visual Projection Field.—Our introspective judgments upon the sizes and shapes of things in the visual field vary as a function of what may be called our *attitude* towards the field in question. If we view the latter strictly as a three-dimensional volume, these sizes and shapes show a high degree of constancy. However, we can regard it in another manner, namely, as projected upon a true plane which is perpendicular to the line of sight. Under this attitude, we find that sizes decrease progressively with distance from the eye, and that forms vary radically as functions of the angles between the axes of things and the lines of view. The common-sense attitude towards the visual field seems to be primarily to consider it as a volume, but there are always some symptoms of the projectional tendency. These are particularly noticeable in connection with very distant things, the sizes of which seem always to be dependent upon their distances. Similarly, although we may see the rim of a cup as a circle, even when we are not looking directly into the vessel, we probably never escape entirely from the eliptical impression which comprises its configuration upon the projection plane.

Such considerations suggest that there is something inherently projectional about the entire visual field. It seems to have the properties of a two-dimensional system which has been artificially stretched or thickened perpendicularly to its natural plane. It is not impossible for practice to undo this effect, so that the visual patterns become substantially two-dimensional. This is particularly easy when one eye is closed. Seeing, as on a plane, is especially cultivated by artists. The plane can be located at any desired distance in the depth dimension, all of the color surfaces can be condensed upon it, and the resulting constant depth can then be neglected.

Introspectively, the visual projection field is roughly circular in shape, fading off into nonexistence at the edges. It may be regarded as being made up of elementary unit areas of color, each of which corresponds to a just noticeable difference in position along each of the two dimensions. Such elementary areas can be conceived as being themselves without internal spatial complexity, and as being constitutive of the field. Each point in the field must be filled by a color at all times, or it cannot continue to exist. Consequently, any concrete exemplification of such a field must constitute a two-dimensional color pattern.

The visual projection field has certain natural coördinates. The fixation point may be taken as an origin, and either the vertical or the horizontal as a reference axis. The method of polar coördinates then enables us to specify any position or group of positions in terms of an angle with the axis and a distance from the origin. Color patterns may be described, if desired, in such terms.

COMPOSITE VISUAL PERCEPTION; PSYCHO-PHYSIOLOGICAL RELATIONS

175. General Analysis of the Problem.—We may now turn to a consideration of the psychophysiological relationships which hold between the visual field and the objective stage of the response. It should be recalled that the original assumptions of our argument prevent us from identifying any of the spatial facts or experiential things, found within the visual field, with physical space relationships or objects which may happen to be before the physical eye at about the same time. We have spoken freely, above, about the "empirical eye," but this is not to be identified in any sense with the anatomical eye or eyes. Consequently, the problem is exclusively one of *correlation* between the empirical space facts and those which are involved in the response situation. Any attempt to *identify* factors between these two systems would be wholly absurd.

Now, in spite of the impossibility of identifying the things in visual consciousness with the objects which are in front of the eyes, it is very easy to demonstrate the functional dependency of the former upon the latter. It is also easy to show that this relationship is established through the medium of something which operates in straight lines between the object-points and the eyes. Even if we did not find ourselves apparently looking at the world from behind our eyes, the latter could be proven to be critical points for visual experience, by the process which we call obstruction of vision. If we move one small object so that it constantly eclipses another, it travels in a straight line from the latter to a point midway between the eyes. This fact is probably responsible not only for the impression that we see things through the eyes, but also, originally, for the physical conception of *light,* as an agency which passes along these lines and is intercepted by the obstructing object.

In the present state of physical science, we are familiar with many ways, in addition to vision, of demonstrating the existence and paths of light rays. Consequently, we can make use of them to specify the objective field of the visual response process. This field can be defined, approximately, as that portion of objective space which is traversed by all of the light rays which enter either of the two eye-pupils. It includes the surfaces of objects from which the light is reflected and the pathways along which the light reaches these surfaces from the source. However, the most important part of the specified space region is that which lies between the reflecting surfaces and the eyes. This more limited region consists of two cones having their apices at the respective pupils and having common bases on the reflecting surfaces. At a considerable distance from the eyes, this doubleness can be disregarded, the system being referred to a Cyclopean average eye-position. However, the most helpful treatment consists in considering each eye separately, the general principles which apply to one being the same as those for the other, characterizing the facts of *monocular vision*. Vision of this sort can be studied experimentally if one eye is closed or totally obscured. The added factors which appear when both eyes act together are characteristic of *binocular* vision, and are of particular importance in relation to the dimension of *depth* in the visual field.

176. Angular Relationships of the Projection Field.— Suppose that we restrict ourselves, in the first instance, to the monocular situation. We may then trace out the paths of all of the rays which enter the pupil of the given eye at any time, and thus determine the objective field that is involved. For most purposes, we can neglect the area of the pupil and treat it as a point, but if we wish to be quite exact we must deal with the paths of the rays through the so-called nodal point of the eye. The resulting diagram comprises a *sheaf of rays converging* upon this point from a restricted selection of objects in the environment. (See Fig. 14.) When the eyes move, this abstract sheaf also moves to cover a different group of objects. Now, such a system of radiating lines can best be specified in terms of *angular measures*. If we consider a group of lines which correspond with the natural subdivisions of the reflecting surfaces before the eye, each component of surface will be represented by a definite *solid angle*. Linear distances along the surfaces will correspond with plane angles between particular lines in the ray sheaf. Any given pattern of reflecting surface elements can be translated into a characteristic solid angular pattern of rays, on this basis.

It can now be demonstrated that the pattern of colors on the subjective "projection field" is determined by the

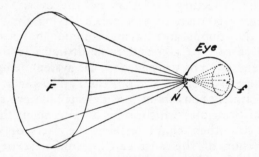

FIG. 14. THE OCULAR RAY SHEAF.

The figure represents a three-quarters view of the eye from the rear, showing the paths of the rays from a circular surface. The total cone of rays acting upon the eye at any time is, of course, much larger than shown. *F* is the fixation point in the environment while *N* represents the nodal point of the eye and *f*, the fovea.

distribution of particular kinds of radiant energy and related variables over the monocular ray sheaf, expressed wholly in angular terms. The positions of the objective factors in question along the lengths of the rays is immaterial. For each element of surface on the projection field, there is a corresponding element of solid angle in the ray sheaf. The size of a color area on the projection field is determined objectively by a solid angular size, while shape depends similarly upon an angular contour. Any patterned sheaf of rays can be projected upon a plane which is perpendicular to the central ray, and the pattern upon this plane will be approximately the same geometrical form as that of the colors on the subjective projection plane. Such similarity is possible, in spite of the qualitative differences which exist between the colors and the corresponding radiant energies, because both systems are spatial plane figures.

In specifying the exact relationships between such subjective and objective projection patterns, it is necessary to establish a correspondence between their reference axes, and to select appropriate units of measurement. It is found that the subjective fixation point corresponds approximately with the central ray of the monocular sheaf, while the horizontal axis is determined roughly by the geodetic horizontal. The peripheral limits of the subjective projection field are determined approximately by those of the sheaf. The units of measurement on the subjective side will naturally be just noticeable differences in position, while on the objective side they may be angular units such as the degree or the radian. Given these principles, we are in a position to discuss the relationships between the two patterns in an accurate manner.

If the similarity between the patterns were exact, there would be nothing further to do beyond establishing proportionalites between the corresponding measures of position. However, the similarity is actually imperfect. It is qualified in two different ways, first, by loss of detail and, second, by distortion. Under each qualification, we may consider the subjective projection field pattern as if it were an *optical image* of the objective pattern, formed by a lens. Such images always have less detail than have the corresponding objects, because of the finite resolving power of the lens. They are also more or less distorted. The discovery of these relationships between consciousness and the object field is independent of our knowledge of the eye as an optical instrument. Although an explanation is suggested in terms of the optical system of the eye, such an explanation is not actually adequate to all of the demonstrable facts.

177. Visual Acuity.—The low absolute resolving power of ordinary vision with respect to the physical object field is demonstrated at once when we consider that this field is teeming with electrons, light quanta, and other molecular constituents which are beyond the range of the most high-powered of microscopes. If we regard the individual proton as the finest existent physical detail, we can say that the latter is about one trillionth (10^{-12}) the size of the smallest detail which the eye can detect at the standard reading distance of 30 centimeters. The exact value of the resolving power depends upon numerous conditions, which include: illumination intensity, contrast, the form of the pattern which is concerned, position in the visual field, etc.

When two dark lines upon a white background are employed, the minimum separation which permits them to elicit a corresponding impression of doubleness in the center of the visual field is about one minute of arc, under good illumination. The reciprocal of the measure of the minimum visible separation in minutes is usually taken as the value of the *visual acuity*. When the object consists of lines abutted at their ends, a departure from linearity as small as one second of arc can sometimes be detected.[273] Towards the periphery of the visual field the acuity decreases, having a value of ⅟₁₅th at 10 degrees from the center, ⅟₅₀th at 25 degrees, and ⅟₂₀₀th at 40 degrees, relative to the value at the center. It is a logarithmic function of illumination intensity, or of brightness, up to about 60 millilamberts. Some of these relationships will be discussed in greater detail in the chapters on visual sensation.

It is probable that we should not regard these visual acuity measures as representing ultimate subjective space limens, since they stand for relationships between the object field and consciousness rather than for an introspective analysis of the latter. The smallest possible difference in position in the subjective visual projection field is not decreased by lowering the illumination, but the representation of objective patterns is blurred by this process in accordance with a definite law. The magnitude of this blurring will have to be expressed in terms of subjective space units which are independent of such losses of definition.

The facts of visual acuity show that the correspondence

between the patterns of the visual projection field and those of the objective phase of the response is limited to a macroscopic analysis of the latter. Detail which has a structure finer than that which is represented by the a־uity limit finds no distinctive correlate in the visual consciousness. All of the structural components which lie inside of a single confusion circle or threshold angle must be represented as an average. The angle or area, over which such averaging occurs, varies with illumination, angle with the central ray of the optic sheaf, etc. Thus, we are not dealing strictly with a point-to-point or even a part-to-part correspondence, but with an overlapping mosaic of averages, which are variable in their scopes and degrees of overlap from one region of the field to another. This kind of relationship is also found in the case of an object and an image which is formed of it by a lens suffering from aberrations that increase towards the periphery of the image field.

It will be recognized that, on account of the angular specification of the regions of confusion in relation to the visual projection field, the linear or areal magnitude of the smallest detail which can be separately represented in consciousness must depend upon the distance of the object from the eye. Thus, on the basis of a one minute limen, we find the following values: at a distance of 30 centimeters, 0.009 centimeters or 90 microns; at 100 feet, ⅓ inch; at one mile, 1½ feet; at one light-year, about 1700 million miles. In spite of their tremendous physical magnitudes, the nearest fixed stars are far too small to present any detail to the eye, but any object—no matter how small a visual angle it may subtend—can be visually represented as a point of light if it stands in isolation against a dark background, and gives off a sufficient quantity of visible radiant energy. Optical devices, such as telescopes and microscopes, which decrease the size of the minimum visible, accomplish this result by increasing the visual angular separation between the objective details.

178. Topographical Distortions of Form.—A careful study of the forms of the color patterns upon the subjective projection field, in relation to those of the determining objective projections, reveals certain definite distortions. The most general of these is the so-called barrel distortion which has been studied quantitatively by Helmholtz, Donders, Drualt and others.[274] The nature of this effect is shown in Fig. 15. The pattern on the visual field, corresponding

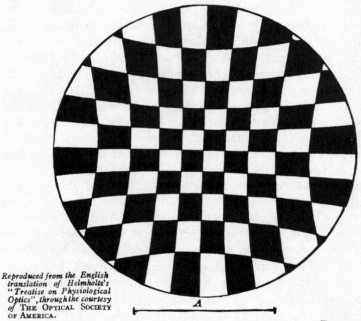

Reproduced from the English translation of Helmholtz's "Treatise on Physiological Optics", through the courtesy of THE OPTICAL SOCIETY OF AMERICA.

FIG. 15. TO DEMONSTRATE BARREL DISTORTION IN THE EYE.

This figure, due to Helmholtz, represents a checkerboard which has been distorted in a manner opposite to the barrel-shaped distortion of ordinary images upon the retina of the eye. Hence, if the figure is held close to the eye, it will be seen as a rectilinear checkerboard, undistorted.

to an objective rectilinear checkerboard, is curvilinear, with contours which are concave towards the center of the field. Elements of surface in the periphery of the field are shortened along their radial dimensions. We also find distortions of an astigmatic type, in which vertical contours are represented differently from horizontal ones. These are readily demonstrated by means of the charts used by oculists, and vary widely from one individual to another. Chromatic aberrations and irradiations are also found.[275] Under conditions of everyday life, these defects of vision are not very noticeable, but they can easily be shown in the laboratory.

Perhaps the commonest irradiation phenomenon consists in the "rays" which are seen about a star or other luminous point at night. These rays have a definite pattern which is the same for all stars within the visual field of a single individual; but the pattern varies with the individual. Purplish objects, such as certain railway signals, may be seen as a bluish and a reddish spot superimposed in bad registration: a phenomenon of chromatic aberration. Objects which are very close to the eye are represented with an extreme degree of blur so that their edges have a penumbral character, as if they were "out of focus." This may also occur in the case of distant objects, when one is looking at near ones. Very bright objects may be surrounded by a haze or halo. None of these effects can be referred to the objective phase of the response.

One of the most interesting cases of visual misrepresentation is that introduced at the so-called blind spot. This is an area having its center about 15 degrees from the fixation point on the horizontal axis of the field nasally, and about six degrees in diameter. Objective details which correspond with this area receive no representation in consciousness, when only a single eye is concerned. The color within the area in question is determined by the same objective variables which also determine its immediate environment. Details represented in the vicinity of the blind spot are subject to distorted localization. Under pathological conditions, such as those of scotoma, retinitis, hemianopia, and the like, similar phenomena may be observed with respect to other and larger portions of the visual field.

179. Geometrical Optical Illusions.—There is another class of distortions which seem to be functions, not of the location of the figure or its parts in the visual field, but of the form of the figure itself.[276] In some cases, orientation within the field is the determining factor. Thus, if the object is a straight line of constant length, its visual representation is apt to be longer when in the vertical than in the horizontal position. (See Fig. 16.) The letter, S, or

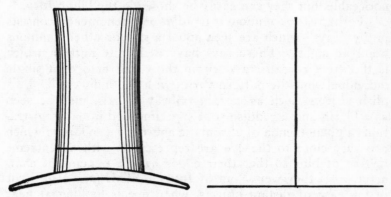

FIG. 16. ILLUSION OF VERTICAL AND HORIZONTAL LENGTHS.

The lengths of the vertical and horizontal lines, and the height and breadth of the hat are equal, objectively, although, in the visual presentation, the vertical dimension is the greater of the two.

the numeral 8, yields upper and lower halves of about equal size, in the conventional position, but striking inequality

FIG. 17. INFLUENCE OF DETAIL UPON APPARENT VISUAL LENGTHS.

The figure shows objectively equal distances, embracing various amounts of detail. In general, the distances which contain the most detail are represented visually as the greatest.

when inverted: 8 or S. This indicates a principle that the uppermost of two similar figure components will tend to be represented as larger than the lowermost one. Two objectively equal lengths, one of which embraces more features or details than the other, are represented as unequal. The one with the greatest internal complexity of configuration appears the longer.   (See Fig. 17.)

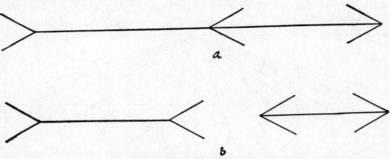

a

b

FIG. 18.   THE MÜLLER-LYER ILLUSION.

The two divisions of the horizontal line in *a* are objectively equal although, in the corresponding visual experience, they are markedly unequal. Similar considerations apply to the two separate figures in *b*.

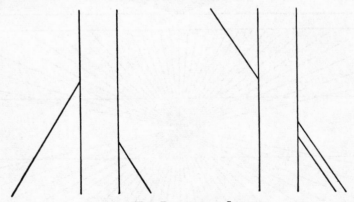

FIG. 19.   THE POGGENDORFF ILLUSION.

In the figure on the left, the two diagonal lines would meet objectively, on the left vertical line, if extended, although visually the right-hand diagonal is displaced downwards.   In the figure on the right, the lower and not the upper of the two diagonals on the right is objectively continuous with the diagonal on the left.

Certain combinations of lines at an angle to other lines or distances which are to be compared, have the effect of shortening or lengthening the representations of such lines or distances. The most striking example of this effect is the familiar Müller-Lyer illusion, shown in Fig. 18. The demarcated distances are clearly unequal in the visual presentation, but not in the objective figure. A similar illusion, in which the "error" is one of direction rather than of length, is given by Fig. 19. The diagonal lines which are objectively

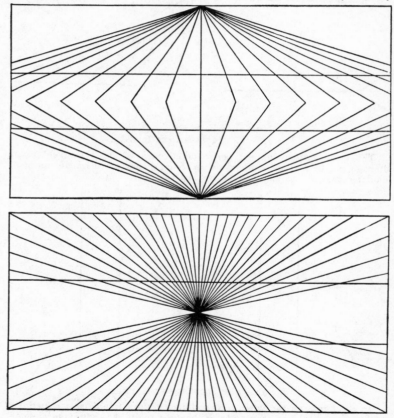

FIG. 20. ILLUSIONS OF CURVATURE.

The horizontal lines in the two figures are objectively straight, although their visual representations are curved.

in a straight path are represented visually as displaced from such a relationship. In Fig. 20, straight lines in the object yield curved lines in the visual field. An illusion involving areas is shown by Fig. 21.

When we class these relationships as illusions, we can only mean that there is a failure of the forms of the visual projection field patterns to be reasonably similar to those of

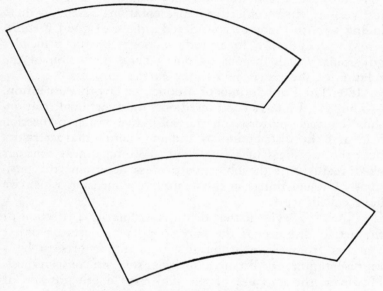

FIG. 21. JASTROW'S ILLUSION OF AREA.

The areas of the two sections of this figure are objectively equal, although the upper one is represented, visually, as smaller than the lower one.

the object patterns. However, there is no reason, *a priori,* to expect similarity rather than some other type of functional relationship. In fact, the high degree of similarity which actually obtains between the subjective and objective configurations in the majority of cases creates a rather difficult problem, because the pattern on the cerebral cortex is certainly very dissimilar to that of the corresponding object. (*Cf.* Volume III.) When we say that a line which is "actually" straight "looks" curved, or "appears" curved, we are using vague language which can only be interpreted to mean that the subjective visual pattern is different in the indicated manner from the objective one. However, if we say that the objective line "appears *to be*" curved, we are indulging in a reprehensible confusion of concepts. Objective lines never "appear," in the sense of being given in consciousness, and if they did they would no longer be objective. If their subjective representations resemble them in any way, this may be considered a piece of good fortune.

We shall return to a study of some of the principles governing visual illusions, in our general discussion of the relation of the visual field to the cortical process.

180. The Foundations of Monocular Depth Perception. —Thus far, we have considered only the functional relationships between patterns on the subjective visual projection field and the distribution of radiant energy characteristics over the ray sheaf of a single eye. We must next consider what features of the objective process determine the positions of visual things in the subjective dimension which we have called depth.

Now, it is evident that depth is ordinarily a function of the actual distance of the corresponding objects or object features from the anatomical eyes. It purports to be a representation of distances of this sort in consciousness. However, the measure of the subjective depth position of a thing is by no means proportional to that of the corresponding objective distance; and such relationships as actually exist between the two quantities are somewhat unreliable. As an object is moved away from the eye, the depth of the corresponding conscious representation increases rapidly at first, then more slowly, and eventually comes to a substantially constant value, following a law resembling that of the curve in Fig. 22. The exact constants which enter into this law vary with conditions that are logically distinct from the actual distance. However, the majority of these conditions are to some extent functions of distance or combine with the latter to yield integral effects significant of distance.   They comprise the so-called *monocular or secondary criteria* of depth.

If we follow our established method of beginning at the most remote points in the response propagation, we must first consider the part played by the source of radiant energy. Where this is the direct object of vision, it is subject to considerations similar to those which apply to objects which reflect, transmit or scatter the light from a source.   However, the position of the source with respect to such objects is of importance in determining the degree of illumination

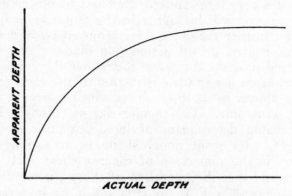

FIG. 22.   APPARENT DEPTH AS A FUNCTION OF ACTUAL DEPTH.

The curve shows, qualitatively, the manner in which the experiential distance of a visual thing from the empirical eye, varies as a function of the physical distance of the corresponding object from the physiological eye.

of their various parts, and thus governs the patterns of shadow, shade and highlight which are presented to the eye.   Now, even when the light source, itself, does not receive direct representation in consciousness, its position, intensity and form may be given indirectly, to comprise what Buehler [277] calls *illumination perspective*.   This impression is evidently determined by the orientation, density and sharpness of the shadows which occur in the illuminated field. The shadow pattern not only indicates the nature and position of the source, but it usually assists in throwing the illuminated objects into relief.   The positions of the shadows are informative concerning the relative positions of the objects in three-dimensional space, when the position of the source is established. Illumination perspective is least operative under conditions of out-of-door vision, in the open on a cloudy day, when the light source consists of the whole sky and shadows are practically non-existent.

Another characteristic of the monocular mosaic which may influence the depth impression is the relation of the bases of objects to the horizon, when the latter is visible. In the ideal case, where the ground is a perfect plane or a segment of a very large sphere, the bases of objects resting upon the ground will be higher in the objective projection pattern the further the objects are removed from the eyes. This is, of course, on the assumption that the eyes are in their normal position about five feet above the ground. A further criterion lies in the obstruction of the rays, emitted from one object, by another object which is nearer to the eye in the same line. The angular size of an object is also a very reliable determinant of its depth position in the visual field. Its projectional shape is indicative of its orientation in the dimension of the ray sheaf. It is customary to add that the operation of these criteria depends upon "familiarity" with the objects which are involved, but such familiarity obviously cannot be regarded as a property of the objects themselves, and hence cannot enter into the perceptual analysis. From our standpoint, we can only note that the objective relationships which we have just considered actually do play a part in determining depth perception in many cases. The effectiveness of all such determining factors is of course conditional upon cortical factors, some of which may be congenital but many of which depend upon "experience."

Another important depth-determining factor lies in what is commonly called *aerial perspective*. This consists in the proportion of scattered light which is added to the rays coming from objects at different distances from the eyes. Ordinarily, this scattered light is due to haze or smoke distributed more or less uniformly at all points between the objects and the eyes, so that it integrates to a value which is approximately proportional to the distance. Owing to the fact that the haze causes a greater relative change in the brightnesses of the darker, as compared with the lighter, regions of a visual pattern, it can readily be distinguished from brightness changes due to variations in illumination. The depth-determining properties of such scattered light involve its wave-length composition (corresponding to the subjective chroma) as well as its photometric intensity. Distances are characteristically *blue,* particularly in certain climates, such as that of California.

It is evident that although haziness provides a quantitative criterion of relative distance when the haze density is constant, it is unreliable, as an absolute criterion, to the extent in which the density can vary. There seems to be a certain standard minimum density which is characteristic of ordinary atmosphere, but when the density increases excessively, as in a fog, aerial perspective tends to lose its importance as a depth-determining factor. However, when the atmosphere is extremely clear, as it frequently is in Switzerland, objects which are really at a great distance may be represented as being relatively quite close to the eye. Buehler claims that the scattering of light by ordinary air over short distances, as within a small room, furnishes a basis for volumic perception of space under practically all circumstances. We may agree with Katz (*cf.* page 258, above), however, that this view is lacking in empirical foundation.

·181. **Diplopia and Disparation.**—All of the factors which we have thus far considered as determinants of depth can operate within strictly monocular vision. However, the simple experiment of closing one eye suffices to show that depth is enhanced in binocular, as compared with monocular vision. The difference is not very great under ordinary circumstances; it is by no means true that the subjective visual field is reduced to a plane when only a single eye is used. The most striking additional phenomenon, which can be observed with two eyes instead of one, consists in the *double representation* of objects at certain distances. Just what objects will be doubly represented depends upon the angle of convergence of the central portions of the ray sheaves of the two eyes. The central rays are identified by the requirement that, within the eye, they pass through the centers of the retinal foveas. Their paths in space are called the *lines of regard;* their point of intersection, the *point of regard* or *fixation;* and the plane which they determine: the *plane of regard.* (See Fig. 23.) Given any fixed angle of

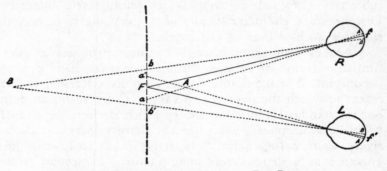

FIG. 23. DIAGRAM TO SHOW BINOCULAR RAY RELATIONS.

f and *f'* represent the positions of the foveas of the right and left eyes, respectively. *F* is the external point of fixation. *Ff* and *Ff'* are the two lines of regard, and the plane *fFf'* (the plane of the paper) is the plane of regard. Images of the points, *A* or *B*, will fall upon non-corresponding points of the two retinas. In the case of *A*, the disparation is "crossed" (heteronymous), while in that of *B*, it is uncrossed (homonymous). The double images of *A* will be projected at the points *a* and *a'*, at the distance of the fixation point, while those of *B* will be projected at *b* and *b'*, respectively.

convergence, the tendency towards doubling or *diplopia* is a function of the distance of the corresponding object from the eyes. Hence the phenomenon in question becomes a possible determinant of depth perception.

In order to understand the objective factors which are involved in this situation, we must study the relationships holding between the two sheaves of rays that converge upon the respective eyes from the same object field. We note, first, that in the majority of cases the optical patterns of the two sheaves will be at least slightly different, because of the different points of view of the respective eyes. (See Fig.

24.) Unless the objects are at an infinite distance, or are restricted to a plane so as to be symmetrically related to both lines of regard, the projections of the same object field pattern in the directions of the separate eyes, will yield different configurations. This means that the pattern on the subjective projection field will vary according as the right or the left eye is used; and that if both eyes are involved simultaneously there should be doubling, at least in some parts of the representation. Now, we find that, for the normal case, there is never any double representation of object details which lie at the point of regard. The

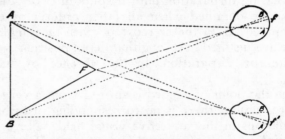

FIG. 24.   DIAGRAM TO SHOW DIFFERENCES IN RAY PATTERN FOR THE TWO EYES IN THE CASE OF A SOLID OBJECT.   .

The two eyes are represented as forming images of a triangular prism. It will be seen that, when fixation is directed to the point, *F*, the points, *A* and *B*, are disparately represented in the rays sheaves and retinal images.

distance of this point from the eyes may vary from infinity to about five inches, and it may be displaced to the right or left, or upwards or downwards, with respect to the usual reference position along the intersection of the median plane and a horizontal plane through the two eyes, or "straight ahead."

Now, when the point of regard is at a great distance (in excess of about three hundred feet), and all visible objects are at least as distant, there can be no doubling at any point in the visual field. Under these conditions the patterns upon the two ray sheaves are substantially identical, both in form and in relation to the respective lines of regard. If certain objects are now brought nearer, their angular projections within the respective ray sheaves will occupy appreciably different positions with respect to the central rays, and may have different shapes and sizes. However, there is no doubling of the corresponding subjective representation until this so-called *disparation* has reached a critical amount. The exact magnitude of the allowable disparation varies with conditions, but is in the vicinity of half a degree, or many times the monocular acuity limit. However, at angles of disparation as low as ten seconds of arc, we find that the visual thing in consciousness has moved forward appreciably in the dimension of depth. It continues to move forward with increasing disparation until it splits in two. Since this result can be obtained when all other criteria of distance are eliminated, as in the stereoscope with meaningless patterns, we are justified in stating that depth position is directly a function of disparation, in the absence of subjective doubling.

When the point of regard is shifted from a very distant to a nearer object, there is no corresponding disturbance of depth relations in the subjective visual field. Nevertheless, the principles of disparation hold substantially as before. With near vision, however, the disparation can be in either of two directions, "crossed" when the object is nearer than the point of regard and "uncrossed" when it is farther away than the latter. The difference between these two types of disparation is shown in Fig. 23. When the disparation is of the first type, the depth distance of the given thing is less than that of things corresponding to objects at the point of regard. When the disparation is of the second type, the depth is greater than that for the point of regard. It thus appears that disparation operates to determine the depth positions of visual things, with respect to that of the depth position corresponding to the point of regard. However, it provides no basis for locating the latter.

182. **Corresponding Rays, and Horopters.**—A great deal of mental energy has been expended in an endeavor to systematize these facts by means of a doctrine of *corresponding points,* and *horopters.* It is supposed that ex-

actly similar distributions of radiant energy characteristics over corresponding points of the two retinal fields—or upon corresponding ray-sheaves—will yield single vision, accompanied by depth localization in certain subjective reference lines or planes. *Corresponding points* are ordinarily defined

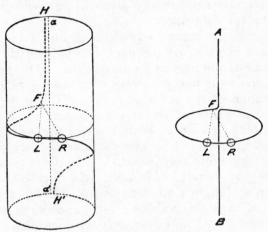

FIG. 25.   HOROPTER DIAGRAMS.

The diagram on the left represents the generalized horopter curve, *HFLRH'*, according to Helmholtz. *L* and *R* symbolize the left and right eyes, respectively, viewed from the rear. The (point) horopter passes through the nodal points of both eyes, circles around an imaginary cylindrical surface, and then turns upwards and downwards, approaching the vertical line, *aa'*, as an asymptote. The point of fixation or regard is represented at *R* (in general, not in the horizontal plane passing through the two ocular nodal points). The exact path of the horopter curve must shift in correspondence with changes in the position of this fixation point, since the latter is always located on the horopter. When the fixation point lies at a definite distance either in the median plane or in the horizontal plane through the ocular nodal points, the horopter assumes the special form represented in the diagram at the right. This consists, approximately, of a horizontal circle and a vertical line, intersecting in the median plane.

by means of an imaginary superposition of the two retinas, but they can be characterized just as readily, and more usefully, in terms of rays or direction lines outside of the eyes. If we imagine the two ray-sheaves to be brought together so that the central rays coincide, and in such a rotational relationship that pencils of rays representing the apparent

verticals for the two eyes also register, then all coincident
rays will be corresponding rays.   However, when the ray-
sheaves are in the positions determined by the normal interocular distance, only very restricted groups of corresponding rays can actually intersect in objective space.   The locus
of such intersections for any given disposition of the two
eyes constitutes a horopter.

In general, the horopter is a curved line, located mainly
in the space in front of the eyes, but passing through the
nodal points of the eyes at its extremities.   The exact form
and position of the horopter vary continuously as a function
of the location of the point of regard.   When the latter is
in the median plane, at an infinite distance, the horopter is
a plane instead of a line.   If the axes of the individual eyes
corresponding to the respective monocular apparent verticals were geometrically parallel, this plane would be a
vertical one at infinity.   However, the fact that the axes
in question are slightly convergent towards the feet of the
observer (at an angle of about $2° 20'$) causes the horopteral
plane to be located approximately in coincidence with an
ideal ground or floor plane.   The existence of a reference
system of this sort is to be attributed to the practical requirements of bodily orientation with respect to the surface upon
which we stand and walk.

When the point of regard is in the median plane, on the
horizontal level of the eyes,—as in straight-ahead vision—
but at a finite distance, the locus of intersecting corresponding
lines consists, approximately, in a circle (of Müller)—which
passes through the points of regard and the nodal points
of both eyes—together with a straight line through the point
of regard.   (See Fig. 25.)   Other positions of the eyes
determine horopteral curves and straight lines having different shapes and directions, but in general the curves are
derived from conic sections, departing continuously in form
from the typical Müllerian circle.   The direction which is
taken by the rectilinear portion of the horopter will depend
not only upon the position of the point of regard, but upon the
angle between the axes for the monocular apparent verticals.

In general, this rectilinear portion will intersect the point of regard and a point approximately at the observer's feet, but would be perpendicular to the plane of the curvelinear portion if the vertical axes were parallel. Horopters of the sort above considered are designated as point-horopters in contradistinction to line-horopters, the latter being surfaces forming the loci of lines (rather than of points) which are seen singly. Usually, the discussion of line horopters is confined to the cases of vertical and horizontal lines, respectively, and the corresponding horopters are known as vertical and horizontal horopters. Their intersections determine the point horopter.

Owing to the fact that the theory of corresponding points yields only a skeleton reference system, it cannot be regarded as furnishing a complete basis for the understanding of the conditions which underlie single vision. In reality, single vision is not restricted to a horizontal circle and a semi-vertical line under any conditions, nor to any other of the mathematically determined horopters. Owing to these facts, it is impossible to ascertain the forms and positions of point-horopters, experimentally, unless we define them in terms of volumes, which include all points that are seen singly for a given position of the point of regard. But such a definition defeats the purpose of the concept as a reference scheme for the study of disparation, and as an explanation of the way in which disparation determines the depth impression. However, Hering [278] has defined the *empirical horopter* in a different way, i.e., as a surface, including the point of regard, which yields the experience of a plane perpendicular to the subjective line of sight. Using vertical threads, Hering finds this surface to be itself a plane at a distance of two meters, but a cylinder concave towards the eyes at a lesser distance and convex in the same direction at a greater distance. These observations demonstrate certain interesting relationships between objective and corresponding subjective shapes in the third dimension, but they have no logical connection with the original definition of an horopter.

The most reasonable resolution of the doctrine of corresponding points appears to be that suggested by Panum,[279] according to whom, for every ray entering one eye, there is a *group* or pencil of corresponding rays entering the other eye. We can readily determine the identity of these groups for various positions of the point of regard, by means of the criterion of singleness of visual representation. But within any such group there must be a ray which yields the *minimum tendency* to diplopia, even if the tendency must exceed a critical value before actual diplopia occurs. Moreover, for each position of the point of regard, we should be able to determine a surface locus of points which show such a minimum tendency. The rays passing through various points on this surface might not yield the theoretical minimum which could be realized in the absence of geometrical restrictions, but they should provide the best values which are possible in practical use of the eyes. Because the relationships in question are probably established upon a practical, rather than upon a purely geometrical, basis it is to be expected that the values will also be the lowest possible under any conditions.

It is obvious that the determination of depth by disparation provides a means for controlling the contours of individual visual things in the third dimension. When the corresponding objects are sufficiently near to the eyes, different points on their surfaces may yield different degrees of disparation, thus governing a definite contour of depths. Things may also stand away, as wholes, from their backgrounds because of a general difference between the disparations which characterize all of their component points and those which go with the background. There are other factors which enter into the determination of the unity of visual things, in contrast with their environments. Among these may be mentioned motion of the whole object with respect to its background. Such motion may be merely projectional; not of the object itself, but of its representation in the ray-sheaves of the eyes in consequence of changing parallax, when the eyes are shifted from one point of view

to another. Such motion parallax, which is particularly
effective when looking out of the window of a moving train,
furnishes a further criterion of distance, and may yield a
very vivid depth impression even in monocular vision.

183. The Basis for Localization of Horopter Points.—
It will be recognized that the theory of binocular disparation
provides us with no immediate basis for the depth positions
of objects corresponding in position to the horopter itself.
The binocular system furnishes variables which are capable
of determining localization with respect to floating axes,
but no criterion for the positions of the axes in question.
The most reasonable hypothesis to account for the depth
locations of horopteral points would appear to be that they
rest upon a kinaesthetic or tactual representation of the
convergence positions of the eyeballs. The location of the
point of regard in objective space could obviously be ascertained from a knowledge of these positions, and the latter
could readily be represented by proprioceptive impulses
emanating from the external ocular muscles, or by tactual
impulses from receptors in the tissues of the orbit. However, experimental tests of these and allied hypotheses have
yielded almost wholly negative results.[280] It appears that,
in the absence of retinal cues, there is no reliable conscious
representation of the convergence point. The degree of
accommodation of the ocular lenses, which might also be
suspected of contributing to depth perception, is similarly
lacking in subjective correlates. Consequently, we must rely
upon some more subtle form of explanation.

At the present point in our discussion, we shall only
indicate the general principles which are probably involved,
since the problem belongs properly under the heading of
cerebration. (See Volume III.) In view of the intimate
relationships which hold between the subjective visual patterns and those which are represented in the ocular ray-
sheaves, it is astonishing that voluntary movements of the
eyes should involve no corresponding movements in the
visual field. Given patterns of radiant energy are displaced
relatively to the ray-sheaves, but the corresponding things

in the visual field remain stationary. This is true, whether the point of regard is displaced in the vertical-horizontal dimensions or whether it moves in the dimension of far to near. In the former case, it is the field of vision or of visibility which moves, and in the latter case, the fixation point. Thus both the projectional and the depth relations of visual things remain unaffected by voluntary eye movement. These considerations show that the reference axes of visual experience as a whole are set subjectively or cortically, by the given system of things, and not by the relations of external objects to the sense-organs. It might be said that the world of visual things is directly a function of the relations of the objects amongst themselves (including the organism), without reference to sensory mechanisms; and in any ordinary situation this statement would have a high degree of truth. However, under experimental or pathological conditions, the relationship in question may break down completely.

Now, the total system of objects which is represented subjectively includes one's own body. A portion of this is given visually, but it receives a much more important representation in kinaesthetic trems. There can be no doubt that the kinaesthetic and the visual features of consciousness are closely interrelated; and it seems likely that the ultimate axes of reference for the visual world are kinaesthetic in nature. In order for the total visual system to move, it must be displaced subjectively with respect to the kinaesthetic system. When the eyes are adjusted voluntarily, there are no changes of this sort, for reasons which are to be sought in the mechanisms of the central nervous organization. However, if the eyes are displaced by means of the finger, or gyrate involuntarily, as in nystagmus, the relation to the kinaesthetic system is disturbed. Thus, in dizziness, the whole visual world seems to revolve around the body, although objectively there is no motion, except that of the eyes. We shall discuss these relationships in greater detail in later chapters.

184. The Stereoscope and Related Instruments.—If it is true that depth is a function of disparation, then it should be possible to produce and to regulate the depth experience by presenting separate plane pictures or diagrams to the respective eyes, when such pictures are made to correspond with the projections of real objects at different distances. This is done in the instrument known as the *stereoscope,* which incorporates optical aids to compensate for the abnormal relations between convergence and accommodation, otherwise introduced in viewing two patterns simultaneously so as to yield single vision. The comparative certainty with which stereoscopic pictures elicit the depth impression shows that disparation is ordinarily the most powerful determinant of this aspect of visual experience. However, if a situation is created in which disparation is opposed by other depth-determining factors, the latter may sometimes prevail. The very interesting instrument, known as the *pseudoscope,* comprises an optical arrangement which presents to one eye the sheaf of rays properly belonging to the other eye; and with the majority of objective configurations it yields an inverted depth pattern. Far objects are represented as near, and near objects are represented as far; convex objective surfaces yield concave ones in consciousness and so on. However, this instrument does not usually succeed in making a human face appear like the inside of a mask. Evidently, the cortical set-up for a face is so well established that disparation factors are unable to reverse it.

When there are no opposing influences, and particularly when the criteria of depth are favorable, the stereoscope enables us to elicit very perfect three-dimensional experiences in the entire absence of the normally corresponding objects. The results are particularly realistic when the stereoscopic pictures are photographically reproduced in full color (as by the autochrome process). The method of colored shadows, which has been applied in certain vaudeville acts, is especially effective because the monocular angular sizes change in synchronism with the disparation, in the proper manner. Such stereoscopic experiments constitute important data in demonstrating the subjective nature of the entire visual world. We have every reason for believing that an arrangement for projecting synchronized stereoscopic motion pictures in full natural color upon the two eye-fields would yield a completely realistic representation of the object situation which had been photographed. In this case the experience would be controlled from a phase in the objective stage of the response which is closer to the eyes than that which ordinarily governs it, and would be independent of a true third dimension in the objective system (*cf*. page 169).

185. Limits of Binocular Depth Perception.—On account of the fact that the degree of disparation, due to the separation of the viewpoints of the two eyes, decreases rapidly with increasing distance, it is to be expected that the control of this factor over the depth impression will diminish as the distance in question becomes greater. Indeed, it is found that at distances exceeding about one hundred meters (328 feet), the binocular criteria become ineffective. At lesser distances, what may be called *disparation acuity,* or the inverse measure of the just noticeable disparation, is practicaly constant when expressed in angular terms, regardless of the distance. The breakdown of disparation as a determinant of depth at distances in excess of one hundred meters is due to the fact that the maximum possible disparation between this distance and infinity is less than the threshold amount. The threshold angle is substantially identical with the minimum difference in visual angle which is detectable monocularly, namely, between five and ten seconds of arc.[281] Values of this order of magnitude are obtained in monocular acuity measurements which involve sudden breaks in the continuity of otherwise straight lines (*cf*. page 328). It is therefore to be supposed that these two acuity measures are dependent upon the same anatomical or physiological factors. It should be obvious that constancy of the angular disparation threshold implies that the just noticeable difference in distance from the eye increases constantly with the distance in question, becoming infinite beyond about one hundred meters. The distance range of the disparation factor can be increased artificially by means of the *telestereoscope,* which was invented by Helmholtz.[282] This instrument effectively increases the interocular distance.

Section 39

COMPOSITE AUDITORY PERCEPTION

Auditory experience is composite in at least two different ways. First, auditory qualities have a definite localization in experiential space, and this space must be conceived as having an auditory structure, in order to make such localization significant. Frequently, a plurality of auditory "images," or of apparent sources, is simultaneously presented within this space, and individuals who have been born blind obviously cannot relate their auditory experiences to visual ones, but nevertheless localize them with more than usual definiteness. Secondly, any auditory image may be complex in a non-spatial dimension, or may show simultaneous, but discriminable, components. Frequently, these are combinations of tones called clangs, chords, etc., but noises may also be separable from simultaneously occurring qualities of any sort. Quite often, the spatial and the qualitative forms of complexity interweave, within the experience, qualitatively distinct sounds being presented at separate points in experiential space.

186. The Auditory Analysis of Sound.—Spatially interpenetrating, but discriminable, auditory qualities are sometimes said to *fuse* in varying degrees. However, such fusion must be construed, not as a process, but as a condition or state, and in the latter sense is significant of various degrees of emergence or separability of the component qualities. The naïve observer finds much more fusion, as a rule, than do musically or psychological trained individuals. This difference may be partly dependent upon the mechanism of introspective report, but in all probability it also involves a real difference in the degree of discreteness of the experiential components.

Now the interpenetrative structure of a musical experience can frequently be correlated with harmonic complexity in the vibrations of the sonorous source, or of the emitted sound waves. From the strictly physical standpoint, such "complex" vibrations do not need to be made up of individualized components, in all cases; since the same material particles may be involved in all aspects of the movements. However, there are numerous, well-established methods by means of which oscillations of this kind can be resolved into formal constituents, and sometimes these constituents are really produced by the mixed action of physically separable sonorous sources. This is true, for example, in the case of the individual piano strings which vibrate when a chord is struck upon the keyboard.

The so-called analytical function of hearing may therefore be regarded as being related to the movements of the sonorous bodies, or to the oscillations of the air particles, in the same manner which characterizes the relations of an harmonic analyzer to these same processes. But in certain cases, as in that of the piano chord, the individual analyzed components can be correlated with discrete mechanical elements. In other cases, they correspond only to conceptually separable aspects of an integral physical process. Thus, the string of a musical instrument may vibrate as a whole, in halves, in thirds, etc., simultaneously, and yield corresponding components in consciousness. Insofar as these components do not emerge distinctly, but are "fused," the constitution of the physical vibrations is represented by the timbre, as previously noted, this being a qualitative and unanalyzed aspect of the experience.

Variations in the degree of analysis, or fusion, between individual observers, cannot, of course, be accounted for on the basis of their immediate environmental conditions, showing no correlation with the latter. However, amount of fusion is a function of the particular acoustic frequencies which are involved, and more particularly of their mathematical relationships to one another. It is found that, in general, greater fusion occurs between components which stand in simple harmonic relations to one another, than under other conditions. Thus, the greatest fusion is that of the octave, representing a ratio of one to two; the next greatest is the fifth, a ratio of two to three; the next the fourth, a ratio of three to four, etc. According to Helmholtz,[283] these phenomena are determined by the fact that the specified combinations of frequencies naturally occur in the sounds emitted by single vibrating bodies, such as strings or air columns, so that they would thus find a basis in the objective phase of the response. We shall have more to say concerning the nature and basis of fusion in the chapter on auditory sensation. (See Volume II.)

187. Psychophysiology of Auditory Localization.— When we are listening to a large orchestra, we ordinarily localize the various instrumental qualities at separate points within experiential space. In general, whether we are dealing with a simple or with a complex auditory experience, the quality tends to have a fairly definite localization, which usually corresponds approximately with the location of the acoustic source in physical or response space. In other words, there tends to be a point-to-point correlation between the two spaces. Complete accuracy in such correspondence ordinarily involves visual cues; the auditory localization is thus partly a function of factors operating through optical channels. But even when the action of such visual or other non-auditory variables is excluded, there is still a definite determination of the localization as a function of the position of the acoustic source with respect to the head of the observer. It is found, however, that the localization may be ambiguous or variable, within conical loci, having as their axes a line passing through the two ears. In other words, the acoustic object or the sound-waves determine the angle of the subjective auditory image with the median (sagittal) plane (which bisects the head, vertically), but fail to determine it in other dimensions. It is found, furthermore, that if the sound is prevented from reaching one of the ears, the localization becomes entirely indeterminate with respect to the real position of the acoustic source, except on the basis of non-auditory factors.

Such observations suggest that the laws of auditory localization can be formulated as functions of the relations of the source, or its emitted sound-waves, to the respective ear positions. The subjective axis of auditory reference moves with the head, and it seems necessary that the localization should be determined by some variable which is a characteristic of the binaural, as opposed to a monaural, system. Such a variable must evidently consist in a *difference* between the sound which acts upon one ear and that which acts upon the other. The differences which are physically conceivable include those in intensity, phase, frequency composition, and "time." Experiments show that all of these factors are involved, under certain circumstances, but that the second one is by far the most important. In order to separate the influences of the several factors, we may arrange an artificial situation, possibly involving two separate sound sources which act individually upon respective ears, these being variable as to intensity, phase, timing or composition in predetermined relationships.

The results of such experiments vary somewhat with frequency, when a substantially pure sinusoidal wave is employed. Banister found that localization is a function of phase difference, over a frequency range from 133 to 1705 cycles per second.[284] Halverson's [285] results indicate that the dependency in question extends from 600 cycles to the upper of limit of audibility (about 15,000 cycles in his experiments). At relatively high frequencies, greater than about 1300, two or more subjectve auditory images may appear simultaneously. Bowlker [286] observed as many as four of these at 3050 cycles. The angular zone, with respect to the sagittal plane within which the sound can be localized is narrowed down, with increasing frequency, above about 500 cycles, until, at the upper limit of audibility, all auditory images are practically confined to the region of the sagittal plane. The dependency of this zone of localizability upon frequency is shown in Fig. 26. When brief, possibly non-sinusoidal stimuli, such as clicks, are employed, the auditory image is localized on the side towards the prior stimulus, following a principle which is substantially identical with that for phase difference.

Under normal conditions, with a single acoustic source, there are substantially no intensity differences between the two ears, for low-frequency sounds; but the head casts appreciable shadows in the case of sounds of high frequency.

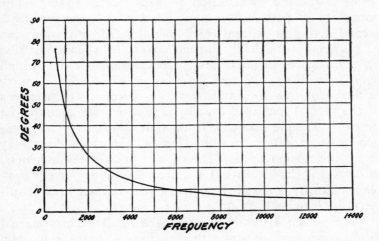

FIG. 26. LIMITS OF AUDITORY LOCALIZATION FOR VARIOUS FREQUENCIES.

This curve, due to Halverson, shows how the limiting angle, for the purely auditory localization of tones, with respect to the sagittal (median) plane of the head, varies as a function of the frequency of a sinusoidal stimulus.

Experiments show that the latter are localized towards the side at which the intensity is greatest, but that when there is a conflict between phase difference and intensity difference, the former is predominant.[287] Intensity differences between low-frequency sounds, artificially produced, yield two auditory images, but do not affect the localization. Considerable variation, from one individual to another, is found in these perceptual relationships.

Section 40

COMPOSITE CONTACT PERCEPTION

188. General Principles of Cutaneous Localization.—
Tactual experience is characterized by a very definite degree
of structuration, or coexistential complexity. This complexity is essentially spatial in character. In the first place,
any simple or elementary contact experience ordinarily possesses a definite localization in experiential space. The
possibility of such localization indicates the existence of a
tactual manifold, within which special tactile variations can
be placed independently of the spaces of vision, audition
or other sense departments. Observations made by and
upon individuals who are defective in these other sensory
fields corroborate this interpretation. Secondly, the contents
of the tactual manifold usually have a definite pattern, the
simplest example probably being that which is given in experiments upon the "two-point limen," in which there may
be an impression of doubleness, as opposed to singleness,
of contact. Practically any required degree of pattern complexity can be realized, however, if the contact area is sufficiently large.

The principles which are involved in elementary tactual
localization, say, of point impressions, seem to rest upon
a part-to-part correspondence between the experiential touch
field and the surface of the body, anatomically or physiologically considered. However, this correspondence is not
between geometrically minute points, but rather between
finite areas, within which localization is indeterminate. The
magnitude of these areas is perhaps constant on the subjective side, but is a function of position, anatomically. Thus,
on the tip of the tongue, the sensory circles, or circles of
confusion, are very small (say, one millimeter in diameter),
whereas in the middle of the back they may be linearly
sixty-seven times as great. In general, the precision of
determination of the subjective localization, with respect to

that of the point of contact of the object upon the skin surface, increases in proportion to the mobility of the corresponding organic member.

It has been claimed [288] that each different location, within the experiential touch field, is characterized by a qualitative distinctiveness. Such a qualitative peculiarity for any given point is said to constitute its "local sign," and it has been supposed that local signs of this kind are the fundamental criteria of location. Now, although we may acknowledge that some qualitative differences of this sort exist, we have no evidence that they are responsible for the correlation which holds between the subjective location of a tactual impression and the cutaneous position of the corresponding object or stimulus. This correlation appears, rather, to be a fundamental psychophysiological datum or principle. It would be quite as reasonable to endeavor to explain the qualitative variations in terms of different localization, as to follow the usual argument regarding local signs.

189. Patterns in the Cutaneous Field.—When two separate pointed objects are placed simultaneously in contact with the skin, the corresponding experience will reveal doubleness of structure only when the objects in question are spaced apart by a distance at least as great as the so-called two-point limen, or space threshold for touch. If the separation is less than this, there will be only a unified areal impression on the experiential field. This area will not necessarily be circular in subjective form, but may be dumbbell-shaped or oval in correspondence with varying degrees of separation of the object points. The magnitude of the liminal distance varies approximately in proportion to that of the indefiniteness of localization in the given portion of the field, ranging from 1.1 millimeters on the tip of the tongue to 67.1 millimeters on the mid-line of the back. At the finger tips, it is about 2.2 millimeters (third finger), and on the palm of the hand, 11.3. The distance is also a function of the *orientation* of the pair of contacting points upon the given region of the body surface, being as a rule less transversely than longitudinally of the trunk or the limbs.

As in the case of localization, the minimal distance is quite uniformly less in proportion to the motility of the given portion of the skin, decreasing regularly with increasing distance from a fulcrum. The magnitudes of these thresholds may also be reduced as much as fifty per cent by practice, in the unpracticed individual. The distance is lessened by applying the two points successively rather than simultaneously, by having them at different temperatures, etc.

Definite localization and representation of the pattern of the contacting object is not restricted to simple pressure influences upon the skin. Ponzo [289] has shown that cutaneous pain, resulting from incipient or actual skin injury, is localized just as accurately as is the tactual quality, the greatest precision being at the tip of the tongue, the end of the forefinger and the middle part of the free border of the lower lip. The least precision is found on the lateral surfaces of the thorax. Thermal action upon the skin yields a localization which is somewhat less accurate than that produced by pressure or injury, cold giving greater precision than does heat. Ponzo found a two-point threshold for cold lying between 0.8 and 3.0 millimeters and, in the same bodily region, a threshold for heat between 2.0 and 5.0 millimeters. The two-point threshold for pain is less than that for pressure, while the latter is less than that for cold.

Weber [290] used the term, "sensory circles," for the boundaries of areas within which multiple contact yields singleness of tactual experience, although as a rule, these areas are not precisely circular in form, on account of the variation of the limen with orientation. If complex contact forms are employed, they tend to produce circular impressions within experience, when the corresponding stimuli include the same numbers of unit sensory "circles," along all diameters. Thus, a geometrical circle may yield the subjective impression of an oval, or *vice versa*. In order that a circle should be appreciated as such by the tip of the tongue, its diameter must be greater than 3.3 millimeters,

while on the skin of the abdomen, a diameter of 55 millimeters is required.

The presentation of a unified tactual object, or thing,
is produced in consciousness when areas of the skin are
affected which are normally excited by single physical
objects, whether or not such action is realized in the given
instance. Thus, contact with opposite surfaces of two adjacent fingers yields such a result, but if the fingers are
crossed, so that a single object makes contact with areas
not ordinarily affected simultaneously under such conditions,
the impression is that of two objects (Aristotle's illusion).
Conversely, under these circumstances, two objects may yield
the impression of a single one.

Katz [291] has recently reported some very extensive
studies upon complex qualitative aspects of tactual experience in relation to their objective conditions. He distinguishes a number of "modes of appearance" in the tactual
field, which are analogous with those found in visual experience. They include surface textures, fluid volume,
flexible solid volume, etc. However, since these impressions
depend upon motion of the skin with respect to the objects,
they may best be considered in the chapters dealing with
temporally conditioned perceptions. Katz also distinguishes
between *touch figure* and *touch ground,* the latter consisting
of intermediate, unfilled portions of the tactual space, in
contrast with those which are occupied by the given
impressions.

Section 41

ORIENTATIVE PERCEPTION (ABSOLUTE KINAES-
THETIC COMPOSITE PERCEPTION)

In our chapter dealing with the components of the perceptual relationship in the kinaesthetic domain, we have
discussed some of the elementary correlations which are
involved. We have seen that it is difficult to describe these

relationships without introducing considerations of structure or pattern. We seem forced to deal, on the introspective side, with specific configurations of psychical components; and the forms in question are found to be functions of concurrent physical constellations. A complete analysis of the introspective relationships shows that we must consider, not only forms of combination among various kinaesthetic constituents, but also the relations of such factors to others which are visual, tactual and auditory in nature. We have distinguished between absolute and relative kinaesthetic experiences, and these two classes of factors combine with each other in characteristic ways. The total kinaesthetic complex, thus formed, is joined in a very coherent manner with the other subjective patterns, and furnishes a general reference system for the latter.

190. The Pattern Psychophysiology of the Kinaesthetic Vertical.—If we regard the impression of the kinaesthetic vertical as being a special, self-sufficient, component of experience, we realize that it must become structurally related in a definite way with other experiential components before it can convey any useful information concerning the disposition of the physical body with respect to the physical vertical. The kinaesthetic vertical might come and go with changes in the gravitational-accelerative force field, but this would not constitute a representation of direction. However, if we introduce the spatial configurations which are comprised by the relative kinaesthetic experiences (*vide* next Section), the vertical may manifest variations in orientation with respect to the latter or *vice versa*. The two types of kinaesthesis combine in the same experiential space; so that the vertical may have a directionality relative to the other kinaesthetic patterns, just as any group of components among the latter may be oriented with regard to further components of the same system. However, the vertical is taken as the fixed or stationary feature and the other constituents are experienced as undergoing changes in orientation. This relational scheme is expanded by the addition of (1) the tactual field, (2) the visual field, (3) the auditory field, and (4) the organic field.

The laws which govern the relation of the kinaesthetic vertical to the other spatial configurations are substantially the same, regardless of the identity of the latter. The simplest situation obtains when all visual cues to the vertical are excluded. This occurs in the dark, when the eyes are closed and when the retinas are stimulated uniformly or in an entirely unfamiliar manner. Under such conditions, there is still a definite orientation of the vertical with respect to the general space pattern, including the meaningless visual presentations. If the head is tipped to one side or the other, the relationship of the vertical to the total kinaesthetic-corporeal system is substantially unaffected. The visual field seems to rotate about the line of sight, but the things within the field retain their original orientations with respect to the vertical.

If the whole body is rotated through a limited arc, as in reclining—whether on the back or on the side—the kinaesthetic-corporeal system rotates with reference to the kinaesthetic vertical, the latter remaining fixed. Hence, it appears that the kinaesthetic vertical behaves as if it were the fundamental angular reference axis of introspective space in general. The other systems of spatial experience derive their orientations by virtue of their relationships to this vertical. This principle holds even when the eyes are viewing familiar objects, but ordinarily, under these circumstances, the lines in the objects which are recognized as vertical, retain their parallelism with the kinaesthetic axis, regardless of all motions of the head or body.

These relationships can be explained perceptually by saying that the kinaesthetic vertical represents the direction of the gravitational force field. The orientation of the relative kinaesthetic, tactual, visual or other subjective space fields, with respect to the kinaesthetic vertical, may be regarded as a function of the orientation of the corresponding objects to the gravitational-accelerative resultant which is acting upon

the body. This resultant is a vector, having a definite directionality in physical space. If the object field rotates with
respect to this vector, the corresponding subjective presentations rotate in an analogous manner with respect to the
kinaesthetic vertical. If, on the other hand, the direction
of the gravitational-accelerative resultant is altered, as on
a merry-go-round, the kinaesthetic vertical usually maintains
its status as a fixed reference axis, and the visual and other
kinaesthetic fields seem to be rotationally displaced.

In this case, we automatically adjust the body so as to
make its vertical axis coincide with the given force resultant,
so that only the visual and auditory fields are tipped. If
the eyes are closed, we believe ourselves to be standing erect,
and if under these conditions we are asked to hold a stick
vertically we place it at a slant with the true vertical, corresponding in angle to the given resultant. Under such
conditions, if the visual environment is sufficiently familiar,
we may intellectually adopt certain visual lines as being true
verticals, but if it is unfamiliar there is an inevitable error
or illusion in our judgment of the visual vertical. This happens, sometimes with disastrous results, in the case of
aviators flying in the clouds, when their machines are ac-
celerating angularly or linearly.

191. Directional Features of Vertigo.—We have already noted, in our discussion of vertigo as a component of
kinaesthetic experience, that it is a function of the rotatory
acceleration of the body or the head. Now, such acceleration, like the gravitational field, is treated in physics as a
vector, which has a definite directionality as well as magnitude. Rotatory acceleration of the body can occur
physically in any plane of space, but any such acceleration
can be resolved into three dynamic components in three
reference planes which are mutually perpendicular. The
quantitative values of the components in these planes serve
to determine the acceleration completely.

If we regard vertigo from the introspective standpoint,
we judge it to be a form of motion and, hence, as having
a temporal aspect. However, there can be little doubt that

an instantaneous cross-section of experience (a consciousness) would still be capable of containing the characteristic vertigo quality. It is also highly probable that under these conditions, the vertigo would not lose its directionality. This corresponds to the physical or mathematical truth that accelerations are independent, for their magnitudes and directions, of any finite span of time, having values at mathematical instants. Consequently, it seems legitimate to consider the directional or orientative features of vertigo in the present chapter.

When the body or the head is set into rotation—say, from right to left—there is a corresponding rotational or vertigo experience which comprises a rotation of the kinaesthetic-corporeal system with respect to the external system of things, as represented primarily by the visual field. This occurs even when the eyes are closed. When they are open, the total impression is enhanced by the purely visual movement of external things with respect to the experiential body, or *vice versa*. This visual movement depends upon a pursuit of stationary objects by the eyes, and hence does not involve any large change in the angular patterns which are operative upon the latter, except in the intervals of non-pursuit; and during these intervals the eye-movement in the opposite direction is so rapid that it is doubtful whether there is any clear vision. If the head is held vertically, the rotation is represented subjectively as about a vertical axis.

If the rotation of the body continues at a constant angular velocity, and if the eyes are kept closed, the subjective impression of rotation disappears, so that the body is now represented as being stationary. If the eyes are opened at this point in the experiment, there is visually perceived rotation, involving blurring of things if the angular velocity is high. The eyes no longer follow stationary objects but move uniformly with the head and the rest of the body. If, now, the objective rotation is stopped, with the eyes closed there is movement of the experiential body in the opposite direction from that of the original rotation. However, we may note that, even here, the subjective rota-

tion is still in the same sense as the acceleration since, in the
case now being considered, the latter is negative and hence
its direction is opposite to that of the velocity which is being
reduced or obliterated. If the eyes are opened, visual things
are found to be revolving with the body in the manner which
is required by the subjective rotation of the latter. This
effect is to be attributed to the nystagmic oscillations of the
eyes which occur in connection with illusory vertigo of this
sort.

If the head is maintained in the vertical position,
throughout these experiments, the subjective rotation will
be in a horizontal plane in all cases. However, if, during
the positive acceleration and motion, the head is held at an
angle to the vertical or if it is displaced from the vertical
during or after rotation, special phenomena occur. Regardless of the position of the head, the impression accompanying
the positive acceleration will be of rotation in a plane corresponding to that of the objective change, although with
due representation of the special position of the head. If
the latter is bent forward and the body is rotated in the
horizontal plane, and then stopped, the opposite rotation
which is then given subjectively will be about a vertical axis,
so long as the head is held in its original position. However, if the head is raised, the plane of the subjective rotation will move with the head, so that the experiential body
may now come to rotate about a horizontal axis. If the
eyes are open, the visual impression of movement will be
consistent with the kinaesthetic one. This is because the
nystagmic movements of the eyes adjust themselves in all
three dimensions of space to the exact plane of the bodily
rotation.

It therefore appears that the delayed perception of
negative rotatory acceleration has a direction which is correlated in three dimensions with the angular orientation of
the head in objective space. If the axis of the head is displaced from the vertical, during rotation, the plane of the
subjective movement will be found to change from that of
the actual movement. The exact orientation of the new

plane will depend upon a resultant of the positive accelerative component in the plane of actual rotation and a negative component in a plane coresponding to the new position of the head. If the position of the head is changed, during rotation at a constant angular velocity after the original vertigo has disappeared, the subjective representation of rotation reappears, and in the proper plane.

We shall consider some further aspects of the vertigo experience in our chapter on temporal perception. (See page 395.)

(See page 395.)

Section 42

BODILY POSTURE PERCEPTION

We have seen that experience contains definite phenomena which represent the motor states and processes of the body. These phenomena are divisible into three general classes: the attitudinal, the tensive, and the exertive, respectively. All three of these groups fall into the category of relative, as opposed to absolute, kinaesthetic experiences. We have already considered the principal facts relating to these experiences, regarded as elements of consciousness. However, as in the case of the absolute kinaesthetic phenomena, it is difficult to deal with certain of them adequately except as patterns. This is particularly true of the attitudinal experiences, which are correlated with postures or changes in posture of the body. The tensive and the exertive types of experience show characteristic distributions in subjective space, but their pattern aspects are less important than are those of the attitudinal class.

192. Attitudinal Patterns and their Psychophysiological Correlations.—It is evident that many aspects of posture can receive representation consciously in visual and tactual terms, but when conditions eliminate such terms, the remaining kinaesthetic experience still shows a very close correlation with the given physical configuration of the organism. The kinaesthetic patterns resemble those of touch, in general quality, although they are much more difficult to analyze introspectively. Their inherent natures are best appreciated when visual accompaniments are eliminated, as, for example, in the experiment cited by Sherrington,[292] of touching any desired finger-tip of one hand by a finger of the other hand, in the dark. Their normal existence is also demonstrated by the serious modifications of consciousness which occur when the nervous structures that underlie them suffer derangement of function, as in locomotor ataxia.

In spite of the rather elusive nature of the attitudinal experiences, they are actually highly definite and characteristic at each instant. Slight changes in pattern are immediately detectable, and the exact form of the experience is of great practical importance to thought and volition. A great deal of our thinking, as we shall see in a later chapter, is actually carried out in terms of such distinctive kinaesthetic patterns, either perceptually or imaginally presented. What the man in the street calls an attitude, or perhaps a "hunch," is really a special kinaesthetic schema of this sort.

Although ordinary introspection does not permit us to formulate kinaesthetic patterns as mosaics of distinct units, arranged in experiential space, it is nevertheless possible to describe any such pattern as a definite spatial form. Each such form is representative of the body as a whole, and all possible kinaesthetic forms can be arranged into a continuous series, involving gradual transitions from one pattern to another. Under normal conditions, the members of such a series stand in correlation with a corresponding series of anatomical attitudes of the body. As the latter are varied, the kinaesthetic forms change to correspond. The objective facts which are here involved are wholly relative between different members of the body, being concerned with the geometrical, kinematical or dynamical relationships between such parts. These facts are to be abstracted from positions or movements which are of the body as a whole, relative to the environment.

The fundamental concept used in expressing the facts in question is that of the *posture,* or static space configura-

tion of the organic parts. Posture is reducible primarily
to patterns of relative angular disposition of the various
portions of the skeleton, although it may also be considered
to involve the tensions in the muscles and tendons, in addition to the pressures at joint surfaces. *Movements* may be
regarded as ordered successions of progressively different
postures. Occasionally, it may be necessary to deal with
postures and movements which exclusively involve soft portions of the organism, such as the eyes, the eye-lids, or the
skin of the forehead, without accompanying skeletal adjustments.

Under normal conditions, the correspondence between
the subjective kinaesthetic pattern and the objective posture
involves a spatial similarity between the two. The subjective schema is an adequate representation of the objective
configuration. However, when some pathological condition
is present, the exact character of the correspondence may be
radically altered. Thus Lewinski [293] reports a case of an
ataxic patient who felt as if his right knee were "turned in,"
while he was actually standing erect. His kinaesthetic forms
thus failed to correspond with the postural facts in a representative manner, but they were none the less definite and
correlated in a special way with the latter. The difficulty
from the patient's standpoint was a lack of resemblance
between his kinaesthetic and his visual impressions regarding
the affected limb.

When changes from one attitudinal configuration to
another occur at a sufficiently high rate, a qualitatively new
kind of experience arises, namely, that of relative bodily
movement. We shall consider the physiological conditions
for this phenomenon in a later chapter.

**193. Tensive and Exertive Patterns and their Correla-
tions.**—There is very little to be said concerning the nature
and determination of patterns which specially involve the
tensive and exertive qualities. These experiences fuse with
the attitudinal patterns, and form with them characteristic
wholes. The magnitudes of the tensive components correspond with our impression of the effort which is being

made to overcome particular objective resistances or other forces. The subjective localization of the tensive factors is determined by the point of application of the forces in question within the organism. Similar statements can be made concerning the exertive experiences, when the forces or amount of work which are objectively involved become excessive.

Section 43

PATTERNS OF ORGANIC EXPERIENCE

It is evident that the various types of internal or organic experience, which we have discussed in a previous chapter, have special distributions within the experiential corporeal field. When these particular qualities arise, they are almost always localized in a fairly definite manner. Thus, hunger is felt in the region of the stomach, lust in the sex organs, the micturitional sensation in the urethra, etc. The general feeling of well-being, or coenaesthesia, tends to permeate the bodily complex as a whole, although sometimes it is more concentrated in some portions than in others. The experiential distribution of these qualities is a function of the location of the corresponding organic conditions within the physical body. However, it is an interesting fact that the subjective and objective distributions do not necessarily resemble each other closely. Thus, the localization of the desire to micturate, in the urethra or the genitalia, does not correspond with the physiological fact that the conditions which gives rise to these feelings are situated in the bladder.

194. "Referred Pain."—The facts of "referred pain" are further illustrations of this point. Head and others [294] have made very elaborate studies, showing how disturbances of the internal organs yield pains, localized on the periphery of the body in definite zones, the identity of which is determined by the location of the organic disturbance in question. Thus, cardiac troubles elicit pains in the neck, shoulders and back; bladder troubles may evoke pains in the back of the legs, and so on. Head has formulated a law of the false

localization of internal pains, according to which "when a painful stimulus is applied to a part of low sensibility in close central connection with a part of much greater sensibility, the pain produced is felt in the part of higher sensibility rather than in the part of lower sensibility to which the stimulus was actually applied." It is to be noted that in spite of the lack of similarity between the subjective and the objective locations, or bodily patterns, in this situation, the two configurations are nevertheless functions of one another. It is, of course, upon this fact that the diagnostic utility of referred pains is based.

Section 44

TOTAL COMPOSITE PERCEPTION

195. The Structure of Consciousness as a Whole.— An unbiased introspective consideration of the structure of consciousness in the adult human being, reveals the fact that all of the various subjective structures which we have considered above are compounded into a coherent whole. In some cases the manner of combination consists in a mere juxtaposition, whereas in others it can more fittingly be described as interpenetrative. In general, we can distinguish quite clearly between the internal and external parts of consciousness or of experience as a whole. The external field is mainly visual, auditory and olfactory, although involving some constituents from contact perception. The various qualities which are thus embraced are compounded within the same spatial manifold, and are thus to a certain extent interpenetrative. A tone or noise can be located at the same point in consciousness as color or a visual thing. Odor can be spread out in the same space which contains visual depth elements. Nevertheless, these various classes of qualities, and the pattern systems which they form, are not so closely united that they cannot be separated. When the eyes are closed, the visual field is reduced to a very flat and unimportant affair, and under these circumstances, the auditory field may still remain very extensive. Deafness may eliminate the auditory field altogether, while leaving the visual one quite intact. Conditions of attention and abstraction may also serve to divorce the various components from one another, at least to some degree.

Somewhat similar considerations apply to the internal field. This field has a surface, which corresponds to that of the organism, and which contains the majority of the contact experiences; while its volume is occupied by the relative kinaesthetic and organic qualities. The last two form a definite, but variable and highly integrated, system. It constitutes the introspectable "self," and it is clearly separated from, but located with respect to, the external space system. The absolute kinaesthetic experiences are concerned with this relationship between the external and internal systems. The kinaesthetic vertical furnishes a general reference axis for the entire experiential mosaic, although it is more closely related to the internal than to the external domains. The vertigo experience, when it is present, is concerned with rotational changes in orientation between the internal and the external systems.

Although this way of treating the constitution of experience may prove to be objectionable to those who are wont to think of consciousness as an unextended entity, candid introspection shows the necessity of some such account as we have just given. Consciousness is essentially a spatial system. It is not necessary, of course, to go to the extreme of claiming that *all* forms of combination of elements within consciousness are extensive, but the majority of them certainly present this aspect. However, subjective space is of various kinds, and is never exactly like the ideal space of geometry or physics. Thus, visual space, as we have seen, has a perspective structure, while auditory space is essentially one-dimensional, when it is not combined with the visual manifold. Relative kinaesthetic space is homogeneously three-dimensional, but tactual space is two-dimensional. Our notion of geometrical space is probably derived from a conceptual combination of the properties of kinaesthetic and visual factors.

196. Psychophysiology of Total Conscious Composition.—The general relationships between the various subjective space systems conform more closely to the pattern of objective facts than would be anticipated from a consideration of their sensory relationships. Thus, it is certainly an introspective fact that, as we walk about in this world, our bodily experiences move as a whole within a much more comprehensive experiential space. This latter may be primarily visual and auditory, but it involves absolute and even relative kinaesthetic components. Although things may move through the visual field, with respect to the ideal axes of this field, our ordinary experience is one of motion of the field rather than of the things. The world at large, considered as a subjective phenomenon, is usually stationary, and the bodily complex moves with respect to it.

Realistic philosophers would undoubtedly interpret these facts in a realistic manner, as indicating that the objective world, itself, is really present within consciousness. However, from the standpoint of psychophysiology, it is almost certain that the facts in question must be explained in terms of highly special and complicated mechanisms within the cerebral cortex. These mechanisms have been developed, and are adjusted, so as to enable consciousness to represent the objective world as adequately as possible. The necessity of such semi-truthful representation is to be found in the relationship between consciousness and the efferent side of the response process. The proper regulation of behavior would probably be impossible if the world jumped about in experience with every movement of the eyes.

From the physical standpoint, motion may always be relative, but, subjectively, either one or the other of two relatively moving portions of experience is very apt to be stationary in an absolute sense. Thus, the kinaesthetic vertical is a stationary axis of this sort in its own dimension, although it can be displaced at right angles to the latter.

When the external space system is displaced relatively to the internal, either one of the two systems must be in motion, the other being stationary within consciousness. The difference between these two conditions is exemplified in a very striking manner in the well-known railway station illusion. A train adjoining the one in which we are seated may begin to move backwards, with the resulting experience that our own train has started to travel forwards. When some cue tells us that this is a mistake, there is a very sudden alteration in the form of consciousness, so that our own system—including the train in which we are sitting—abruptly becomes stationary again. However, during this change, nothing has happened objectively. Similar considerations apply to the phenomena which accompany eye-movements. We shall deal with some of these problems of motion perception, in more detail, in the next chapter.

As a matter of fact, it is impossible to give a comprehensive account of the manner in which the subjective space mosaic is constituted, without reference to factors in addition to those which we have considered in the above discussion of perception. These factors involve such things as images and the corresponding records upon the cerebral cortex. In classical discussions of perception, it is customary to consider the part which is played by such reproductive constituents. We have chosen to treat the topic in a different manner, and to reserve the study of the cortical influences for a later phase of our psychophysiological analysis. The space within which we move about, in experience, is only partially determined in a perceptual way. The greater portion of it is imaginal in character, and rests upon a system of neurograms in the brain.

Of course, if we desired, we might extend the concept of perception to include objective conditions which are located at various remote times in the past, including those at which the memory records in question were laid down. We are forced to admit that, even in the most immediate instances of perception, the active objective variables precede the corresponding consciousness by a small interval of time

Ordinarily, this is less than a second, and it seems undesirable to expand the notion of perception so that it includes objective conditons at substantially more remote times. Our original definition limits it to the relation of experience to the objective phase of a continuous chain of response propagation.

Chapter XII

Temporally Conditioned Perception

197. Statement of the Problem.—Thus far, we have been concerned primarily with psychophysical relationships which do not explicitly involve time. It is highly probable that *processes,* in some sense of the term, are involved in the majority of these relationships, but nevertheless they can all be considered as applying to individual *consciousnesses* or instantaneous cross-sections of experience. We must now consider certain relationships which include time in their essential formulation; depending upon finite amounts of change occurring at finite rates. *Changes* may exist on both sides of the psychophysiological nexus, and the concept of time, as we have seen, is applicable in the same way to both the psychical and the physical manifolds. As a rule, temporal perceptions involve intervals of time and time derivatives, in the physical as well as in the psychical domains. However, in some instances, we may find that time is explicitly involved on one side of the equation, only. Thus, when interrupted visual stimuli yield "fusion," there is a steady state in consciousness which can be described without reference to time, whereas the objective conditions comprise definite temporal variations.

There are two general classes of temporal perception: (1) those which can be described in terms of changes occurring at a fixed point in the experiential field, and (2) those which involve a progression from one point to another. Flicker is an example of the first class, and motion of the second class.

374

VISUAL CHANGE (ESPECIALLY MOTION) PERCEPTION

The temporal phenomena which are observable in the visual field may be divided into two groups, in accordance with the distinction just made, as (1) changes occurring at a single point or fixed area in the field, and (2) motion. Motion perception is by far the more important and common in everyday life, and will receive primary attention in the present discussion. Phenomena of the first class include various forms of "flicker," together with slower or non-periodic alterations in colors.

198. Flicker and Other Color Changes.—General changes in the brilliance, hue or saturation of the things which are presented within the visual field occur in accordance with rather simple psychophysical laws, which relate them to the intensities and wave-length compositions of the objective illumination. Low illumination means a dark visual field, high illumination may yield dazzling brilliance, and so on. However, a careful consideration of these relationships shows that the brilliance and saturation of the subjective illumination is also a function of the *time* which has elapsed after a given objective change has taken place. Thus, if we suddenly enter a darkened room, after having been in out-of-door daylight for some time, the visual field is empty of distinct presentations, being occupied only by a floating luminous haze. But, as time goes on, things gradually appear, until eventually a very satisfactory representation of the object-field may be developed. Similarly, in passing from the dark, after such "adaptation," there may be an intense dazzling which rapidly disappears with lapse of time. Analogous phenomena occur in relation to the wave-length composition, or "color," of the illumination. When we first enter a photographic dark-room, all visual things are suffused with red, but this general effect gradually diminishes with time. We shall discuss the details of these processes in our chapters on visual sensation.

When the change in the intensity or wave-length composition of the light which acts upon the eyes is very rapid, other laws, involving a much shorter time span, are demonstrable. If there is a rapid succession of light and dark phases, or of a different wave-length compositions, the accompanying experience follows these changes, at least partially, up to a certain point, as the frequency increases. However, ultimately, a "critical frequency" is reached at which the experience becomes invariable with respect to time, or shows complete disappearance of the subjective alternation which is known as "flicker." The brilliance, hue or saturation which is established under these conditions is usually a mean between the values which would be characteristic of the given alternating objective phases, if each of them were presented separately and continuously. When illumination changes, either in intensity or in wave-length composition, are very brief, the concomitant alteration in consciousness may involve less departure from the preexistent state than would be the case if a greater duration of the objective change were realized, a fact which is commonly known as "persistence of vision." Under special conditions, particularly those of laboratory experimentation, visual presentations may recur periodically or steadily, when there has been only a single change on the objective side. After-image phenomena, belonging in this class, may best be considered along with the detailed laws governing flicker, in the chapter on visual sensation (see Volume II), since, under ordinary circumstances, these phenomena show a very variable correlation with objective conditions.

199. Subjective Visual Motion Characteristics.—The visual perception of motion constitutes a psychophysiological function which is of the utmost importance from a practical standpoint. Its experimental study has also led psychologists to some very significant theoretical views. The subjective motion phenomena resemble physical motions in certain respects, but differ from them in others. In the vast majority of cases in everyday life, visually presented motions involve the displacement of a definite visual "thing," within the experiential space field. This displacement is "relative" between the given thing and other simultaneously presented portions of the experience. In these respects, the facts are similar to those which characterize physical motions. However, as we have already noted, subjective motions seem to be "absolute," in the sense that one part of the changing experiential mosaic is absolutely at rest, whereas another portion is absolutely in motion. It is true that there may be sudden exchanges of status between the parts in question, without good reason, but this does not affect the truth of the proposition, for any limited phase of the experience. Physical motions are said always to be relative.

Another seeming difference between physical and psychical motion lies in the fact that in some cases (*e.g.*) a visual thing can be in motion without suffering displacement. It may move continuously in a certain direction and yet make no progress. Furthermore, it is alleged that motions can exist in the visual field without inhering in any particular or definite moving thing. Thus, we say that "something moved," without having any clear impression as to the nature of the "something" in question, although there is no doubt about the existence of the motion. The so-called "phi phenomenon" of Wertheimer is described by him as a movement which may be separable from the visual things or images which are present at the same time. The "movement after-image" presents similar aspects. These questions are still under dispute, and we cannot be sure that there is not some sort of vague pre-kinematic "thing" which is moving in all instances. Nevertheless, we are forced to acknowledge that the thing which moves, in these cases, has a very hazy and indefinite nature and that its motional aspect has a much greater clearness than has its static character.

Motion presentations are ordinarily classed as direct and indirect. The latter are of the nature of inferences and depend upon memory or memory-images, the motion being so slow objectively that it arouses no distinctive impression of change, but after the lapse of sufficient time the pattern is cognized as different. Direct motion perception, on the other hand, comprises a definite kind of experience, of a kinematic sort, which is independent of all memory and inference. We are here concerned with this latter type of motion experience.

200. Psychophysiological Correlations of Direct Motion Impression.—The objective conditions under which visual motion impressions arise are somewhat diverse. In the first place, the objective changes may consist either in (1) the real, continuous, displacement of a single object or (2) a stroboscopic series of exposures. The latter is best exemplified in the projection of motion pictures. Under either of these two conditions, there may be motion perception with (a) the eyes stationary or (b) with the eyes pursuing the moving object or image. Motion experiences may also occur when the object is quite stationary and the eyes are moving, and when neither the object nor the eyes is in motion.

Let us first consider the case of a real objective motion. If a continuously moving object enters the field of regard, there is a powerful tendency for the eyes to fixate it and to follow its motion as long as possible. When such pursuit of the object occurs, there is very little displacement of the rays from the object with respect to the line of regard, so that it can be regarded as substantially stationary in relation to the latter. The rays from other objects which are at rest are, however, sweeping across the field of regard. If the tendency to follow the motion of the object is resisted, or if it is too complex to permit of such pursuit, there will be a displacement of the object-rays through the field while those emanating from stationary features of the latter may be motionless. Thus, in both cases, certain definite patterns of radiation are moving across the ray-sheaves of the eyes, and this process can be considered to be a primary condition for the subjective motion impression.

However, it is to be noted that, regardless of the behavior of the eyes, the visual thing corresponding to the moving object shows absolute motion, while the background pattern is at rest. The subjective result seems to be determined by the objective facts and not by the manner of displacement of ray patterns with respect to the line of regard. Nevertheless, we can state the conditions in terms of the processes of the ray-sheaves, by saying that if the latter move with the object, then the visual representation of the object will be in motion; while if they remain stationary, any object whose rays are displaced relatively to them will be represented as moving. In any event, motion of the eyes is perfectly consistent with a stationary state of the visual things which correspond to rays that are sweeping over the field of regard. According to both Aubert [295] and von Fleischl [296] a given movement apprehended by ocular pursuit is subjectively about half as fast as when perceived foveally with the eyes stationary.

201. Threshold Angular Velocity and Path Length.— Both objective and subjective motions are characterized by variability in *velocity,* a concept which includes direction as well as speed. Objective speeds may be expressed in such terms as centimeters per second but, when translated into values which characterize processes in the ray-sheaves, they are best stated in angular units per second. We find that such statements lead to threshold magnitudes which are independent of the distance of the moving object. Motions within the visual field may occur in the vertical, horizontal, or the depth dimensions, or in any possible combination of these. They may also be considered as projected upon the visual projection plane. In the latter case, they are determined in magnitude and direction by the angular speeds in the ray-sheaves, but under other conditions the subjective velocities are more nearly proportional to the objective linear velocities. At great distances, as in viewing a moving railway train in a valley from a hill-top, the subjective speed is angularly determined. In general, the speed in the three-dimensional visual field is proportional to the projection field speed multiplied by the effective depth of the moving thing, combined with a factor for the rate of change of the depth, when this is not zero.

There are both upper and lower absolute thresholds for the direct perception of motion, as regards angular velocity. A motion can either be so slow or so rapid as to be imperceptible. Munck [297] has reported a threshold as low as 34″ per second, although the values usually given lie between 1′ and 2′ per second, in the immediate vicinity of the line of regard. The threshold is higher—10′ per second (Aubert) —when there are no comparison objects in the field of regard. When the position of the moving object is removed from the line of regard, the threshold increases, although less rapidly than does that for the perception of static detail (*cf.* page 328). Thus Aubert and Bourdon [298] found the following values:

TABLE III

Angle with Line of Regard		Velocity Threshhold (per second)	
1°	15′	1′	30″
2°	15′	3′	0″
5°	0′	5′	37″
9°	0′	13′	0″
20°	0′	34′	0″

According to Czermak, [299] the velocity of a thing in the periphery of the visual field is less than in the center, for the same objective angular velocity. Dodge [300] finds that a moving object which is pursued yields a subjective speed three times as great as that going with an unpursued *peripheral* object having an equal velocity.

When the angular speed is increased to such an extent that the object takes less time, in passing through a given arc, than is necessary for a noticeable lapse in the visual effect to occur at any one point, the impression of motion tends to give way to streaking or blurring. If the conditions are such that the "persistence of vision" amounts to .010 seconds, the upper speed threshold for movement through an angle of 20 degrees must be in the neighborhood of

2000 degrees per second. This amounts to a linear speed of 349 feet per second at a distance of ten feet from the eyes.

There is a lower threshold for *length of path* in motion perception. Basler [301] states that, under conditions of daylight illumination, a displacement of 20″ can be detected near the line of regard, when comparison objects are present, while one of 13″ gives a doubtful judgment. This threshold is naturally lower for rapid motions than for slow ones, the figures just given being for optimal conditions. When no comparison objects are present, a displacement of 1′ 15″ is required. It will be noted that these values are of the same order of magnitude as those for static visual acuity, the latter also being widely variable as a function of illumination and the exact sizes and shapes of the objects. Motion acuity also decreases with an increasing angle of the object with respect to the line of regard, but less rapidly than does static acuity. Thus, at 20 degrees from the center, Stern [302] found the former to be about four times as good as the latter. Exner [303] asserts that rapid motion can be perceived between limits too narrow for position discrimination, even when the duration is too small for the perception of succession in the same place; but this proposition is now very doubtful.

202. The Stroboscopic Illusion and Its Determinants. —The fact that motion perception has a path threshold virtually implies that a perfect motion impression can be aroused, without any actual motion of an object, by the discontinuous substitution of one object for another at progressively different points in space. The only requirement for smooth motion under these circumstances would seem to be that the relative displacements of the successive objects should not exceed the path threshold. As a matter of fact, experiment shows that they can be very much greater than this and still yield a satisfactory motion impression. If we consider the process from the standpoint of the ocular ray-sheaves, we realize that the identity of the object from one moment to another is irrelevant, since the ray-patterns would vary in the same manner for a succession of similar objects as for the continuous movement of a single one—except for the negligible discontinuity.

We may study the conditions for the stroboscopic illusion by varying the angular separations and the time intervals between the exposures of the successive objects or images. Starting with a very small interval, two overlapping things are given simultaneously; at a larger interval, there is an impression of the motion of a single thing; while at a much greater interval two different things appear separately and successively. Between the third and second stages, and also between the second and third, there is frequently a phenomenon known as "part-motion" (*Teilbewegung*). This consists in an apparent motion of a single thing between two points, in which, however, the thing disappears from view momentarily somewhere in the middle of its path. Under conditions of considerable angular separation of the successive objects, the pure *phi phenomenon* is observed. This is reported by Wertheimer [304] and his followers as an impression of pure movement, divorced from the initial and terminal positions and the things which occupy the latter. Dimmick,[305] however, finds the phi phenomenon to consist in a "gray flash," filling the space between the two positions. When the succession is too rapid for a "good" motion impression, flashes and changes in brilliance of the successive phases are observable, and there is a sort of "inner motion" within them. Ellis [306] has noted that when successive phases overlap, there may be lines, of the color of the background, at the overlapping boundaries.

Increase in the length of the time interval, of course, slows down the phenomenal speed for a constant angular separation of phases. Using small strips about one degree in width, and separated by about the same distance, Wertheimer found subjective simultaneity with an interval of .030 seconds, good motion at .060 seconds, and discrete succession at over .200 seconds. The times of exposure of the individual phases varied from .005 to .030 seconds. Lincke [307] found that, with a stroboscopically rotating wheel, an impression of motion could be obtained with intervals as

great as .600 seconds.   Fischer [308] has reported uniform
motion with intervals as high as .200 seconds, using a series
of phases each separated by a distance of 1.44 degrees.
These times tend to be greater than the usual values for
"persistence of vision," although they are of a similar order

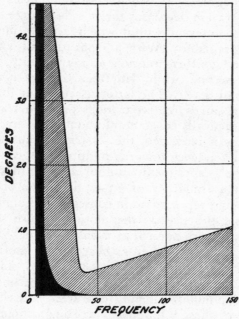

FIG. 27. CONDITIONS FOR SMOOTH MOTION IMPRESSION WITH STROBOSCOPIC
STIMULI.

The abscissae in this figure represent the number of stroboscopic stimuli
presented per second; the ordinates stand either for the (spatial) angular
separation of successive phases or for the apparent angular velocity of the
moving configuration.   Interpreting the ordinates in the first sense, smooth
(non-flickering) motion will be experienced for conditions represented by the
black area of the figure, including the base-line.   Interpreting the ordinates
in the second sense, smooth motion will be experienced for the conditions
represented by the shaded area and the black area taken together.

of magnitude if *complete* persistence is not required.
When the angular separation of successive objects or
phases is increased, there is a tendency for the phenomenal
motion to become jerky, and an adjustment of the phase

intervals may be required to yield the best motion impression. According to Marbe,[309] under conditions resembling those of motion picture projection, the illusion is seriously disturbed at all frequencies for distances greater than 4.5 degrees, and no motion impression of any kind is possible above 12.5 degrees. Wertheimer states that increase in the angular separation decreases the possible range of variation of the phase interval within which a clear impression of motion is obtainable. With a separation of 1.14 degrees, Marbe found uniform motion at a frequency of 4.55 exposures per second, while with 1.44 degrees Fischer found a frequency of 4.54. The latter asserts that the frequency or interval required for separations between 1.44 and 4.32 degrees is practically constant, at about .200 seconds. When the frequency is increased, the separation must be reduced, owing to the tendency towards multiple images.

In Marbe's experiment, all impression of motion had disappeared at a frequency of 83.4, all of the objects in the succession being represented in consciousness simultaneously. (The present practice on the motion picture screen is 24 pictures per second, not 16, as usually stated. It is dictated by considerations of flicker rather than of motion smoothness.) With a separation of 1.14 degrees, motion disappears at frequencies lower than 1.18 per second (Marbe) and has a continuous jumping character between 2.56 and 4.55. Some of these relationships are diagrammed in Fig. 27. In these experiments the eye was permitted to follow the apparently moving object; if the eyes are held stationary the required frequencies are somewhat lowered. The possibility of obtaining an impression of uniform motion with angular separations of successive phases as great as 4.5 degrees shows that the mechanism which determines such continuity is quite distinct from that underlying acuity.

The problem of the subjective nature and the psychophysiological conditions of motion in the dimension of depth seems to have received very little attention from experimenters. In everyday life, this type of motion is probably the most vivid of all, since it frequently represents an object which is bearing down upon us, with impending danger. It must obviously depend either upon the actual approach (or recession) of an object, or upon variations in disparation. The latter may be produced stereoscopically and strobo-scopically. In the case of an actual object, there will also be a correlated change in angular size, which greatly enhances the vividness of the impression, as in experiments with the anaglyphic shadowgraph (*cf.* page 349). Ter Kuile [310] has reported experiments on the visual motions which accompany the stereoscopic presentation of harmonically vibrating points, and finds that they yield depth components.

203. Relation of Visual Motion to Eye Movement.— If it were not for complications due to movements of the eyes, we might claim that visual motion depends primarily upon the displacement of similar contours across the ocular ray-sheaf system. However, in the case of pursuit of an object by the eyes, the contour which corresponds with the moving thing in consciousness is held stationary in the objective field of regard, while the background sweeps across the latter. We might attribute the motion experience, in this case, to the displacement of the background contours across the field, the motion impression being aroused by *relative* displacement and being attached to either the stationary or the displaced thing according to the manner of innervation of the eyes. In voluntary movements which are not of the pursuit type, there is no relative displacement. As in pursuit, the visual field itself shifts over the system of visual things, the latter remaining motionless.

However, in the phenomena which accompany dizziness (see pages 363–365), the background does move, and under conditions of eye movement which closely resemble those of pursuit. The body is stationary, the eyes shift back and forth, while the representations of both the body and the environment in consciousness show rotation about the body axis. Here, we might attribute the visual motion to the general displacement of all contours across the field of regard, but this seems to contradict the principles derived from the study of voluntary glancing movements of the eyes. We may perhaps be able to account for the difference between these two cases on the basis of the demonstrations by Holt[311] and by Dodge[312] that there is "visual anaesthesia" during voluntary eye movements of the latter sort, the functional link between consciousness and the objective world being temporarily broken. However, in vertigo, the motion persists even when the eyes are closed, showing that other factors, of a kinaesthetic type, are definitely incorporated in the total experience.

Certain other illusions of motion introduce further difficulties. If we look at a night sky, with clouds drifting across the moon, the latter usually seems to be in motion while the clouds are represented as stationary. Here, the eyes probably follow the clouds, so that the rays from the moon are displaced across the field of regard, but the illusion seems to be referable primarily to a lack of reference axes for the entire system. An even more radical example of the same sort of effect is provided by the so-called "autokinetic sensation," which consists in irregular drifting movements of a single spot of light seen within an otherwise dark and featureless visual field. This phenomenon does not seem to be conditional upon eye movements, because it occurs when the spot is carefully fixated. We are forced to conclude that no complete specification of the conditions for absolute visual movement (or rest) can be given from the perceptual standpoint. The problem must be solved on the basis of cerebral mechanisms which incorporate such conditions as "familiarity," and the combination of numerous kinds of perceptual influences in rather complex ways.

204. After-Image of Visual Movement.—If we look continuously at a steadily moving object, such as a stream or a waterfall, and then turn our gaze to a stationary object, the latter will be represented in consciousness as moving in the opposite direction. This effect is particularly marked when the eyes were held in a fixed position during the original exposure. The illusory movement is found to be restricted to that portion of the visual field which contained the primary motion experience. If, during the persistence of the motion after-image, an object is moved in opposition to it, a speed of the latter can be found at which the subjective impression is one of rest.

Section 46

AUDITORY CHANGE PERCEPTION

The temporal features of auditory experience are second only in importance to its qualitative variety. Spatial continuity is the dominant structural characteristic of visual experience, but in the auditory domain, temporal continuity is paramount. The exact order in which the various components of auditory experience follow one another determines distinctive form-qualities, which may be simultaneous functions of numerous objective events that are rather widely separated in time. This principle is demonstrated, especially, in music and in language, when the latter is presented in auditory form. These temporal aspects of auditory experience are practically independent of spatial factors. Although our consciousness places the music or the speech in a definite position in subjective space, its temporal features are substantially uninfluenced by the localization. However, we must also consider certain phenomena of *acoustic motion,* which involve a continuous displacement of auditory things or images within experiential space.

205. Beats.—One of the simplest temporal phenomena of audition is that which goes under the name of "beats." These consist in a periodic waxing and waning of a musical tone, when the objective conditions involve two sinusoidal vibrations which differ only slightly in frequency. Purely physical analysis shows that such sounds must periodically summate and interfere with each other, since their phase relations are subject to constant change. It can also be shown, by wholly physical reasoning, that the number of cycles of such interaction, occurring per second, must be

equal to the arithmetical difference between the two frequencies in question. Furthermore, this difference is found to correspond with the number of beats which appear subjectively.

However, beats may also be given in experience when their normal correlatives are objectively absent. Thus, beats can be detected under the proper conditions when one frequency differs from the other by approximately, but not exactly, an integral multiple. The subjective intensities of the beats are at a maximum, under the first condition specified above, when the two interfering sounds are of the same energy; but under the second condition the higher of the two frequencies must ordinarily be less intense than the lower one, in order to yield the optimal effect. It is found, however, in this case, that the required intensity ratio changes radically with the absolute value of the intensity. Numerous further interesting complications regarding beats will be considered in the chapter dealing with auditory sensation.

206. Perceptual Aspects of Rhythm, Melody, and Language.—Closely similar to the experience of beats, we find the impression of auditory *rhythm*. This impression arises in consequence of periodic or regular variations either in the intensity or the wave-length composition of the sound which impinges upon the ears. Intensity variations are, perhaps, the most important. Many different forms of rhythm are found in music and language, and rhythm may also be noted in certain natural, as well as in many mechanically produced, sounds. We shall have more to say concerning this topic in later chapters, dealing with cerebration, where we shall see that the central brain process is frequently responsible for the introduction of rhythms which have no basis in the objective domain. Stimuli or acoustic objects may be given in regular sequences without accent, the latter appearing as a subjective phenomenon only.

The experience of *melody* is, of course, related to a definite succession of different sound frequencies, usually accompanied by a fixed rhythm. Melodies are therefore as varied as are the possible sequential combinations of musical frequencies. In the production of melodies, with their accompanying harmonies, the frequencies which can be used are ordinarily limited to an arbitrary series known as a musical scale. Positions in such scales are commonly proportional to the logarithm of the acoustic frequency. Although scales are arbitrary constructions, the choice of frequencies which they comprise has undoubtedly been influenced by psychophysiological laws, some of which we shall consider in later chapters. (Volume II.)

An infinite number of different melodies is possible, but we find that only a few of them are satisfactory or pleasing. Certain laws, which involve objective terms, have been noted as partially determining the satisfactoriness of melodies. The most important of these is undoubtedly the *law of the tonic,* according to which if we determine the ratios between the various frequencies that are involved in a melody, those frequencies which are represented by the number, 2, or some power of 2, will yield the most satisfactory *ending.* Thus, if we strike the two notes, *c* and *g,* on the piano, having frequencies in the proportion: 2:3, we find that *c* provides the best ending for the phrase. However, if the frequency ratio is as 3:4, then the tone corresponding to 4 will exhibit the greatest degree of "finality." This is a law of temporal auditory sequence, which is independent of the absolute character, or frequency, of the components which are involved.

The *law of cadence* or of falling inflection, states that, other things equal, the lower of two tones in pitch forms the most satisfactory ending. Another principle is the *law of return,* which asserts that a melody is best terminated by returning to its tonal starting point. The construction of melodies on the basis of a musical scale, which involves identical frequency ratios between adjacent members, is also probably a fundamental requirement for the generation of pleasing melodies. This is called by Ogden [313] the *law of equal intervals.* The temporally related constituents of a melody are sometimes said to present a special attribute, called "tonality," which arises from the relationship of the tones to one another, and demands the objective conditions which we have just specified, for the production of the most pleasing results. The explanation of these relationships can, of course, only be found by studying the manner of determination of the melodic experience in the cerebral, or possibly the afferent nerve, processes.

Language presents us with phenomena of auditory sequence which are even more complicated than are those which are given in music. In general, it is clear that the succession of vowels and consonants, in experience, is determined by the temporal order of the corresponding complex acoustic vibrations which impinge upon the ears. Each speech sound has a normal duration which is essential to its intelligibility. The vowel sounds are ordinarily about ten times as protracted as are the consonants. On long distance telephone lines, the fact that certain frequencies travel more rapidly than do others, introduces disturbances in the temporal relationships between speech components, thus greatly decreasing intelligibility. Language, in its modern forms, is essentially arbitrary, although it may exemplify some principles of rhythm and melody. Its most interesting psychological relationships are found in connection with the part which it plays in thought. Consideration of these matters may best be postponed to the chapters on cerebration. (Volume III.)

207. Auditory Motion.—If a source of sound is moved in objective space, the localization of the corresponding auditory image tends to be similarly displaced in subjective space. However, if the objective movement is very rapid, the experience reduces to a mere change in loudness. Lane found that when a telephone receiver, emitting a pure sinusoidal wave, revolves in a circle about an observer's head, the motion impression ceases at three revolutions per second.

The sound-wave conditions for such auditory motion are naturally to be sought in a progressive variation in the phase differences between the sounds at the two respective ears. This should be true, at any rate, for sinusoidal vibrations of medium frequency. It is found, in fact, that if separate sound sources are applied to the two ears, and that if the phase relations are altered in the manner just indicated, the subjective auditory image moves from right to left, or *vice versa,* in experiential space. The most convenient way of obtaining such a variation in phase difference consists in using two sounds which differ slightly in frequency, between the two ears. Such sounds would yield beats, if they were applied simultaneously to one or both ears. When they are separately applied, the effect is that known as *binaural beats,* consisting, typically, in a periodic displacement of the subjective localization. The exact character of the movement varies with the individual observer. The auditory image may pass straight through the head from right to left and back again, or it may revolve in a circle entirely outside of the head. A relatively small number of observers report merely a change in loudness, and this is the general result when the frequency of the beats is high.

The auditory image lies in the median or sagittal plane of the head when the phases are in agreement, and otherwise it is localized on the side of the head which leads in phase. As a rule, there is a correlated variation in loudness, maxima occurring at: (1) phase agreement, (2) 30 or 40 degrees before oppositon, or (3) 30 or 40 degrees after opposition. According to Lane,[314] binaural beats cannot be obtained with frequencies which are greater than one thousand cycles per second. No experiments appear to have been made to test the stroboscopic principle in the auditory domain.

Section 47

CONTACT CHANGE PERCEPTION

In the domain of contact perception, we find that we must deal with qualitative and intensive changes at a single point in the cutaneous field, and also with relative motion over the field. The skin is moved actively over objects more frequently than conversely. In the former case the experience is of a stationary object, over which the tactual field is displaced, and the corresponding tactual thing in consciousness has a characteristic contact quality or "feel." We may divide the discussion of these phenomenon and their conditions under the headings of (1) vibration perception, (2) dynamic qualities and (3) tactual motion.

208. Perception of Vibration and Texture by Contact. —Perhaps the simplest form of temporally conditioned perception in the domain of touch consists in the so-called "sense of vibration." When a rapidly vibrating object, such as a tuning fork, is brought into contact with the skin, the accompanying experience is "rough," or differs characteristically from smooth contact. The experience has a definite temporal texture which is correctly characterized as "vibratory." However, if the frequency of the objective vibration is made sufficiently high, smoothness results. Earlier investigators placed the limit at 1552 cycles per second, but the recent studies of Gault [315] have raised this to 2600. Both Gault and Katz [316] find that differences in the acoustic form of the objective vibrations can produce qualitative variations in the corresponding experience. Thus, a frequency variation of nine per cent can be detected, while vowels and other speech forms yield characteristic subjective impressions.

Dynamically Produced Tactile Qualities.—Motion of the skin surface across that of an object is necessary to generate those characteristic contact qualities which receive the name of *texture.* We may consider these experiences as being referable either to characteristic changes in the nature of the contact at fixed points on the skin or to the movement of similar types of contact from one point to another. The recent studies of Katz [317] have shown that movement is an indispensable prerequisite to most of the contact experiences which concern us in everyday life. He distinguishes between the following four principal "modes of appearance," in tactual presentation: (1) palpation of surface, which is dependent upon the motion of the skin over objects having characteristic textures, (2) spatial touch quality, which may be elicited, for example, by moving the hand through a liquid; (3) volumic touch phenomena, corresponding, for instance, to the compression of a mass of cotton wool by the fingers, and (4) mediate perception of surface, which accompanies the exploration of the surface of one body by means of another which is used as an instrument. Katz has also made careful studies of the conditions under which various "modifications" of tactual experience are realized. In this category, he includes the qualitative variations from rough to smooth, hard to soft, and the like. He employs the term, "specifications," to designate touch experiences or attributes which give information concerning the kind of material (metal, stone, wood, etc.) of which an object is made up.

If the skin is brought into contact with paper, or other objects having characteristic textures, and if great care is taken to avoid sliding or relative movement in the plane of the skin, it is impossible to discriminate different degrees of roughness and smoothness. If the relative movement has a speed which exceeds 60 centimeters per second, there is a tendency for roughness to give way to smoothness even when the surface is actually rough. At lower speeds than three centimeters per second, smoothness is aroused with great difficulty although roughness can still be evoked. According to Katz, movements in the plane of the skin yield impressions of roughness versus smoothness, while movements perpendicularly to this plane underlie experiences of softness versus hardness. These correlations hold for passive as well as active movement, but are favored by the latter. In spite of the fact that such touch qualities possess a dynamic basis, they frequently seem introspectively to have a nature which is independent of time. This corresponds to the fact that the perceived properties of the object are spatial rather than temporal in nature. Physiologically, the basis of many of these perceptions is probably identical with that of the "vibration sense."

209. Movement of Things in the Cutaneous Field.— A different type of tactual dynamic impression is aroused when an object, usually of small area, moves over the skin, while the latter is stationary. This occurs in everyday life in the case of crawling insects, flowing drops of water, etc. Early studies by G. Stanley Hall[318] showed that there is representation of movement, and its direction, when the objective distance which is traversed is only about one quarter that required to yield an impression of double contact. Movements over very small distances may have an illusory directionality, and there is a marked tendency for them to be represented as towards the head. When the rate of movement is two millimeters per second, threshold distances varying from 0.20 millimeters, on the forehead, to 0.85 millimeters, on the back, were found. Using a traveling point carrying an electrical voltage and thus capable of arousing pain, highly varied qualitatively different experiences were evoked. In general, a constant objective rate of movement is accompanied by variations in the subjective speed.

Later investigations of tactual movement, by Benussi,[319] Hulin[320] and others have been directed towards the study of stroboscopically produced impressions. In these experiments, pressure is applied at one point, shortly after it is released at a neighboring one. The accompanying experience is usually that of movement if the intervening interval is brief. However, Benussi did not confirm Wertheimer's idea that there can be an experience of pure movement in the absence of a "thing" which moves. One of his most interesting observations was of a so-called "bow" movement, in which the illusory moving thing jumped into space above the skin and settled back again at the final point of rest. Hulin found several different types of subjective movement, analogous to those demonstrated in the visual case by Wertheimer. The best movement impressions occur when there is an interval of .075 seconds between the removal of the first object and the application of the second one.

Thalman[321] has demonstrated the possibility of producing an after-image of movement in the tactual domain.

Section 48

BODILY MOVEMENT PERCEPTION

In harmony with classifications which we have already established, we may distinguish between absolute and relative perceptions of bodily movement. The former involve translations or rotations of the body as a whole, with respect to axes fixed in space, either subjective or objective, whereas the latter have to do with changes in bodily posture.

210. Conditions for Absolute Movement Impression. —There is very little to be added to our discussion of the conditions for the kinaesthetic vertical or the directionality of vertigo, in previous chapters. We have there treated the static characteristics of these phenomena, while recognizing that it is difficult to divorce these characteristics from temporally conditioned aspects. However, there is a dearth of quantitative data regarding the phenomena of change in orientation. It is obvious to introspection that the speed of rotation of the body, in vertigo, varies in degree as well as in direction, and that active departures from vertical orientation show similar quantitative differences. These aspects of the dynamic experiences can undoubtedly be correlated in definite ways with their objective conditions.

211. Conditions for Relative Bodily Movement Perception. —The study of relative kinaesthetic perceptions is divided by Sherrington [322] into passive and active, according as the bodily members are moved by external forces or under the influence of their own musculatures. The classical researches of Goldscheider [323] upon the sense of bodily movement showed that passive angular displacements of the limbs as small as 0.22 degrees evoke an experience of bodily movement, under the most favorable conditions. The threshold was found to be four or five times as great for peripheral joints, such as those of the fingers, as for proximal ones, such as those of the shoulders. In order that a movement impression should arise, the speed of displacement had to exceed 0.3 degrees per second in the case of the shoulder, increasing to 12.5 degrees per second for the first joint of the finger. If we measure the sensibility to angular movement in terms of the product of the minimal excursion and the reciprocal of the threshold speed, we find that the shoulder is over forty times as sensitive as the finger joint. Störring [324] has reported thresholds for horizontal movement about the elbow joint, as small as ½₀₀th of a degree. He attributes the difference between his results and those of Goldscheider to the extreme care taken by the latter to eliminate cutaneous factors.

Goldscheider found that the least perceptible *active* movement was practically the same as in the case of the passive type.   A slight increase in sensibility was noted in the former case.   It is possible to execute voluntary movements which are so small as to fail of all representation in consciousness.   Extremely accurate movements are also possible to individuals who are entirely lacking in kinaesthetic experience.   However, the experiments of Loeb [325] show that the duplication of movements between two homologous limbs usually involves gross errors.   These errors increase as the initial position of the limb departs from its limiting position.

212. Change in the Domain of Internal Organic Experience.—In order to make our discussion systematically complete, we should consider the perceptual laws governing changes within the domain of organic experience. Everyone will recognize that such changes are very common, but, in most cases, their physical conditions can readily be inferred from those which underlie the various characteristic experiences in their static aspects. Thus, the throb of a headache is referable to periodic changes in the pressure on the brain meninges, due to the pulse wave; the onset of hunger goes with a gradual change in the chemical condition of the stomach walls, while the hunger pangs are associated with the contractions of the latter; the insidious rise of sexual feeling accompanies increasing tumescence of the generative organs, etc. There is little to be added to common-sense knowledge, at the present time, from the scientific standpoint.

Section 49

THE PERCEPTION OF CHANGE AND TIME IN GENERAL

213. The Status of "Abstract Time Perception."—In preceding Sections, we have considered some of the detailed relationships which hold between the temporal characteristics of response objects and the functionally associated aspects of experience. In addition to considering such special relations, it is customary in psychological textbooks to deal with the perception of time in general or in the abstract. However, if we are correct in the proposition which we have laid down, in our introductory discussion, that there is no such entity as pure or empty time, then there can certainly be no problem as to the perceptual relationships of time in this sense. The most that we can do is to trace the temporal relations which hold between experience and changes which occur in various stages of the response process. Nevertheless, the temporal attribute presents certain rather unique features in the psychophysical situation. Like space, it is exhibited by both the physical and the psychological systems, but within the latter domain its application is universal, while that of spatial form has limitations. Moreover, introspective time presumably resembles physical time more closely than introspective space resembles physical space. The universality of time of course stands simply for that of *change,* and without change there would be no psychophysical problem.

In attempting to deal with time in the abstract, we must compare separate concrete facts with respect to their temporal or change features. In certain instances, one group of facts may be physical and the other psychical, while in other cases, two or more psychical phenomena may be considered. Thus, we may compare the duration of a presentation with that of the stimulus which determines it, or, on the other hand, we may compare the duration of one auditory experience with that of another auditory—or perhaps a visual—experience. Such temporal comparisons may involve questions either of simultaneity or of duration. With regard to the former, we contrast the simultaneous with the successive, while with reference to the latter, we distinguish between the temporally longer and the temporally shorter.

Psychologists have frequently differentiated between "filled" and "empty" time, but from the attributive nature of time in general, it follows that all observable time must be "filled." Time is manifest only in concrete enduring entities or processes. The distinction in question arises from attention to some particular department of sensation or perception. If we are considering the objective or afferent conductional stages of any specified response pathway, we note that the degree of its activity may vary as a function of time (i.e., the chronometer reading). Sometimes, the afferent nerve process may be very intensive, while at other times it may have a zero value. Under the latter conditions, the time for this particular sense department is comparatively "empty," but reports upon the temporal characteristics of the corresponding consciousness are nevertheless concerned with the concrete experiential phenomena that are substituted for the sensations which would accompany more intensive afferent activity.

214. Psychophysical Inertia and Temporal Acuity.— Now, if objective or stimulus factors are varied in time there will be correlated *changes in experience* unless certain limiting conditions are exceeded. The psychical change may fail either (1) because the objective alteration is too small, i.e., is subliminal in amount, or (2) because the change is cyclic in nature and is excessively rapid. Under other conditions there will be a psychical alteration regardless of the speed of the objective modification. However, in general, the speed of the psychical change will be lower than that of the corresponding objective or stimulus change. The former will lag behind the latter. This fact can be expressed by saying that the perceptual system manifests *inertia;* it behaves like a mechanical mass in relation to the temporal course of the forces which act upon it.

The most feasible method of measuring this inertia

factor seems to be to employ the cyclic type of objective change and to determine the highest (or critical) frequency at which any change can be detected introspectively. *Fusion,* or apparent simultaneity of the subjective consequences of individual stimulus phases, occurs at frequencies or time intervals between successive phases which are readily measurable by physical methods. In addition to facts already presented we shall consider further details of certain experiments of this sort in our chapters on sensation, below. Table IV summarizes some of the more important results.

It will be noted, from this table, that the smallest interval between successive stimuli which will yield an impression of succession in experience is of the order of magnitude of one-thousandth of a second. The exact limiting value will certainly vary with special conditions, such as intensity, adaptation, and the like. However, we are justified in inferring that details in objective changes which are temporally finer than about a thousandth of a second must fail of perceptual representation in all cases. There are, of course, many

TABLE IV

MINIMAL APPRECIABLE TIME INTERVALS BETWEEN VARIOUS STIMULI [326]

	Thousandths of a Second
Between two electrical sparks	2.0
Between two electrical stimuli on the same retinal area	17.0
Between two pressure stimuli on same spot of finger	27.7
Between two light stimuli on the same retinal area (foveal)	44.0
Between two light stimuli on the same retinal area (peripheral)	49.0
Between tactual and optical stimuli	50.0
Between auditory and optical stimuli	60.0
Between two noise stimuli	64.0
Between optical and tactual stimuli	71.0
Between peripheral and foveal optical stimuli	76.0
Between optical and auditory stimuli	160.0

Where the stimuli are of different kinds the order of naming in the table indicates that of their temporal succession in the experiment.

objective processes, acting upon the organism, which possess great temporal complexity within the span of a thousandth of a second. Thus, about a trillion electromagnetic oscillations occur in a "light wave" during this interval. There is nothing in the objective world to set a limit at one-thousandth of a second, so that this, and similar, magnitudes must be regarded as constituting a sort of *temporal acuity* index for the perceptual relationship.

The figures in Table IV show that such temporal acuity varies widely as a function of the particular sensory department which is involved. Facts which will be presented in our discussion of sensation, below, indicate that the fundamental limitation, or the basic inertia factor, lies in the maximal frequency at which separate impulses can be aroused in the afferent nerve conductors. The sense-organs, with the possible exception of the tactual and the auditory, markedly add to this inertia effect. Certain aspects of the cerebral process contribute an even greater resistance to change. These aspects are manifested in experience by the lethargy of recognition, association, judgment, volition and allied phenomena, as contrasted with sensation. The latter comprises those features of experience that are most closely correlated with objective or stimulus variables, which seem to be limited in the detail of their temporal representation primarily by the sense-organ and afferent nerve inertias.

215. The Temporal Overlap of Psychical Representations.—It follows from the above considerations that psychical transitions or *events* that are attributable to objective changes must have finite durations which are always greater than those of the corresponding objective events. The limiting duration of such a psychical event would be that which would accompany an instantaneous objective or stimulus change, if the latter were possible. The percentage prolongation of the psychical transition, in terms of the objective one, must evidently increase with increasing rapidity of the latter. We can infer from these considerations that the subjective representations of successive physical events will overlap temporally if the latter are in close succession. With a sufficient degree of such overlap, the events will be judged as simultaneous.

This temporal smearing of the perceptual representations is partly responsible for the notion of the psychological "specious present," which we have already discussed (*cf.* page 197 above) and have rejected as a fundamental concept. As described in picturesque language by James,[327] the contents of the specious present are "in a constant flux, events dawning into its forward end as fast as they fade out of its rearward one, and each of them changing its time-coefficient from 'not yet,' or 'not quite yet,' to 'just gone' or 'gone,' as it passes by." As James indicates, we tend to identify the present with the average temporal overlap of unit events of this sort; but it is obviously unnecessary and absurd to treat this interval as a group of contemporaneous instants. Consciousness does not extend itself along the time dimension; it is only the representations of objective events within *experience* which are thus extended. This prolongation is not limited by the more sensory inertia factors, since after-image, memory after-image, and other perseverative effects tend to increase it in a very effective way. The complete system of relationships between the experiential consequences of any single objective event suggest the existence of a plurality of serially related inertia factors, and the maximal temporal overlap is determined by the greatest of them. However, in general, the greater the persistence or inertia, the lower the intensity of the process, so that as the overlap increases along the time dimension, it decreases in the dimension of degree.

216. Higher Aspects of Time Perception.—Helmholtz has suggested that the manner of temporal sequence perhaps constitutes the only respect in which psychical facts can accurately duplicate the corresponding features of physical facts. The law of an objective change may apply quite accurately to the correlated subjective one, provided that the process is not too rapid. As a matter of fact, it seems that the same sort of relationship can obtain for spatial properties. James,[328] however, contends that such approximate reduplication of temporal pattern is not sufficient to establish a good temporal perception; he says that a mere "succession of feelings" cannot constitute a "feeling of succession"; something additional seems to be needed to bind the feelings together temporally. This contention is interesting primarily as an example of the perversity of the awareness psychology (*cf.* page 63, above). The subjective phenomenon is not a series of discrete, instantaneous events —which require binding together to make them continuous. It is, rather, a single modulated entity which changes, not only continuously through time, but at any instant.

However, although one temporal process is certainly a good representation of another similar process, we do not need to deny that experience embraces particular phenomena which are set off specifically by the temporal aspects of other concurrent phenomena. Such secondary developments appear in the phenomena of motion perception (the "phi phenomenon" and allied effects), as well as in "thoughts about" the temporal properties of things, comparisons of such properties, volitional processes released by them, etc. The facts of motion perception have already been considered (*cf.* pages 375–387 and Volumes II and III.) The introspective and volitional reactions may be concerned either with the simultaneity or the duration aspects of the primary phenomena; and the temporal characteristics of the reactions may frequently become confused—under the "psychologist's fallacy"—with those of the facts which they purport to describe or indicate. The study of such processes belongs properly under the categories of thought and action, but a few outstanding observations may be mentioned here for the convenience of the reader.

Experiments by numerous observers have shown that, in the comparison of auditorily presented intervals, the percentage error shows a minimum at a value of about 0.72 seconds.[329] Vierordt [330] found that intervals averaging 0.62 seconds were most readily or "comfortably" attended to. Intervals less than 0.55 seconds seem "hurried," whereas those in excess of about 1.80 seconds are inconveniently long. Judgments of this sort are probably determined by the natural time spans of certain cerebral processes which are involved in discrimination or action. (*cf.* Volume III.)

When attention is directed to a single sensory department, short intervals of "filled" time are judged as longer than equal intervals of "empty" time. With longer intervals, exceeding the "comfortable" period noted by Vierordt, filled time seems shorter in passing, but longer in retrospect. "Filled time," in this case means a series of varied and interesting events, which distract the attention from temporal judgments while the events are transpiring. Subsequently, however, the duration is gauged by the number of distinctive memory images which can be recalled. The retrospective time increases, not only with the number of events, but with their original novelty, so that the time impression may be assumed to depend upon the amount of neurographic recording which has occurred. As we grow older, dearth of novelty reduces such recording, and time seems, retrospectively, to be moving more rapidly than in youth.

Conclusion of Volume One

The first volume of this work, here concluded, consists of three Parts. The first deals with the definition of psychological knowledge, and endeavors to establish psychology as a science of immediate experience, or consciousness, and its conditions. The second Part treats of the fundamental factors and relationships which are involved in a study of the principal one among such conditions: the physiological mechanism of the nervous system. The third Part considers the main facts of *perception*, treated as a relationship between experience and objects or objective variables.

The second volume of this work will treat of *sensation*, regarded as a psychophysiological relationship between experience and factors in the afferent nervous arc, which starts with the sensory stimulus and ends in the sensory areas of the cerebral cortex.

The third volume will be devoted to *cerebration* and *action*. The former term stands for the relation between experience and the essential processes of the cerebrum. The term, action, is used to denote the psychophysics of the efferent nervous arc, the correlation holding between experience and motor reaction.

The fourth volume will deal with the philosophy of the mind-body relation, and will attempt to show how epistemology, cosmology and ethics can be developed scientifically on the basis provided by the data of psychophysiology.

BIBLIOGRAPHY

1. *Cf.* BUEHLER, K. Der Krise der Psychologie, Jena, 1927.
2. COMTE, A. The Positive Philosophy, Eng. trans. by H. Martineau, London, pp. 22–25.
3. *See* ROBACK, A. A. Behaviorism and Psychology, Cambridge, Mass., 1923.
4. *Cf.* WELLS, H. G. The Outline of History, 3rd edition, New York, 1921, Chap. XI.
5. TYLOR, E. B. Anthropology, New York, 1909, Chap. XIV.
6. GOMPERZ, T. Greek Thinkers, English trans. by L. Magnus, New York, 1905, 3 vols.
7. CUSHMAN, H. E. A Beginner's History of Philosophy, Boston, 1910, vol. 1, pp. 241–261.
8. JOWETT, B. The Dialogues of Plato, 3rd edition, London, 1892, vol. 2, pp. 159–266.
9. ARISTOTLE. A Treatise on the Principle of Life, Trans. by W. A. Hammond, London, 1902.
10. MARTIN, L'ABBE JULES. St. Augustine, 2nd edition, Paris, 1923.
11. SERTILLANGES, A. E. Saint Thomas D'Aquin, Tome I, Paris, 1910.
12. *See* BURTT, E. A. The Metaphysical Foundations of Modern Physical Science, New York, 1927.
13. KOCH, A. Die Psychologie Descartes, München, 1881.
14. RATNER, J. The Philosophy of Spinoza, New York, 1927, and McKEON, R. The Philosophy of Spinoza, New York, 1928.
15. LEIBNITZ, G. W. VON. The Monadology, Trans. by R. Latta, Oxford, 1898.
16. HOBBES, T. Complete Works. Collected by Sir W. Molesworth, London, 1839. Vol. 1. Concerning Body, pp. 101–132 (materialism); vol. 2. Leviathan, pp. 1–17 (secondary qualities).
17. BORELLI, G. A. Die Bewegung der Tiere. Übersetzt von Max Mengeringhausen, Leipzig, 1927, 69 pp.
18. LA METTRIE, J. O. DE. Man a Machine, Eng. trans., Chicago, 1912.
19. CABANIS, P. J. G. Rapports du physique et du moral de l'homme. Paris, 1824.
20. D'HOLBACH, P. H. D. The System of Nature, Trans. by H. D. Robinson, Boston, 1877.
21. BERKELEY, G. A New Theory of Vision, London, 1709.
22. HUME, D. A Treatise of Human Nature, 2 vols., New York, 1898.
23. KANT, I. Critique of Pure Reason, Trans. by F. Max Müller, London, 1881.
24. FICHTE, J. G. The Science of Ethics, Trans. by A. E. Kroeger, London, 1897.

25. Münsterberg, H. Psychology: General and Applied, New York and London, 1914.

26. Schelling, F. W. J. von. Einleitung zu seinem Entwurf eines Systems der Naturphilosophie, Jena, 1799.

27. Hegel, G. W. F. Philosophy of Mind, Trans. by W. Wallace, Oxford, 1894.

28. Schopenhauer, A. The World as Will and Idea, Trans. by R. A. Haldane and J. Kemp, 3 vols., London, 1907.

29. Hartmann, K. R. E. von. The Philosophy of the Unconscious, Eng. trans., Vol. 1, 2nd edition, London, 1893.

30. Joly, H. Les grands philosophes—Malbranche, Paris, 1901.

31. See Hoppe, G. Die Psychologie des Juan Luis Vives, Berlin, 1901.

32. Locke, J. An Essay Concerning Human Understanding. Edited by A. C. Fraser, Oxford, 1894.

33. Hartley, D. Observations on Man, London, 1791.

34. Priestley, J. Disquisitions Relating to Matter and Spirit, 2 vols., Birmingham, 1782.

35. Reid, T. The Works of Thomas Reid. Edited by Sir W. Hamilton, 8th edition, Edinburgh, 1895, Vol. 1.

36. Mill, James. An Analysis of the Phenomena of the Human Mind, 2 vols., London, 1869.

37. Mill, J. S. A System of Logic, Seventh edition, New York, 1887, pp. 591–594.

38. Hamilton, Sir Wm. Lectures on Metaphysics and Logic, edited by the Rev. H. L. Mansel and John Veitch, 4 vols., Edinburgh, 1859.

39. See Waule, Leon de. Condillac et la psychologie anglaise contemporaine, Paris, 1891.

40. Herbart, J. F. Textbook in Psychology, Eng. trans. by Margaret K. Smith, New York, 1891.

41. See Jones, H. The Philosophy of Lotze: the Doctrine of Thought, Glasgow, 1895.

42. Treviranus, G. R. Biologie, oder Philosophie der lebenden Natur für Naturforscher und Aerzte, Erster Band, Göttingen, 1802–1822.

43. Huxley, T. H. Methods and Results, London, 1893, pp. 130–165.

44. Lamarck, Jean B. P. de M. Philosophie zoölogique, Paris, 1873.

45. Darwin, C. The Origin of the Species, 2 vols., New York, 1872.

46. Spencer, H. The Principles of Psychology, Vol. 1, London, 1870.

47. Lewes, G. H. Problems of Life and Mind; Problem I, The Study of Psychology, Boston, 1879–1880.

48. Clifford, W. K. Lectures and Essays. Edited by Leslie Stephen and Sir F. Pollock, London, 1879.

49. Huxley, T. H. Ibid. (Ref. 43), pp. 166–198.

50. Galton, Francis. Inquires into the Human Faculty and its Development, London, 1883.

51. Woods, F. A. The Influence of Monarchs, New York, 1913, and other writings.

52. Quelelet, A. Anthropometrie en mesure des différentes facultés de l'homme, Bruelles, 1871.

53. PEARSON, KARL. Studies in Biometrika. See bibliography in BROWN, W. and THOMSON, G. H. The Essentials of Mental Measurement, Cambridge, 1921.

54. *See* BATESON, W. Mendel's Principles of Heredity, Cambridge (Eng.), 1909.

55. DE VRIES, HUGO. The Mutation Theory, Eng. trans. by J. B. Farmer and A. D. Darbishire, Chicago, 1909.

56. BREWSTER, SIR DAVID. The Stereoscope. London, 1856. A Treatise on Optics, New Ed., Phila., 1854.

57. WOLLASTON, W. H. On the Nature of the Refraction and Dispersion of Colors, etc. *Phil. Trans. Roy. Soc.,* London, 1802.

58. GOETHE, J. W. VON. Zur Farbenlehre, Tübingen, 1810.

59. NEWTON, SIR I. Optics, London, 1730.

60. YOUNG, T. On the Theory of Light and Colours, *Phil. Trans. Roy. Soc.,* 1802, vol. 92, pp. 12–48, esp. pp. 46–47. See also The Wave Theory of Light; Memoirs by Huygens, Young and Fresnel. Ed. by Henry Crew, New York and Cincinnati, 1900.

61. PURKINJE, J. E. Beobachtungen und Versuche zur Physiologie der Sinne, I. Prag, 1823; II. Berlin, 1825.

62. MÜLLER, J. Zur vergleichenden Physiologie des Gesichtssinnes des Menschen und der Thiere, Leipzig, 1826.

63. MÜLLER, J. Ueber die phantastischen Gesichtserscheinungen, Coblenz, 1826.

64. DU BOIS-REYMOND, EMIL, Untersuchungen über thierische Elektrizität, 2 vols., Berlin, 1849.

65. KOENIGSBERGER, L. Hermann von Helmholtz, Trans. by F. A. Welby, Oxford, 1906.

66. HELMHOLTZ, H. VON. Physiological Optics, 3 vols., American Ed., 1924.

67. HELMHOLTZ, H. VON. On the Sensations of Tone, Trans. by A. T. Ellis, 2nd English edition, London, 1885.

68. VERWORN, MAX. Irritability, New Haven, 1913.

69. SHERRINGTON, C. S. The Integrative Action of the Nervous System, New York, 1906.

70. LUCAS, K. The Conduction of the Nervous Impulse, London, 1917.

71. HERING, E. Zur Lehre vom Lichtsinne, Wien, 1878.

72. KRIES, J. VON. Abhandlungen zur Physiologie der Gesichtsempfindungen, Hamburg and Leipzig, 1897.

73. KÖNIG, A. Gesammelte Abhandlungen zur Physiologischen Optic. Leipzig, 1903.

74. NAGEL, W. Handbuch der Physiologie des Menschen., Braunschweig, 1905.

75. WEBER, H. Wagner's Handwörterbuch der Physiologie, 1846, Bd. III, Teil ii, S. 481.

76. FECHNER, G. Elemente der Psychophysik, Leipzig, 1899.

77. FECHNER, G. Zend-Avesta oder die über Dinge des Himmels und des Jenseits, Hamburg and Leipzig, 1901.

78. WUNDT, W. The Principles of Physiological Psychology, Trans. by E. B. Titchener, London, 1904.

79. *See* RUCKMICK, C. A. The History and Status of Psychology in the United States, *Amer. J. of Psychol.,* 1912, vol. 23, p. 517. See also CATTELL,

J. McK., Early Psychological Laboratories, in Feelings and Emotions, Worcester, Mass., 1928, pp. 423–433.

80. *See* RUCKMICK. *Ibid.* (Ref. 79) p. 520.

81. MÜNSTERBERG, M. Hugo Münsterberg, His Life and Works, New York, 1922.

82. BORING, E. G. Edward Bradford Titchener, *Amer. Jour. of Psychol.*, 1927, vol. 38, pp. 489–506.

83. GALL, F. J. On the Functions of the Brain and Each of its Parts, Trans. by W. Lewes, Boston, 1835.

84. FLOURENS, M. J. P. Reserches expérimentales sur les properties et fonctions du système nerveau, Paris, 1842.

85. FRITSCH, G. T. und HITZIG, E. Die elektrische Eregbarkeit des Grosshirns, Arch. für Anat. Physiol. etc., 1870, 300–332.

86. FERRIER, D. The Croonian Lectures on Cerebral Localization, London, 1890.

87. BOUILLAUD, J. B. *Archives de médicine,* 1825. BROCA, P. P. Remarques sur le siége de la faculté du langage articuli. *Bul. de la soc. anat.,* 1861, 2 ser., tome 4; also: Du siège de la faculté du langage articuli dans l'hemisphere gauche des cerveau. *Bul. la soc. d'anthropol.,* June, 1865.

88. FLECHZIG, P. Gehirn und Seele, 2te Auflage, Leipzig, 1896.

89. GOLTZ, F. Ueber die Verrichtungen des Grosshirns, Bonn, 1881.

90. MUNK, H. Ueber die Functionen der Grosshirnrinde, Berlin, 1881.

91. JANET, P. The Major Symptoms of Hysteria, New York, 1907.

92. CHARCOT, J. M. Clinique des maladies du système nerveux, Paris, 1893.

93. FREUD, S. A General Introduction to Psychoanalysis, New York, 1921.

94. BERMAN, L. The Glands Regulating Personality, New York, 1921.

95. CANNON, W. B. Bodily Changes in Pain, Hunger, Fear, and Rage, New York, 1915.

96. JAMES, W. The Principles of Psychology, New York, 1890, vol. 2, pp. 522–528.

97. ANGEL, J. R. Functional Psychology. *Psychol. Rev.,* vol. 14, 1907, pp. 61–69.

98. BEER, T., BETHE, A., and VON UEXKÜLL, J. Vorschlage zu einer objectivirende Nomenclature. *Biol. Centralbl.,* 1899, Bd. 19, S. 517.

99. HEYMANS, G. Einführung in die Metaphysik auf Grundlage der Erfahrung, Leipzig, 1905.

100. BERGSON, H. Matter and Memory, Trans. by N. M. Paul and W. S. Palmer, London, 1919.

101. HOLT, E. B. The Freudian Wish, New York, 1916.

102. WATSON, J. B. Psychology as a Behaviorist Views It. *Psychol. Rev.,* 1913, vol. 20, pp. 158–177.

103. KOFFKA, C. Growth of the Mind, Eng. trans. by R. M. Ogden, London, 1924, pp. 12–22.

104. FROST, E. B. Can Biology and Physiology Dispense with Consciousness? *Psychol. Rev.,* 1912, vol. 19, pp. 246–252. Cannot Psychology Dispense with Consciousness? *Psychol. Rev.,* 1914, vol. 21, pp. 204–211.

105. WEISS, A. P. A Theoretical Basis of Human Behavior, Columbus, 1925.

106. TOLMAN, E. C. A New Formula for Behaviorism. *Psychol. Rev.,*

1922, vol. 29, pp. 44–53. Concerning the Sensation Quality—a Behavioristic Account, *Psychol. Rev.*, 1922, vol. 29, pp. 140–145.

107. HUNTER, W. S. Human Behavior, Chicago, 1928.

108. PERRY, R. B. A Behavioristic View of Purpose, *Jour. of Philos.*, 1921, vol. 18, pp. 85–105.

109. WERTHHEIMER, M. Experimentelle Studien über das Sehen von Bewegung. *Zeits. f. Psychol.*, 1912, vol. 61, pp. 161–278.

110. KOFFKA, C. Perception: An Introduction to Gestalt Theory. *Psychol. Bull.*, 1922, vol. 19, pp. 531–585. Also, article: Psychologie, in Max Dessoir's Lehrbuch der Philosophie, Die Philosophie in Ihren Einzelgebeiten, Berlin, 1925, S. 497–603, esp. S. 526–565.

111. KÖHLER, W. Die physichen Gestalten in Ruhe und in Stationeren Zustand. Berlin, 1920.

112. EHRENFELS, C. VON. Ueber Gestaltqualitäten. *Vierteljsch. f. wiss. Philos.*, 1890, vol. 14, pp. 249.

113. OGDEN, R. M. Are There Any Sensations? *Amer. Jour. of Psychol.*, 1922, vol. 33, pp. 247–254.

114. HELSON, H. The Psychology of Gestalt. *Amer. Jour. of Psychol.*, 1925, vol. 36, pp. 342–370, 474–526; 1926, vol. 37, pp. 25–62, 189–223.

115. *Cf.* WELD, H. P. Psychology as Science, New York, 1928.

116. McDOUGALL, W. Body and Mind, 5th edition, London, 1922.

117. McDOUGALL, W. Outline of Psychology, New York, 1923, p. 39.

118. CALKINS, M. W. The Self in Scientific Psychology, *Amer. Jour. of Psychol.*, 1915, vol. 26, pp. 495–524; also First Book of Psychology, New York, 1910, p. 274.

119. McDOUGALL, W. Outline of Psychology, New York, p. 39.

120. STOUT, G. F. Manual of Psychology, 3rd edition, London, 1913.

121. For a critical review of these doctrines, see TITCHENER, E. B., Functional Psychology and the Psychology of Act. II. *Amer. Jour. of Psychol.*, 1922, vol. 33, pp. 43–83.

122. ANGELL, J. R. The Province of Functional Psychology, *Psychol. Rev.*, 1907, 14, 61–91.

123. JAMES, W. The Principles of Psychology, New York, 1907, vol. 1, pp. 1 and 8.

124. *Cf.* HÖFFDING, H. Outlines of Psychology, Trans. by M. E. Lowndes, London, 1891.

125. ROYCE, J. Outline of Psychology, New York, 1903, pp. 1–2.

126. MÜNSTERBERG, H. Psychology, General and Applied, New York, 1914, pp. 10–14.

127. WARD, J. Psychological Principles, Cambridge (Eng.), 1919, p. 28.

128. On the psychology of pure experience see AVENARIUS, R. Kritik der reinen Erfahrung, Leipzig, 1888–1890; MACH, E. Contributions to the Analysis of Sensations, 1886, Eng. trans., 1897, 5th ed., revised 1914; KÜLPE, O. Outlines of Psychology, 1893, Eng. trans., 1909; and TITCHENER, E. B., Textbook of Psychology, New York, 1910. See also WELD, H. P. Psychology as Science, Chaps. 2 and 3.

129. HOLLINGWORTH, H. L. Psychology, Its Facts and Principles, New York, 1928, pp. 1, 9, and 17.

130. WUNDT, W. Outlines of Psychology, Eng. trans. by C. H. Judd, New York, 1907, p. 3. See also WELD, H. P. Psychology as Science, pp. 55–61.

131. TANSLEY, A. G.   The New Psychology and Its Relation to Life, London, 1920.

132. I have attempted to correct this neglect in my recent book, The Fundamentals of Human Motivation, D. Van Nostrand, New York, 1928.

133. WARREN, H. C.   Human Psychology, Boston, 1911, p. 13.

134. BENTLEY, M.   The Field of Psychology, New York, 1924, pp. 189–208.

135. BETHE, A.   Dürfen wir den Anreisen und Bienen psychische qualitäten zuschreiben? Arch. f. ges. Physiol., 1898, Bd. 70, S. 15–100.

136. WATSON, J. B.   Behavior; An Introduction to Comparative Psychology, New York, 1914, p. 1.

137. WATSON, J. B.   Psychology from the Standpoint of a Behaviorist, New York, 1919, pp. i and viii.

138. HOLT, E. B.   The Freudian Wish and its Place in Ethics.   Supplement; Response and Cognition, New York, 1915, pp. 153–208.

139. HOLT, E. B.   The Concept of Consciousness, London, 1914.   The New Realism, New York, 1912.

140. PERRY, R. B.   Reply to Professor Calkins, Jour. of Philos., 1928, vol. 24, pp. 683–685, esp. p. 684.

141. WEISS, A. P.   A Theoretical Basis of Human Behavior, Columbus, 1925, pp. 13 and 70.

142. JAMES, W.   Does Consciousness Exist? in Essays in Radical Empiricism, New York, 1912, pp. 1–38.

143. JAMES, W.   The Principles of Psychology, vol. I, New York, 1890, pp. 342–350.

144. Quoted by MOORE, J. S.   The Foundations of Psychology, Princeton, 1921, pp. 77–78, from TITCHENER, E. B., Philos. Rev., vol. 15, p. 94.

145. MACH, E.   Contributions to the Analysis of Sensation.   Eng. trans., Chicago, 1897, pp. 1–41.

146. McDOUGALL, W.   Outline of Psychology, New York, 1923, p. 16.

147. TITCHENER, E. B.   An Outline of Psychology, New York, pp. 13 and 7.

148. HOLLINGWORTH, H. L.   Op. cit. (Ref. 129), p. 20.

149. LADD, G. T.   Outlines of Descriptive Psychology, New York, 1898, p. 20.

150. BERKELEY, G.   An Essay Towards a New Theory of Vision, London, 1709.

151. HOLLINGWORTH.   Op. cit. (Ref. 129), p. 9.

152. MACH, E.   Erkenntnis und Irrtum, 2te Auflage, Leipzig, 1906, S. 8–11.

153. BURTT, A. E.   Op. cit. (Ref. 12), pp. 75 and 69.

154. See McDOUGALL, W.   The Fundamentals of Psychology, Psyche, 1924, vol. 27, p. 17.

155. RUSSELL, B.   Scientific Method in Philosophy, Chicago, 1914.   The Analysis of Matter, London and New York, 1927.

156. HOLLINGWORTH, H. L.   Op. cit. (Ref. 129), pp. 18–21.

157. JAMES, W.   A Pluralistic Universe, New York, 1909, Lect. 5.

158. MACH, E.   Op. cit. (Ref. 145), pp. 8–14.

159. BERGSON, H.   Time and Free Will, Trans. by Pogson, London, 1910, p. 226.

160. KÖHLER, W.   Op. cit. (Ref. 111).

161. HELSON, H.   Op. cit. (Ref. 114), Amer. Jour. of Psychol., 1925, vol. 36, footnote, p. 346.

162. HELSON, H. *Ibid.* (Ref. 161), p. 361.

163. BERGSON, H. Matter and Memory, London, 1911, p. 235. Time and Free Will, London, 1910, Chap. I–II.

164. TITCHENER, E. B. The Psychology of Feeling and Attention, New York, 1908, pp. 171–188.

165. FECHNER, G. T. *Op. cit.* (Ref. 76), vol. 1, p. 54.

166. HERBART, J. F. A Textbook in Psychology. Trans. by M. K. Smith, New York, 1891, Chap. II–III.

167. *Cf.* RUBIN, E. Visuell wahrgenommene Figuren, Copenhagen, 1921, pp. xii + 244.

168. EHRENFELS, C. VON. Ueber Gestaltqualitäten, *Vierteljsch. f. wiss. Philos.*, 1890, vol. 14, S. 249.

169. *Cf.* RUSSELL, B. The Analysis of Matter, London, 1927, p. 133.

170. MILL, J. S. *Op. cit.* (Ref. 37).

171. EHRENFELS, C. VON. *Op. cit.* (Ref. 168).

172. WUNDT, W. Beiträge zur Theorie der Sinneswahrnehmung, Leipzig, 1862.

173. WUNDT, W. Outlines of Psychology, 2nd Ed., Trans. by C. H. Judd, London and New York, 1902, p. 365.

174. MILL, J. S. *Op. cit.* (Ref. 37).

175. For a modern example of an erroneous argument of this sort, see HERRICK, C. J. The Brains of Rats and Men, Chicago, 1926, pp. 301 and 307.

176. BERGSON, H. Creative Evolution, Trans. by A. Mitchell, New York, 1911.

177. YERKES, R. Introduction to Psychology, New York, 1911, pp. 245–300.

178. TITCHENER, E. B. A Beginner's Psychology, New York, 1917, pp. 22–26.

179. LEIBNITZ, G. W. VON, The Monadology, Eng. trans. by R. Latta, Oxford, 1898, pp. 331–333.

180. JAMES, W. The Will to Believe, New York, 1897, pp. 153–159. PEIRCE, C. A. Chance, Love and Logic, New York, 1923.

181. BERKELEY, G. The Works of George Berkeley. Ed. by A. C. Fraser, Oxford, 1901, vol. 11, pp. 153–192.

182. BROWN, W. and THOMPSON, G. H. The Essentials of Mental Measurement, Cambridge, 1921, p. 149.

183. HEAD, H. Sensation and the Cerebral Cortex, *Brain,* 1918, vol. 41, pp. 57–253.

184. For a careful but inconclusive discussion of this assumption see BURTT, E. A. The Metaphysical Foundations of Modern Physical Science, New York, 1927, pp. 305–327.

185. SWINDLE, P. F. Positive After-Images of Long Duration, *Amer. Jour. of Psychol.*, 1916, vol. 27, pp. 324–334.

186. For a diagram of the visual conduction path see Quain's Anatomy, Ed. by E. A. Schäfer, London, vol. 3, part 1, 1908, p. 240.

187. CUSHING, H. A Note upon the Faradic Stimulation of the Post Central Cyrus in Conscious Patients, *Brain,* 1909, vol. 32, pp. 44–53.

188. LASHLEY, K. S. Studies in Cerebral Functions in Learning, *Jour. of Animal Behavior,* vol. 2, pp. 310–331; also The Effects of Long Continued Practise on Cerebral Localization, *Jour. of Comp. Psychol.,* vol. 1, pp. 453–468.

189. HERRICK, C. L. The Brains of Rats and Men, Chicago, 1926.

190. See TILNEY, F. and RILEY, H. A. The Form and Functions of the Central Nervous System, New York, 1928, pp. 905–911.

191. CUSHING, H. Removal of a Subcortical Cystic Tumor at a Second-Stage Operation Without Anaesthesia, *Jour. of the Amer. Med. Assoc.,* 1908, vol. 50, pp. 847–856, esp. p. 851.

192. McCOMAS, H. C. Extravagances in the Motor Theories of Consciousness, *Psychol. Rev.,* 1916, vol. 23, pp. 397–406.

193. MÜLLER, J. Elements of Physiology. Trans. by W. Baly, M.D., London, 1842, pp. 1059–1087.

194. SHERRINGTON, C. S. *Op. cit.* (Ref. 69), pp. 115–149.

195. EINSTEIN, A. The Principle of Relativity, including papers by Lorentz, Einstein, Minkowski, and Weyl. Trans. by W. Perrett and G. B. Jeffery, London, 1923, pp. 75–91.

196. BERGSON, H. Time and Free Will. Trans. by F. L. Pogson, London, 1910, pp. 100–106.

197. TITCHENER, E. B. A Beginner's Psychology, New York, 1917, pp. 122–124.

198. KANT, E. Critique of Pure Reason, 2nd edition, New York, 1907. Trans. by Max Müller, vol. 2, pp. 24–33.

199. LADD, G. T. Outline of Descriptive Psychology, New York 1898, pp. 299–300.

200. JAMES W. *Op. cit.* (Ref. 96), p. 196.

201. JAMES, *ibid.* (Ref. 96), pp. 608–610.

202. See FAIRBANKS, A. The First Philosophers of Greece, London, 1898, pp. 112–120.

203. WASHBURN, M. F. The Animal Mind, 2nd edition, New York, 1917, pp. 27–37.

204. LORENTZ, H. A. The Theory of Electrons, Leipzig, 1909.

2 5. SPEARMAN, C. The Abilities of Man, London, 1927, p. 32.

206. PILLSBURY, W. B. The Fundamentals of Psychology, New York, 1922, p. 294.

207. HOLLINGWORTH, H. L. *Op. cit.* (Ref. 129), p. 115.

208. TITCHENER, E. B. A Textbook of Psychology, New York, 1910, p. 364.

209. JAMES, W. *Op. cit.* (Ref. 96), vol. 2, pp. 2–3.

210. WUNDT, W. *Op. cit.* (Ref. 130), p. 99.

211. HUNTER, W. S. General Psychology, Chicago, 1919, p. 217.

212. BREESE, B. B. Psychology, New York, 1917, p. 197.

213. SHERRINGTON, C. S. *Op. cit.* (Ref. 69), Lects. 4 and 9.

214. The color terminology which is used in this book is that adopted by the Optical Society of America. See TROLAND, L. T. The Report of the Committee on Colorimetry for 1921, *Jour. of the Optical Soc. of Amer.,* 1922, vol. 6, pp. 571–572.

215. See PLANCK, M. The Theory of Heat Radiation, Eng. trans. by M. Masius, Phila., 1914.

216. KÜLPE, O. Outlines of Psychology, Trans. by E. B. Titchener, London, 1915, p. 122.

217. KÖNIG, A. Über die Anzahl der Unterscheidbaren Spectralfarben und Helligkeitsstufen, *Zeitsch. für Psychol. u. Physiol. der Sinnesorg.,* 1895 Bd. 8, S. 375–380.

218. DIMMICK, F. L.   An Experimental Study of Visual Movement and the Phi Phenomenon, *Amer. Jour. of Psychol.*, 1920, vol. 31, pp. 317–332.

219. *Cf.* LADD–FRANKLIN, C.   Colour and Colour Theories, New York, 1929, pp. 33–36.

220. TITCHENER, E. B.   A Textbook of Psychology, New York, 1910, p. 63.

221. TITCHENER, E. B.   *Ibid.* (Ref. 220), pp. 52–55.

222. KATZ, D.   Die Erscheinungsweisen der Farben, *Zeitsch. f. Psychol.* Erg. Bd. 7, S. 425, 1911.

223. TROLAND, L. T.   The Measurement of Visual Stimulation Intensities. *Jour. of Exper. Psychol.*, 1917, vol. 2, pp. 1–33.

224. HERING, E.   Zur Lehre vom Lichtsinne. Wien, 1878, S. 66–69.

225. JAENSCH, E. R.   Parallelgesetz über das Verhalten der Reizschwellen bei Kontrast und Transformation. *Zeitsch. f. Psychol.*, 1920, Bd. 85, S. 342–352.

226. BUEHLER, K.   Handbuch der Psychologie, Teil I, Der Structure der Wahrnehmung, Heft I, Die Erscheinungsweisen der Farben, Jena, 1922, S. 28–35.

227. KATZ, D.   Neue Beiträge zu den Erscheinungsweisen der Farben, Luftlicht und Beleuchtungseindruck. *Zeitsch. f. Psychol.*, 1924, Bd. 95, S. 29–36.

228. BUEHLER, K.   *Loc. cit.* (Ref. 226), S. 75–89.

229. HERING, E.   Grundzüge der Lehre vom Lichtsinn, Berlin, 1920, S. 13–20.

230. BUEHLER, *loc. cit.* (Ref. 226), S. 8–11.

231. SCHUMANN, F.   Die Repräsentation des leeren Raumes in Bewusstsein. Eine neue Empfindung. *Zeitsch. f. Psychol.*, 1920, Bd. 85, S. 224–244.

232. MARTIN, M. F.   Film, Surface, and Bulky Colors and Their Intermediates. *Amer. Jour. of Psychol.*, 1922, vol. 33, pp. 451–480.

233. KATZ, D.   Die Erscheinungsweisen der Farben und ihre Beeinflussung durch die individuelle Erfahrung. *Zeitsch. f. Psychol.*, 1911, Erg. Bd. 7, S. 1–31.

234. HELMHOLTZ, H. v.   Physiological Optics, 3 vols., English trans., 1924, vol. 2, p. 283.

234. HELMHOLTZ, H. VON.   Physiological Optics, 3 vols., Eng. trans., 1924,

236. PRIEST, I.   Preliminary Note on the Relation between the Quality of Color and the Spectral Distribution of Light in the Stimulus. *Jour. of the Opt. Soc. of Amer.*, 1920, vol. 4, pp. 388–401.

237. MUNSELL, A. H.   A Color Notation, Boston, 1905.

238. RIDGWAY, R.   Color Standards and Color Nomenclature, Washington, 1912.

239. OSTWALD, W.   Die Farbenlehre, Bd. 1, 2, Leipzig, 1921.

240. TROLAND, L. T.   Report of the Committee on Colorimetry of the Optical Society of America, 1920–1921, *Jour. of the Optical Soc. of Amer.*, 1922, vol. 6, pp. 571–572.

241. BUEHLER, K.   *Op. cit.* (Ref. 226), S. 12 *ff.*

242. On tonal attributes, etc., see OGDEN, R. M.   Hearing, New York, 1924, esp. pp. 48–199.

243. RICH, G. J.   A Study of Tonal Attributes. *Amer. Jour. of Psychol.*, 1919, vol. 31, pp. 21–164.

244. TITCHENER, E. B.   A Textbook of Psychology, New York, 1910, p. 95.

245. MILLER, D. C.   The Science of Musical Sounds, New York, 1916, lecture IV.

246. WENTE, E. C.   The Thermophone, *Phys. Rev.,* 1922, vol. 19, 2nd Ser., pp. 333–345.

247. FLETCHER, H.   Physical Measurements of Audition and their Bearing on the Theory of Hearing, *Jour. Franklin Instit.,* 1923, vol. 196, pp. 289–326.

248. JOHNSON, K. S.   Transmission Circuits for Telephonic Communication, New York, 1927, pp. 3 *ff.*

249. On the perception of distance of acoustic sources, *cf.* MYERS, C. S. Textbook of Experimental Psychology, Cambridge (Eng.), 1911, Part 1, p. 278.

250. On reverberation, *cf.* OGDEN, R. M.   Hearing, New York, 1924, pp. 5–7.

251. ZWAARDEMAKER, H.   Die Physiologie des Geruchs, Leipzig, 1895, S. vi + 324.

252. HENNING, H.   Der Geruch, *Zeitsch. f. Psychol.,* 1916, Bd. 74, S. 203 *ff.*

253. MACDONALD, M. K.   An Experimental Study of Henning's System of Olfactory Qualities, *Amer. Jour. of Psychol.,* 1922, vol. 33, pp. 535–553.

254. HENNING, H.   Die Qualitätenreihe des Geschmacks, *Zeitsch. f. Psychol.,* 1916, Bd. 74, S. 212.

255. HENSEN, V.   Vortrag gegen den sechsten Sinn, *Arch. f. Ohrenhlk.,* 1893, Bd. 35, S. 161–177.

256. BASTIAN, C.   The Muscular Sense, *Brain,* London, 1887, vol. 10, p. 1.

257. EINSTEIN, A.   Relativity, the Special and General Theory, English trans. by R. W. Lawson, New York, 1920.

258. DODGE, R.   Thresholds of Rotation, *Jour. of Exp. Psychol.,* 1923, vol. 6, pp. 107–137.

259. HEAD, H. and RIVERS.   Studies in Neurology, by Henry Head, 2 vols., London, 1920, pp. 242–256.

260. GOLDSCHEIDER, A. und BLECHER, A.   Versuche über die Empfindung des Widerstandes. *Arch. f. Physiol.,* 1893, S. 536–549.

261. FREY, M. VON.   Studien über den Kraftsinn, *Zeitsch. für Biol.,* 1914, Bd. 63, S. 129–154.

262. WEBER, E. H.   See Wagner's Handwörterbuch der Physiologie, 1846, Bd. iii, Tl. ii, S. 488–588.

263. MERKEL, J.   Die Abhängigkeit zwischen Reiz und Empfindung, *Phil. Stud.,* 1889, Bd. 5, S. 245–291.

264. JACOBI, C.   Untersuchungen über Kraftsinn, *Arch. f. Exper. Pathol. u. Pharmakol.,* Leipzig, 1893, Bd. 32, S. 49–100.

265. HERING, E.   Ueber Fechner's psychophysiches Gesetz, Wien, 1875, S. 22.

266. LUCIANI, L.   Human Physiology, 5 vols., London, 1917, vol. 4, pp. 58–125.

267. CANNON, W. B.   Bodily Changes in Pain, Hunger, and Fear, New York, 1915.

268. CARLSON, A. J.   Hunger, Appetite, and Gastric Juice Secretion in Men During Prolonged Fasting, *Amer. Jour. of Physiol.,* 1918, pp. 120–145.

269. TITCHENER, E. B.   Textbook of Psychology, New York, 1910, p. 192.

270. TITCHENER, E. B.   *Ibid.* (Ref. 269), p. 184.

271. HENLE, F. G. J.   Allgemeine Anatomie, Leipzig, 1841, S. 728.

272. SCHUMANN, F. Die Repräsentation des leeren Raumes in Bewusstsein. Eine neue Empfindung. *Zeitsch. f. Psychol.,* 1920, Bd. 85, S. 224–244.

273. FRENCH, J. W. The Unaided Eye, III, *Trans. of Opt. Soc.,* 1920, vol. 4, pp. 127–147.

274. On barrel distortion see AMES, A. JR. and PROCTOR, C. A. Dioptrics of the Eye, *Jour. of the Opt. Soc. of Amer.,* 1921, vol. 5, pp. 80–85.

275. HARTRIDGE, H. The Chromatic Aberration and Resolving Power of the Eye, *Jour. of Physiol.,* 1918, vol. 52, pp. 175–246.

276. For a thorough discussion of Visual Illusions, see LUCKIESH, M. Visual Illusions, Their Causes, Characteristics and Applications, New York, 1922.

277. On illumination perspective, see BUEHLER, K. Handbuch der Psychologie, Teil 1, Heft 1, Die Erscheinungsweisen der Farben, Jena, 1922, S. 84–88.

278. HERING, E. Beiträge zur Physiologie, Leipzig, 1861–1864. Fünftes Heft, 1864, S. 296. (Several pamphlets, not reprints, are bound in this volume.)

279. PANUM, P. L. Physiologischen Untersuch uber das Sehen mit zwei Augen, Kiel, 1858, S. 62.

280. See RIVERS, W. H. R. Vision, in Schäfer's Textbook of Physiology, vol. 2, pp. 1133–1135.

281. *See* HELMHOLTZ, H. VON. Handbook of Physiological Optics., Eng. Trans., vol. 3, p. 375.

282. HELMHOLTZ, *ibid.* (Ref. 281), p. 674.

283. HELMHOLTZ, H. VON. The Sensations of Tone, London, 1885, pp. 65–102.

284. BANISTER, H. The Effect of Binaural Phase Differences on the Localization of Tones at Various Frequencies, *Brit. Jour. of Psychol.,* 1925, vol. 15, pp. 280–307.

285. HALVERSON, H. M. The Upper Limit of Auditory Localization, *Amer. Jour. of Psychol.,* 1927, vol. 38, pp. 97–106.

286. BOWLKER, T. J. On the Factors Serving to Determine the Direction of Sound, *Phil. Mag.,* 1908, 6 ser., vol. 15, pp. 323–327.

287. BANISTER, H. A Suggestion towards a New Hypothesis Regarding the Localization of Sound, *Brit. Jour. of Psychol.,* 1926, vol. 17, pp. 142–153.

288. LOTZE, R. H. Outlines of Psychology, Eng. trans. by G. T. Ladd, Boston, 1886, pp. 47–61.

289. PONZO, M. Étude de la localisation des sensations thermiques de chaud et de froid, *Arch. ital. de biol.,* 1913, vol. 60, p. 218–231.

290. WEBER, E. H. See Wagner's Handwörterbuch d. Physiologie, Bd. iii, Abth. ii, S. 529 *ff.*

291. KATZ, D. Der Aufbau der Tastwelt, *Zeitsch. f. Psychol.,* Erg. Bd. 11, 1925.

292. SHERRINGTON, C. S. The Muscular Sense, in Schäfer's Text-Book of Physiology, vol. 2, Edinburgh and London, 1900, p. 1013.

293. LEWINSKI. Ueber den Kraftsinn, *Virchow's Arch.,* 1879, Bd. 77, S. 145.

294. HEAD, H. On Disturbances of Sensation with Especial Reference to the Pain of Visceral Disease, *Brain.* 1893, vol. 16, pp. 1–169; 1894, vol. 17, pp. 339–480; 1896, vol. 19, pp. 153–276.

295. AUBERT, H. Die Bewegungsempfindung, *Arch. f. d. ges. Physiol.,* 1886, Bd. 39, S. 347–370. Also 1887, Bd. 40, S. 459–479.

296. VON FLEISCHL, E. Physiologisch-Optische Notizen (2te Mittheilung) *Sitzungsber. d. Akad. Wien, math.-naturwiss. Kl.,* 1882, Bd. 86, Abth. 3, S. 17.

297. MUNCK, G. W. See article "Gesicht und Sehen" in Gehler's Physikalisches Wörterbuch, 1828, 4, S. 1457.

298. BOURDON, B. La perception visuelle de l' espace, Paris, 1902, pp. 201–204.

299. CZERMAK, J. Ideen zu eine Lehre von Zeitsinn, *Sitzungsber. d. Akad. Wien, math.-naturwiss. Kl.,* 1851, Bd. 24, S. 231–236.

300. DODGE, R. The Participation of Eye Movements in the Visual Perception of Motion, *Psychol. Rev.,* 1904, vol. 11, pp. 1–14.

301. BASLER, A. Über das Sehen von Bewegungen, *Arch. f. ges. Physiol.,* 1906, Bd. 115, S. 582–601.

302. STERN, W. Die Wahrnehmung von Bewegungen vermittelst des Auges. *Zeitsch. f. Psychol.,* 1894, Bd. 7, S. 321–326.

303. EXNER, S. Ueber das Sehen von Bewegungen und die Theorie des Zusammungsetzten Auges. *Sitzungsber. d. Akad. Wien, math.-naturwiss. Kl.,* 1875, Bd. 72, S. 156–189.

304. WERTHEIMER, M. Experimentelle Studien über das Sehen vom Bewegung, *Zeitsch. f. Psychol.,* 1912, Bd. 61, S. 161–278.

305. DIMMICK, F. L. *Op. cit.* (Ref. 218).

306. ELLIS, W. F. Studies in the Physiology and Psychology of Visual Sensations and Perceptions, *Amer. Jour. of Physiol.,* 1901, vol. 5, pp. 462–486.

307. LINKE, P. Die Strobokopischen Täuschungen und das Problem des Sehen von Bewegungen. *Psychol. Stud.,* 1907, Bd. 3, S. 393–545.

308. FISCHER, O. Psychologische Analyse der Stroboskopischer Erscheinungen, *Phil. Stud.,* 1886, Bd. 3, S. 128–156.

309. MARBE, K. Theorie der kinematographischen Projectionen, Leipzig, 1910.

310. TER KUILE, T. E. Stereokinematoskopie, dichopisch gesehener harmonischer Punktbewegungen, *Arch. f. d. ges. Physiol.,* 1919, Bd. 174, S. 233–243.

311. HOLT, E. B. Eye-Movement and Central Anaesthesia, *Psychol. Rev. Mon. Suppl.,* 1903, vol. 4, pp. 3–45.

312. DODGE, R. Visual Perception during Eye-Movement, *Psychol. Rev.,* 1900, vol. 7, pp. 454–455.

313. OGDEN, R. M. *Op. cit.* (Ref. 242), pp. 130 and 140–149.

314. LANE, C. E. Binaural Beats, *Phys. Rev.,* 1925, 2nd Ser. vol. 26, pp. 401–412.

315. GAULT, R. H. On the Upper Limit of Vibrational Frequency that can be Recognized by Touch, *Science,* 1927, vol. 65, pp. 403–4c4.

316. KATZ, D. Der Aufbau der Tastwelt, *Zeitsch. f. Psychol.,* Erg. Bd., 1925, Bd. 11, S. xii + 270.

317. KATZ, D. *Ibid.* (Ref. 316), S. 270 *ff.*

318. HALL, G. S. and DONALDSON, H. H. Motor Sensations on the Skin, *Mind,* 1885, vol. 10, pp. 557–572.

319. BENUSSI, V. Kinematohaptische Erscheinungen, *Arch. f. d. ges. Psychol.,* 1913, vol. 29. Also, 1917, vol. 36, pp. 59–135.

320. HULIN, W. S. An Experimental Study of Apparent Tactual Movement, *Jour. of Exp. Psych.*, 1927, vol. 10, pp. 293–320.

321. THALMAN, W. A. The After-effect of Movement in the Sense of Touch, *Amer. J. Psychol.*, 1922, vol. 33, pp. 268–276.

322. SHERRINGTON, C. S. See article in Schäfer's Text-Book of Physiology, p. 1014–1016.

323. GOLDSCHEIDER, A. Physiologie des Muskelsinnes, Leipzig, 1898, S. 182–183.

324. STÖRRING, G. Experimentelle Beiträge zur Lehre von den Bewegungs- und Kraftsempfindungen. *Arch. f. die ges. Psychol.*, 1912., 1912, Bd. 25, S. 179.

325. LOEB, J. Untersuchungen über die Orientierung in Fühlraum der Hand und in Blickraum. *Arch. f. d. ges. Physiol.*, 1890, Bd. 46, S. 1–45. See Schäfer, *ibid*, p. 1017.

326. LADD, G. T. and WOODWORTH, R. S. Elements of Physiological Psychology, New York, 1911, p. 475.

327. JAMES, W. *Op. cit.* (Ref. 142), vol. 1, p. 630.

328. JAMES, W. (Ref. 96), vol. 1, p. 628.

329. JAMES, W. *Ibid.* (Ref. 96), p. 617.

330. VIERORDT, K. Der Zeitsein Nach Versuchen. Tübingen, 1868.

INDEX

A

Aberration, chromatic, 331
Acceleration, angular, 307
  sense of, 305–306
Achromatic series, 247
Act, psychology of, 44, 63, 65
Action, 221, 404
Activity, 9
Acuity, cutaneous, 357–359
  temporal, 398–400
  visual, 327–329
  visual motion, 381
Adaptation, visual, 375
Adrenin, 35
Affection, 168
Afferent conduction and conscious-
  ness, 174–176
After-images, 174
After-image, visual movement, 377,
  386–387
Air, desire for, 311, 314
All or none principle, 29
Analepsis, 315
Analysis, 208
  by stages, 238–239
  criticisms of, 108–110
  harmonic, 352
  pattern, 239
  structural, 107, 108–110
  temporal, 106, 107, 130–132, 240
Anaxagoras, 13
Anaximander, 12, 14
Anaximenes, 12
Angell, J. R., 36, 46
Angular velocity, visual, 379–381
Animal behavior, 52–53
Animatism, 9–10
Animism, 9–11
Aquinas, Saint Thomas, 15
Arabians, 15
Aristotle, 14, 22

Aristotle's illusion, 359
Articulation, acoustic, 278–279
Aspects of experience, 107
Association areas and consciousness,
  179–181
Astigmatism, 330
Atomism, psychological, 110, 137–138
Attitude, kinaesthetic, 366
Attributes, 107, 120–126
  measurement of, 122–128
  nature of, 120–121
Aubert, H., 379, 380
Auditory change perception, 387–391
Auditory elements, 269–271
Auditory perception, composite, 351–
  356
Augustine, Saint, 15, 22
Autokinetic sensation, 386
Avenarius, R., 47
Awareness, 60, 63–64
Axon, 189

B

Bacon, Francis, 15
Banister, H., 354
Basler, A., 381
Beats, auditory, 387–388
  binaural, 391
Bechterew, V., 53
Beer, T., 36, 53
Behavior, 76–78
Behaviorism, 36, 38–39, 52–55, 144
  argument against, 76–78
  as physiology, 76
Bentley, M., 52
Benussi, V., 40, 394
Bergson, H., 37, 108, 109, 115, 118,
  136, 197
Berkeley, Bishop, 19–20, 70, 151
Bernard, C., 26
Bert, P., 26

419

Index

Index

Qualities, tensive, 304
  tensive, psychophysiology of, 308–310
  unknown, 119
Quality, and quantity, 117–118
  systems, properties of, 118–120
Quantitative series, law of, 117
Quantity and difference, 118
Quetelet, A., 27

R

Ragona Scina experiment, 261
Raumfarben, 261
Ray-sheaf, visual, 325–327
Rays, corresponding, 342–343
Realism, 68–69, 146, 154–155, 371
Receptor process and consciousness, 172–174
  process, visual, 171–172
Receptors, 241–242
  classification of, 242
Reflection coefficient, 262
Reflex, simple, 160
Regard, lines of, 340
  plane of, 340
  point of, 340
Reid, Thomas, 23
Relations, functional psychophysical, 143–145
Response, 214
  and experience, 153–155
  arc, structure of, 156–160
  functions, 158
  levels of, 160
  nature of, 156–160
  objective stage of, 229–231
  parameters, 160
  pattern, 160
  propagation, 156–159
  stages, 158–160
Retina, 193
Return, law of, 389
Rhythm, auditory, 388
Ridgway color system, 264
Rotation, bodily, perception of, 306–307
  sense of, 362–365
Roughness, 293
Royce, J., 47
Russell, B., 45, 81, 93

S

Saltiness, 294
Saturation, 249
Scales, musical, 271
Schelling, F. W. J. von, 21
Schopenhauer, A., 21
Schumann, F., 260, 321
Self-determination, 150
  psychology of, 44
  the, 61, 150
Sensation, 214, 221, 403
  concept of, 215–216
  history of, 27–30
Sensational analysis, 229
Sense data, 68
Sense-organs, physiology of, 28–29
Sensibility, kinaesthetic, 303–310
Sensory circles, cutaneous, 356, 358
Shadows, 258
Sherrington, C. S., 29, 189, 366, 395
Sight, line of, 319
Simultaneity, psychical, 203–204
  psychophysical, 201–203
Smell prism, 283
Socrates, 22
Soul, 61–63
  defunct in psychology, 42–43
  theory, history of, 7–11
Sound, auditory analysis of, 351–353
  distribution, curves, 275
  frequency, 275
  intensity, 275
  nature of, 274
  source, 279
  sources, 276–278
Sourness, 294–295
Space, auditory, 272, 281
  Euclidean, 88
  experiential, 88, 129–130
  perception, acoustic, 279–281
  physical, 81
  subjective, 370, 372
  thresholds, visual, 321
  visual, 261, 319, 321–323
Spearman, C., 213
Spencer, Herbert, 27
Spinoza, B., 17
Stages, of response, 158–160
Stereoscope, 349